PROGRESS IN

Nucleic Acid Research and Molecular Biology

VOLUME 40

PROGRESS IN
Nucleic Acid Research and Molecular Biology

edited by

WALDO E. COHN

Biology Division
Oak Ridge National Laboratory
Oak Ridge, Tennessee

KIVIE MOLDAVE

Department of Biology
University of California, Santa Cruz
Santa Cruz, California

Volume 40

ACADEMIC PRESS, INC.

Harcourt Brace Jovanovich, Publishers

San Diego   New York   Boston
London   Sydney   Tokyo   Toronto

Academic Press, Inc.
San Diego, California 92101

United Kingdom Edition published by
ACADEMIC PRESS LIMITED
24-28 Oval Road, London NW1 7DX

Library of Congress Catalog Card Number: 63-15847

ISBN   0-12-540040-3   (alk. paper)

PRINTED IN THE UNITED STATES OF AMERICA
91 92 93 94   9 8 7 6 5 4 3 2 1

Contents

msDNA of Bacteria

Bert C. Lampson, Sumiko Inouye and Masayori Inouye

Vertebrate Protamine Genes and the Histone-to-Protamine Replacement Reaction

Rafael Oliva and Gordon H. Dixon

Aminoacyl-tRNA Synthetase Family from Prokaryotes and Eukaryotes: Structural Domains and Their Implications

Marc Mirande

Nucleosome Positioning: Occurrence, Mechanisms, and Functional Consequences

Robert T. Simpson

Specific Interaction between RNA Phage Coat Proteins and RNA

Gary W. Witherell, Jonatha M. Gott and Olke C. Uhlenbeck

Superoxide Dismutases

Wayne Beyer, James Imlay and Irwin Fridovich

Genetics of Human Alcohol-Metabolizing Enzymes

Akira Yoshida, Lily C. Hsu and Michio Yasunami

DNA Helicases of Escherichia coli

Steven W. Matson

Abbreviations and Symbols

All contributors to this Series are asked to use the terminology (abbreviations and symbols) recommended by the IUPAC-IUB Commission on Biochemical Nomenclature (CBN) and approved by IUPAC and IUB, and the Editors endeavor to assure conformity. These Recommendations have been published in many journals (1, 2) and compendia (3) and are available in reprint form from the Office of Biochemical Nomenclature (OBN); they are therefore considered to be generally known. Those used in nucleic acid work, originally set out in section 5 of the first Recommendations (1) and subsequently revised and expanded (2, 3), are given in condensed form in the frontmatter of Volumes 9–33 of this series. A recent expansion of the one-letter system (5) follows.

SINGLE-LETTER CODE RECOMMENDATIONS[a] (5)

Symbol	Meaning	Origin of symbol
G	G	Guanosine
A	A	Adenosine
T(U)	T(U)	(ribo)Thymidine (Uridine)
C	C	Cytidine
R	G or A	puRine
Y	T(U) or C	pYrimidine
M	A or C	aMino
K	G or T(U)	Keto
S	G or C	Strong interaction (3 H-bonds)
W[b]	A or T(U)	Weak interaction (2 H-bonds)
H	A or C or T(U)	not G; H follows G in the alphabet
B	G or T(U) or C	not A; B follows A
V	G or C or A	not T (not U); V follows U
D[c]	G or A or T(U)	not C; D follows C
N	G or A or T(U) or C	aNy nucleoside (i.e., unspecified)
Q	Q	Queuosine (nucleoside of queuine)

[a]Modified from *Proc. Natl. Acad. Sci. U.S.A.* **83**, 4 (1986).
[b]W has been used for wyosine, the nucleoside of "base Y" (wye).
[c]D has been used for dihydrouridine (hU or H_2 Urd).

Enzymes

In naming enzymes, the 1984 recommendations of the IUB Commission on Biochemical Nomenclature (4) are followed as far as possible. At first mention, each enzyme is described *either* by its systematic name *or* by the equation for the reaction catalyzed *or* by the recommended trivial name, followed by its EC number in parentheses. Thereafter, a trivial name may be used. Enzyme names are not to be abbreviated except when the substrate has an approved abbreviation (e.g., ATPase, but not LDH, is acceptable).

REFERENCES

1. *JBC* **241**, 527 (1966); *Bchem* **5**, 1445 (1966); *BJ* **101**, 1 (1966); *ABB* **115**, 1 (1966), **129**, 1 (1969); and elsewhere.† General.

2. *EJB* **15**, 203 (1970); *JBC* **245**, 5171 (1970); *JMB* **55**, 299 (1971); and elsewhere.†

3. "Handbook of Biochemistry" (G. Fasman, ed.), 3rd ed. Chemical Rubber Co., Cleveland, Ohio, 1970, 1975, Nucleic Acids, Vols. I and II, pp. 3–59. Nucleic acids.

4. "Enzyme Nomenclature" [Recommendations (1984) of the Nomenclature Committee of the IUB]. Academic Press, New York, 1984.

5. *EJB* **150**, 1 (1985). Nucleic Acids (One-letter system).†

Abbreviations of Journal Titles

Journals	*Abbreviations used*
Annu. Rev. Biochem.	ARB
Annu. Rev. Genet.	ARGen
Arch. Biochem. Biophys.	ABB
Biochem. Biophys. Res. Commun.	BBRC
Biochemistry	Bchem
Biochem. J.	BJ
Biochim. Biophys. Acta	BBA
Cold Spring Harbor	CSH
Cold Spring Harbor Lab	CSHLab
Cold Spring Harbor Symp. Quant. Biol.	CSHSQB
Eur. J. Biochem.	EJB
Fed. Proc.	FP
Hoppe-Seyler's Z. Physiol. Chem.	ZpChem
J. Amer. Chem. Soc.	JACS
J. Bacteriol.	J. Bact.
J. Biol. Chem.	JBC
J. Chem. Soc.	JCS
J. Mol. Biol.	JMB
J. Nat. Cancer Inst.	JNCI
Mol. Cell. Biol.	MCBiol
Mol. Cell. Biochem.	MCBchem
Mol. Gen. Genet.	MGG
Nature, New Biology	Nature NB
Nucleic Acid Research	NARes
Proc. Natl. Acad. Sci. U.S.A.	PNAS
Proc. Soc. Exp. Biol. Med.	PSEBM
Progr. Nucl. Acid. Res. Mol. Biol.	This Series

†Reprints available from the Office of Biochemical Nomenclature (W. E. Cohn, Director).

Some Articles Planned for Future Volumes

Molecular Structure and Transcriptional Regulation of the Salivary Gland Proline-Rich Protein Multigene Families
 DON M. CARLSON, JIE ZHOU AND PAUL S. WRIGHT

Recognition of tRNAs by Aminoacyl-tRNA Synthetases
 LADONNE SCHULMAN

Ribosome Biogenesis in Yeast
 H. A. RAUÉ AND R. J. PLANTA

Structural Elements in RNA
 MICHAEL CHASTAIN AND IGNACIO TINOCO, JR.

Nuclear RNA-Binding Proteins
 JACK D. KEENE AND CHARLES C. QUERY

Amplification of DNA Sequences in Mammalian Cells
 JOYCE L. HAMLIN, TZENG-HORNG LEU, JAMES P. VAUGHN, CHI MA AND PIETER A. DIJKWEL

Molecular Biology Approaches to Genetic Defects of the Mammalian Nervous System
 J. GREGOR SUTCLIFFE AND GABRIEL H. TRAVIS

Lens Proteins and Their Genes
 HANS BLOEMENDAL AND WILFRIED W. DE JONG

msDNA of Bacteria

Bert C. Lampson,
Sumiko Inouye
and Masayori Inouye[1]

Department of Biochemistry
Robert Wood Johnson Medical School
University of Medicine and Dentistry of
New Jersey
Piscataway, New Jersey 08854

Recent discoveries in our laboratory and in the laboratory of Werner Maas have clearly demonstrated the presence of a new type of retroelement found on the chromosomes of at least two different bacterial groups: the soil microbe *Myxococcus xanthus* (*1*) and the enteric bacterium *Escherichia coli* (*2, 3*). This element encodes a reverse transcriptase (RT) that closely resembles those of retroviruses and other retroelements. In addition, it is responsible for the production of an unusual, extrachromosomal RNA–DNA molecule known as msDNA (multicopy, single-stranded DNA). The msDNA molecule consists of a short single strand of DNA joined, at its 5′ end, to a nucleoside in the middle of a single strand of RNA; specifically the 5′ end of the DNA chain is joined to the 2′ position of an internal guanosine residue of the RNA molecule, forming a unique 2′,5′ phosphodiester bond between RNA and DNA. This unusual structure is a hallmark of the abundant, but functionally obscure, msDNA and remains perhaps the most peculiar of many unusual features of the msDNA system. Because the msDNA-synthesizing systems of bacteria encode RT but, to our present knowledge, lack some of the other features of retroviruses, such as long terminal repeats and virions, the systems have been termed "retrons" (*4*).

[1] To whom correspondence may be addressed.

1

Progress in Nucleic Acid Research
and Molecular Biology, Vol. 40

A number of short reviews have appeared recently about msDNA (4–6). This article provides a comprehensive discussion of the msDNA-retron system. Although much remains to be discovered, this review provides insight into the molecular mechanisms of msDNA biosynthesis, its functions, and the evolutionary implications of the retron element.

I. Structure of msDNA

The msDNA-retron system was first discovered in the soil bacterium *M. xanthus* (7). *Myxococcus xanthus* has been studied extensively as a model system of developmental biology, because, when deprived of certain nutrients, individual cells form multicellular aggregation centers, which then develop into fruiting bodies containing spores (8, 9). When total chromosomal DNA from *M. xanthus* is electrophoresed on a 5% acrylamide gel, as first observed during a study to determine the relative size of the genome (10), a small but abundant satellite DNA is detected upon staining with ethidium bromide. This extrachromosomal DNA is present in a high copy number, estimated at 500–700 copies per cell genome in *M. xanthus*, and is therefore designated multicopy, single-stranded DNA, or msDNA (7). Subsequent work established that msDNA is a complex of DNA and RNA. The msDNA from the closely related myxobacterium *Stigmatella aurantiaca* is similarly estimated to exist at about 500 copies per cell (11).

The msDNA molecule probably exists free of the chromosome in the cell cytoplasm, and can be isolated by the same methods used to isolate plasmids. For *M. xanthus*, msDNA is found in all developmental stages, from vegetative cells to even inside the myxospore (12). Aside from the myxobacteria, msDNA is also found in some *E. coli* strains. Analysis of these msDNA molecules reveals a large degree of nucleotide sequence diversity among them, with little, if any, primary sequence homology in either the DNA strand or the RNA strand. However, in spite of their primary structural diversity, all msDNAs share important secondary structures, including the following.

A. Single Strand of DNA Covalently Linked to a Single Strand of RNA

Ribonuclease A-treated, gel-purified preparations of msDNA can be sequenced directly after radioactive labeling of the 5′ end with T4 polynucleotide kinase (EC 2.7.1.78). Chemical cleavage by the Maxam and Gilbert method (13) reveals that the DNA of msDNA from *M. xanthus* is a single strand of DNA of 162 nucleotides (7). However, a large portion of the 5′ radiolabel can be removed during piperidine cleavage and almost completely removed by alkaline hydrolysis, indicating that the 5′ end of the

DNA chain contains a labile ribonucleotide (7). Later work established that the DNA of msDNA is covalently linked to a short single strand of RNA (14). This RNA is observed when exponentially growing cells of *M. xanthus* are pulse-labeled with [^{3}H]thymidine, yielding a labeled msDNA band of about 240 bases when RNA preparations are electrophoresed on a 5% acrylamide gel. When the same material is treated with RNase A prior to gel electrophoresis, the labeled msDNA band is reduced to about 162 bases, indicating that an RNA of 70–80 bases has been removed. This RNA part of Mx162 has been sequenced directly, using base-specific RNases, and shown to consist of 77 nucleotides (see Fig. 1).

Figure 1 presents the complete nucleotide sequences and proposed secondary structures of the five different msDNAs that have been analyzed so far. The msDNAs are identified by two letters designating the genus and species of the host cell and a number that corresponds to the size of the DNA strand in number of nucleotides. For the msDNA of *M. xanthus* (Mx162), the DNA chain folds into a long, stable stem–loop structure based on sequence complementarity, and the RNA strand forms short stem–loops as well. This is supported by the observations that the DNA strand of msDNA can be cleaved by the endonuclease *Hae*III, indicating that this restriction site is formed in the double-stranded stem region of the folded molecule. Likewise, regions of the RNA chain resistant to base-specific RNases used for sequencing correspond to proposed stem–loop regions (7, 14).

B. 2′,5′ Branch Structure

Experiments to determine the nucleotide sequence of the single strand of RNA linked to the 5′ end of msDNA showed that this RNA can be labeled with both [γ-^{32}P]ATP, using T4 polynucleotide kinase, and [^{32}P]pCp, using RNA ligase (14, 15), indicating that it has both a free 5′ end and a free 3′ end. In addition, as exemplified by Ec67 (see Fig. 2), when the base-specific sequencing reactions for the RNA of msDNA are electrophoresed on a sequencing gel, a large gap appears in the banding pattern of the "sequence ladder." This indicates that all of the RNA fragments above the gap contain extra material that cannot be removed by the RNases, thus increasing the size of each fragment (and slowing migration through the gel). The extra material is DNA, covalently joined to an internal residue of the RNA. For Mx162, the 2′ hydroxyl at the 20th residue (guanosine) of the RNA is linked to the 5′ end of the DNA strand (14). This linkage, therefore, is a 2′,5′ phosphodiester bond between the 20th nucleoside (guanosine) of the RNA strand and the first nucleoside (dC) of the DNA strand (Fig. 1). This branch structure is further confirmed by the ability of a debranching enzyme, 2′,5′ phosphodiesterase, to cleave the 2′,5′ linkage between the RNA and the DNA, which is otherwise impervious to RNases (2, 3, 11, 14). This debranch-

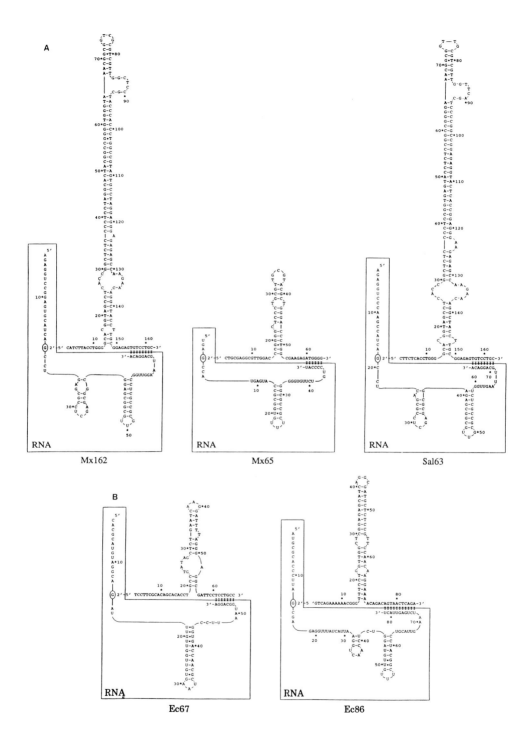

A

Mx162   Mx65   Sal63

B

Ec67   Ec86

ing enzyme has been purified (*16, 17*) from HeLa cells and normally converts the branched RNA "lariats," which form as intermediates during the splicing of pre-mRNA, into linear strands by a specific cleavage at the 2' side of the 2',5' phosphodiester bond (*16, 17*).

All msDNAs examined in structural detail have the unique branched linkage joining the RNA and DNA strands. In addition, the branched residue is, in all cases, a specific internal guanosine residue near the 5' end of the RNA segment. For RNA lariats generated from mRNA splicing, there is a strong preference for adenosine as the branched residue (*18*). In the case of msDNA, a specific guanosine residue appears to be required for the synthesis of the branch linkage (see Section II,F).

C. Hybrid, Base-Paired Structure

As depicted in Fig. 1, the extreme 3' end of the DNA strand of Mx162 contains an octanucleotide sequence complementary to the octanucleotide sequence at the 3' end of the RNA chain. This allows the overlapping 3' ends of the DNA and RNA to form an RNA·DNA base-paired region. The presence of this "hybrid" region has been shown by demonstrating that the 3' end of the RNA moiety is sensitive to RNase-H digestion, which attacks only the H-bonded RNA within it (*19, 20*). The presence of this short RNA·DNA segment in the msDNA molecule is a result of the mechanism by which msDNA is synthesized via RT (described in Section II). Although of variable length (from 6 to 11 bases), this H-bonded region is present in all msDNA molecules.

D. Complex with Protein

Experiments designed to isolate native msDNA from cell extracts point to a more complex structure. DNA–protein binding assays, using the gel-retardation method, show that one or more proteins, derived from *M. xanthus* cell extracts, specifically bind endogenous Mx162 *in vitro*. This suggests that msDNA may exist as a complex with protein(s), with most of the DNA strand bound to protein (*21*). The native msDNA–protein complex sediments in glycerol density gradients at 14 S, while Mx162 free of protein

FIG. 1. Primary and secondary structures of msDNAs. The complete nucleotide sequences of the DNA strand and the RNA strand (boxed regions) of five msDNAs are shown. The proposed secondary structure for each msDNA is also presented and is based on sequence complementarity. The guanosine residue in the RNA containing the 2',5' branch linkage with the DNA strand is circled. Each msDNA is identified by two letters representing the genus and species of the host cell and a number corresponding to the size of the DNA strand in number of nucleotides (bases). Thus, Mx162 and Mx65 are from *M. xanthus*, strain DZF1 (*14, 35*); Sa163 is from *S. aurantiaca*, strain DW4 (*15*); Ec67 is from *E. coli*, hospital isolate, Cl-1 (*2*); and Ec86 is from *E. coli* B (*3*).

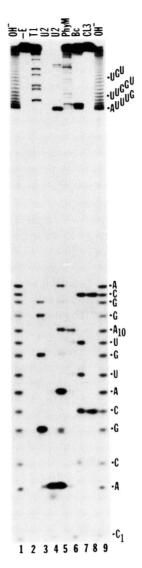

FIG. 2. Determination of the sequence of RNA nucleotides in the branched RNA linked to msDNA-Ec67 of *E. coli*. The 5′ end of purified RNA linked to msDNA was labeled with [γ-³²P]ATP and T4 polynucleotide kinase. The labeled RNA was sequenced by limited digestion with base-specific RNases (1). Lanes OH⁻ are partial alkaline hydrolysis ladder (cleavage at every base); lane −E is no enzyme treatment of the labeled RNA; lane T1 is digestion with RNase T1 (cleavage at G); lanes U2 are RNase U2 (cleavage at A); lane PhyM is RNase PhyM (cleavage at U or A); lane Bc is RNase *B. cerus* (cleavage at U or C); and lane CL3 is RNase CL3 (cleavage at C). The large gap in the sequence ladder is due to msDNA joined to the rG residue at position 15 by a 2′,5′ phosphodiester linkage.

sediments at only 2 S (21). Some of the msDNAs from E. *coli* also appear to exist as complexes with protein. Although the protein(s) associated with the msDNA from *M. xanthus in vivo* has not been identified, recent experiments with E. *coli* suggest that the retron-encoded RT is associated with msDNA. This is described in more detail in the discussion on the purification of the RT from E. *coli* Cl-1 (Section II,E).

II. Synthesis of msDNA

A. Genetic Locus Encoding msDNA

The gene coding for the RNA and DNA strands of msDNA was discovered by using msDNA as a hybridization probe. When Mx162, purified from *M. xanthus*, is radioactively labeled by nick translation and hybridized against a Southern blot of chromosomal DNA digested with several restriction enzymes, a single-hybrid fragment appears. This means that msDNA is encoded by a unique, single-copy chromosomal locus (7). Like *M. xanthus*, the gene encoding msDNA in E. *coli* is also a single-copy chromosomal locus. A comparison of all known msDNA coding regions reveals that this locus contains three genes organized in a similar manner, as shown in Fig. 3. A gene called *msd* codes for the DNA portion of msDNA. A second gene (*msr*) is situated 5' to 3', in the opposite orientation of *msd*, and codes for the RNA chain. Thus, the genes *msd* and *msr* are convergently oriented, so that their respective 3' ends overlap by several bases. This overlap is equivalent to the H-bonded DNA·RNA structure formed by the overlapping 3' ends of the RNA and DNA chains in the msDNA molecule. For Mx162, the overlapping *msd–msr* genes, like the hybrid structure of the msDNA they produce, comprise eight base-pairs (14).

Determination of the nucleotide sequence in the vicinity of the *msd–msr* genes revealed a closely linked open reading frame (ORF). This ORF is located immediately upstream from *msd*, but is transcribed in the same direction as *msr* (as shown in Fig. 3). The initiation codon of the ORF is situated as close as 19 base-pairs from the start of the *msd* gene for the Ec86 retron of E. *coli* B, but as much as 77 base-pairs for the Mx162 retron of *M. xanthus* (1, 3).

Another conserved feature of the chromosomal locus that codes for msDNA is a set of inverted repeat sequences, designated a1 and a2. Sequence a1 is located just upstream from the start of the *msd* gene, while sequence a2 is positioned immediately 5' to the G residue in the *msr* gene that forms the 2',5' branch linkage in the msDNA molecule (Fig. 3). The inverted repeats display a large degree of nucleotide sequence diversity among the different known loci encoding msDNA, as well as differences in size. For example, the inverted repeats found in the retron locus encoding

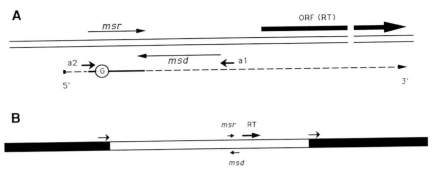

Fig. 3. Arrangement of genes in the retron element responsible for the production of msDNA. A single-copy retroelement on the bacterial chromosome contains the region required for the production of msDNA. All known msDNA coding regions contain three genes organized in a similar manner, as shown in (A): A gene, *msd*, codes for the DNA strand of msDNA. A second gene (*msr*) is situated, 5′ to 3′, in the opposite direction and codes for the RNA strand of msDNA. A closely positioned ORF codes for the RT. Transcription of this region initiates at or near the 5′ end of *msr* and extends beyond *msd* to include the ORF. A set of inverted repeat sequences, a1 and a2, is also conserved among msDNA coding regions (short arrows). The circled G corresponds to the residue in the RNA that will contain the 2′,5′ branch linkage in msDNA (see also Fig. 6). (B) For the *E. coli* retron Ec67, the region encoding msDNA is only a small part of a large element found on the chromosome (open bar). The junction of the Ec67 retron with the host chromosome is flanked by 26-base directly repeated chromosomal sequences, as shown by arrows. The figure is not drawn to scale.

Mx162 are 34 nucleotides long, while the inverted repeats for the Ec86 retron of *E. coli* B are only 12 bases in size. Despite their diversity, these repeat sequences are located in the same positions (as shown in Fig. 3) for all known loci encoding msDNA. As discussed in more detail below (Section II,F), the position of these inverted repeat sequences is critical to the synthesis of msDNA.

B. Transcription of the *msr–msd* Locus

When *M. xanthus* cells are labeled with [³H]thymidine in the presence of rifampicin, an RNA polymerase inhibitor, incorporation of label into msDNA is blocked. This seems to indicate that synthesis of msDNA depends on transcription by RNA polymerase (*12, 22*). Mapping experiments with S1 clearly demonstrate that transcription from the chromosomal locus for the msDNA of *M. xanthus* (Mx162) is initiated at about 75 base-pairs 5′ from the start of the *msr* gene, and extends at least 70 base-pairs beyond the *msd* gene (*14*) (Fig. 3). Transcription may, in fact, extend beyond this point to include the ORF, thus forming one long transcript. This appears to be the case for the chromosomal locus encoding the msDNA from *E. coli* B (Ec86). S1-

mapping indicates that transcription begins at or near the 5' start of the *msr* gene, extends through the *msd* gene, and continues into the ORF just downstream (3). In addition, a *lacZ* fusion construction, to produce an ORF– *lacZ* protein for the Ec86 retron, demonstrated that deletion of the region −14 to −170 5' from the start of the *msr* gene reduced both β-galactosidase activity and msDNA production, suggesting that production of msDNA requires the transcription of a long region encompassing the genes *msr* and *msd* and the ORF (3).

C. msDNA-Retron Unit[2]

Recent mapping studies indicate that the chromosomal region required for the synthesis of msDNA (*msd, msr,* and the ORF) is only a small part of a larger genetic element, the retron. In the case of *E. coli*, at least, it appears that the retron element was incorporated into the genome during the recent evolution of this species (see Section III). The original 11.5-kilobase (kb) *Eco*RI fragment cloned from the chromosome of *E. coli* strain Cl-1 (a hospital isolate) contains the region involved in the synthesis of Ec67 (a region about 3.5 kb in size). However, this fragment does not cross-hybridize to any region of the K-12 chromosome. By screening chromosomal sequences flanking both sides of the 11.5-kb *Eco*RI fragment, the junction site, at which the unique sequences of the retron element end and sequences homologous to the K-12 chromosome begin, was identified on the chromosome of the *E. coli* strain Cl-1. The junction sites for retron Ec67, which define the ends of the element, span a distance longer than 30 kb. Retron Ec67 is flanked by directly repeated chromosome sequences, about 26 base-pairs in size. Both ends of the retron contain additional direct repeats and inverted repeat sequences (M.-Y. Hsu, M. Inouye and S. Inouye, unpublished). Retron Ec67 appears to have integrated into the chromosome of the *E. coli* strain Cl-1 at a site corresponding to 19 minutes on the K-12 chromosome. Retron Ec67 thus resembles transposon-like elements that have generated small sequence duplications at the site of insertion on the chromosome (23, 24).

D. ORF Encodes an RT

All retrons so far examined contain an ORF closely linked to the genes *msr* and *msd*, which code for the msDNA molecule. In addition, the associated ORF appears to be essential for the production of msDNA. For example, when the carboxy-terminal portion of the 586-aminoacid ORF found in retron Ec67 is deleted, no Ec67 msDNA is produced (2). Likewise, if most of the 320-aminoacid ORF associated with the msDNA-retron system of *E. coli* B is deleted, there is no detectable Ec86 (3).

---

[2] See Note Added in Proof (p. 24) for recent information on topics concerning msDNA.

Deletion mutations have also been constructed for the ORF associated with Mx162 from *M. xanthus* (25). Here residues 12–142 of the 485-aminoacid ORF of Mx162 were replaced with a kanamycin-resistance gene. The ORF containing the deletion mutation was exchanged for the wild-type gene on the chromosome of *M. xanthus* by homologous recombination; myxobacteria lack a plasmid system to express gene mutations constructed in *E. coli* (25). The deletion mutation as well as a disruption mutation (insertion of a kanamycin-resistance gene) of this ORF greatly reduced the level or copy number of the Mx162 produced by *M. xanthus*. Deletion of the amino-terminal region of the ORF does not, however, appear to completely destroy the activity of the presumed protein product, as a small level of msDNA is still produced.

Before the closely associated ORF was discovered, it was proposed (*14*) that the msDNA molecule is synthesized by reverse transcription of an RNA precursor. This was based primarily on the discovery of a large, stably folded RNA precursor molecule encoding the *msr–msd* region of the Mx162 retron from *M. xanthus*. The closely linked ORF was, therefore, examined for aminoacid sequence similarities with known retroviral RTs.

Detailed sequence alignments have been generated for many retroviral-encoded polymerase genes (RTs). A particularly well-conserved region of 94 amino acids among five viral polymerase genes contains 10 highly conserved residues (*26*). Although the overall level of aminoacid sequence similarity between different RTs is very low, the same 10 amino acids are invariably conserved and reflect the conservation of function and secondary structures unique to RTs. An expanded set of 13 highly conserved amino acids within seven conserved regions among 37 RT-like sequences correlates with secondary structural elements (*27*). When the ORFs associated with msDNA are aligned with retroviral RT sequences, 12 of the 13 strictly conserved amino acids are present in two of the four msDNA-linked ORFs (Ec86 from *E. coli* B, Ec67 from *E. coli* Cl-1, and Mx162 and Mx65 from *M. xanthus*) aligned in Fig. 4. The presence of these highly conserved amino acids, diagnostic for RT, strongly argues that the ORF situated downstream from the region encoding msDNA codes for an RT similar to those encoded by retroviruses and other retroelements.

An additional similarity in aminoacid sequence is apparent at the carboxy-terminal region of the Ec67 ORF from *E. coli* Cl-1. An alignment of this region (residues 466–586) with the carboxy-terminal region of two retroviral polymerase sequences, from human immunodeficiency virus type 1 (HIV-1) and human T-lymphotropic virus type 1 (HTLV-1), shows significant similarity (16–17% identical) (*2*). This carboxy-terminal region is considered to be responsible for RNase-H activity associated with retroviral RT, and re-

```
                                K            R
HIV    213 KISKIGPENP YNTPVFAIKK KDSTKWRKLV .DFRELNKRT QDFWEVQLGI 261

Ec86    37 LRLLTYTADF KYRIYTVEKK GDEKRMRTIY QPSREL.KAL QGWV...LRN  82
Ec67    32 NVLYRIGSDN QYTQFTIPKK G..KGVRTIS APTDRL.KDI QRRICDLLSD  78
Mx162  170 AFHREVDTAT HYVSWTIPKR D..GSKRTIT SPKPEL.KAA QR...WVLS. 212
Mx65   139 SIHRPRERVR HYVTFAVPKR S..GGVRLLH APKRRL.KAL QR...RMLA. 181
                        o          •              o   •  •        •

                                                             D
HIV    262 PHP....... .......... .......... AGLKKK.KSV TVLDVGDAYF 283

Ec86    83 ILDKL..... S.SSPFSIGF E.KHQSILNN ATPHIGANFI LNIDLEDFFP 125
Ec67    79 CRDEIFAIRK I.SNNYSFGF E.RGKSIILN AYKHRGKQII LNIDLKDFFE 126
Mx162  213 ...NVV.ERL P.VHGAAHGF V.AGRSILTN ALAHQGADVV VKVDLKDFFP 256
Mx65   182 ...LLV.SKL P.VSPQAHGF V.PGRSIKTG AAPHVGRRVV LKLDLKDFFP 225
                        oo         oo       •   o o      •o •oo

HIV    284 SVPLDEDFRK YT........ .......... .AFTIP.SIN NETPGIRYQY 313

Ec86   126 SLTANKVFG. VFHS.L.... .......... .GYN.RLISS VLTKICCYK. 156
Ec67   127 SFNFGRVRG. YFLS..NQDF .......... .LLN.PVVAT TLAKAACYN. 161
Mx162  257 SVTWRRVKGL LRKGGLREGT STLLSLLSTE APREAVQFRG KLLHVAKGP. 305
Mx65   226 SVTFARVRGL LIALGYGYPV AATLAVLMTE SERQPVELEG ILFHVPVGP. 274
               •    o  o                                o

                P  G                            Y   DD
HIV    314 NVLPQGWKGS PAIFQS...S MTKILEPFKK QNPDIVIYQY MDDLYVGS.D 359

Ec86   157 NLLPQGAPSS PKLANLICSK LDYRIQGYAG SR.GLIYTRY ADDLTL.SAQ 204
Ec67   162 GTLPQGSPCS PIISNLICNI MDMRLAKLAK KY.GCTYSRY ADDITI.STN 209
Mx162  306 RALPQGAPTS PGITNALCLK LDKRLSALAK RL.GFTYTRY ADDLTF.SWT 353
Mx65   275 RVCVQGAPTS PALCNAVLLR LDRRLAGLAR RY.GYTYTRY ADDLTF.S.. 320
               •• o•• •    o          o o     o       o   o o• o•• o   •

                                       G           K        (L)
HIV    360 LEIGQHRTKI EELRQH.... .....LLRWG LTTPDKK... HQKEPPFLWM 397

Ec86   205 ......SMKK V...VKARD FLFSIIPSEG LVINSKKTCI SGPRSQRKVT 244
Ec67   210 KNTFPLEMAT VQPEGVVLGK VLVKEIENSG FEINDSKTRL TYKTSRQEVT 259
Mx162  354 KAKQPKPRRT QRPPVAVLLS RVQEVVEAEG FRVHPDKTRV ARKGTRQRVT 403
Mx65   321 .GDDVTALER VR...ALAAR Y....VQEEG FEVNREKTRV QRRGGAQRVT 362
                                       •         •o         oo

           G
HIV    398 GYELHPDKWT VQPIVLPEKD SWTVNDIQKL VGKLNWAS 435

Ec86   245 GLVISQEKVG .....IGREK YKEIRAKIHH IFCGKSSE 277
Ec67   260 GLTVNR.... ..IVNIDRCY YKKTRALAHA LYRTGEYK 291
Mx162  404 GLVVNAAGKD APAARVPRDV VRQLRAAIHN RKKGKPGR 441
Mx65   363 GVTVNT.... ..TLGLSREE RPRLRAMLHQ EARSEDVE 394
               •          o        oo  o
```

FIG. 4. Aminoacid sequence alignment of four known msDNA-RTs—Ec86, Ec67, Mx162, and Mx65—and the RT from human immunodeficiency virus (HIV). A portion of the aminoacid sequence of the four known msDNA–RTs is aligned with the RT region of the HIV polymerase sequence. The 13 amino acids that are strictly conserved among 37 RT sequences (27) are shown above the HIV sequence. Most of the bacterial RTs share 12 of the 13 conserved amino acids, a leucine (in parentheses) being the exception. Numbers indicate the aminoacid residues, beginning at the amino terminus. ●, Amino acids shared by all five proteins; ○, residues shared by the bacterial RTs.

quired for virus replication (28). The ability to distinguish a separate functional domain is based on a significant resemblance between the aminoacid sequence at the carboxy-terminal portion of retroviral polymerases and the sequence of RNase H from *E. coli* (29). In addition, mutational analysis with the separate expression of one or the other of the two activities confirms the predicted designation of an amino-terminal DNA polymerase activity and a carboxy-terminal RNase-H activity for retroviral RTs (30). Similarly, Fig. 5 shows the predicted functional domains for the four bacterial RTs based on aminoacid sequence similarities with the retroviral activities. As mentioned, the Ec67-RT from *E. coli* Cl-1 was predicted to have an associated RNase-H activity similar to that of retroviral RTs. The other msDNA RTs (Ec86-RT from *E. coli* B and Mx162-RT and Mx65-RT from *M. xanthus*) appear to lack the RNase-H domain (Fig. 5).

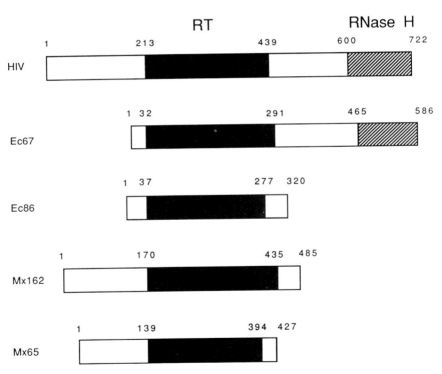

FIG. 5. Proposed functional domains for each of the four known msDNA-RTs are shown based on amino-acid sequence similarity with retroviral polymerase sequences. The RT and RNase-H domains for the human immunodeficiency virus polymerase are also shown (27, 29).

E. Purification and Activity of msDNA-RT

In agreement with the predicted activity, based on the aminoacid sequence of the msDNA ORF, crude extracts prepared from *E. coli* cells harboring the cloned Ec67-retron show RT activity when poly(rC)·oligo(dG) is the template/primer (2). The RT encoded by the Ec67 retron has been further purified by cloning a 5-kb *Pst*I–EcoRI restriction fragment containing part of the retron from the host chromosome into a plasmid vector. The recombinant plasmid (pCl-1EP5b) contains the retron genes *msr*, *msd*, and the RT-ORF, and this 5-kb region appears to supply all of the information needed to produce msDNA in an *E. coli* K-12 strain. As discussed in section III,A, *E. coli* K-12 does not contain a native msDNA or retron element. The Ec67-RT was purified from an *E. coli* K-12 strain harboring plasmid pCl-1EP5b, and shown to exist as a large complex with its endogenous product, msDNA. The complex sediments in a glycerol density gradient as a 20.5-S particle with an approximate M_r of 600,000–700,000. The complex is composed of several units of the Ec67-RT and a molecule of Ec67 msDNA. The Ec67-RT from the purified complex migrates at an M_r of 65,000 after electrophoresis in sodium dodecyl sulfate, which is in good agreement with the predicted M_r of 67,227 for the monomer form of the Ec67-RT (*31*).

The purified Ec67-RT complex can synthesize cDNA *in vitro* using a 5-S rRNA as a template annealed to a small, synthetic DNA primer, and can produce a double-stranded DNA using a synthetic 50-base DNA as a template annealed to a small, synthetic DNA as a primer. The purified RT complex can also utilize the msDNA molecule itself as a natural template to synthesize new DNA. Since the msDNA molecule contains a short H-bonded RNA·DNA (hybrid) region formed between the 3′ ends of the DNA strand and the RNA strand (Fig. 1), this structure serves as a natural, intramolecular primer. The purified Ec67-RT produces two major DNA products when Ec67 is used as a template/primer. A 103-base, single-stranded DNA is formed by extending the 3′ end of msDNA using the RNA of msDNA as a template, and a 60-base double-stranded DNA product resulting from the converse reaction in which the 3′ end of the RNA is extended, using msDNA as a template (*31*).

Similar reaction products are observed (3) when a partially purified preparation of the RT produced by the Ec86 retron from *E. coli* B is allowed to react with Ec86 serving as a template/primer. Here, a 144-base product is formed by the action of RT, which extends the 3′ end of msDNA until it stops at the branch point of the RNA template. Similar experiments have also shown that the purified Ec67-RT can use heterologous msDNAs, Ec86 and Mx162, as template/primers to extend the synthesis of msDNA in vitro (*31*). However, *in vivo* complementation experiments show that a retron RT cannot complement the production of a heterologous msDNA. For example, if a plasmid containing just the genes *msd* and *msr* from the Ec67 retron is transformed into *E. coli* B, the endogenous retron-encoded RT of *E. coli* B cannot promote the synthesis of the exogenous Ec67. Other combinations also show that a retron-RT can complement only the synthesis of its own homologous msDNA (M.-Y. Hsu and S. Inouye, unpublished).

F. Mechanism of msDNA Synthesis

Several lines of evidence now point convincingly to the original model, which proposed that msDNA is synthesized by reverse transcription of an RNA precursor (*14*). These include, for example: (1) production of msDNA is completely blocked by rifampicin, an antibiotic that inhibits RNA polymerase; (2) expression of the region encoding msDNA begins with the synthesis of a long mRNA beginning upstream from *msr* and extending beyond the *msd* gene to include the ORF; (3) conserved inverted repeat sequences allow the mRNA to fold into an important secondary structure; (4) the closely linked ORF encodes a protein that resembles a typical retroviral RT in both aminoacid sequence and activity *in vitro*; (5) deletion or disruption of the ORF blocks msDNA synthesis; and (6) analysis of intermediate products formed during the synthesis of msDNA in an *in vitro* system is consistent with reverse transcription of an RNA template.

The mechanism proposed for the formation of msDNA is illustrated in Fig. 6 and proceeds as follows. Synthesis of msDNA begins with transcription of a long RNA that starts upstream from *msr*, encodes the RNA strand, and extends to include *msd* encoding the DNA strand and the ORF encoding the RT. Two inverted repeat sequences, designated a1 and a2 (Fig. 6, arrows), and sequences b1 and b2, which exist within the *msd* region, allow the long mRNA molecule to fold into a stable stem–loop structure. This secondary structure positions the rG residue, which will contain the branched linkage in msDNA (circled "G" in Fig. 6), in such a way as to be accessible for priming DNA synthesis. Correct positioning of the branched rG in the folded RNA is critical for the synthesis of msDNA. If mutations are introduced into either inverted repeat a1 or a2 of the RNA from retron Mx162 of *M. xanthus*, creating a base-pair mismatch, the stem structure immediately adjacent to the branched rG is disrupted, preventing the synthesis of msDNA (*32*). In addition, the inverted repeats a1 and a2, although different in their primary sequences, are, in all known retrons, found in the same location immediately upstream from the branched rG residue (a2) and immediately upstream from the start of the DNA coding region (a1) (Fig. 6).

After the formation of a secondary structure in the precursor RNA, a priming reaction (step 2, Fig. 6) and initiation of reverse transcription (step 3) follow the formation of the branched linkage between the 2' OH of the rG

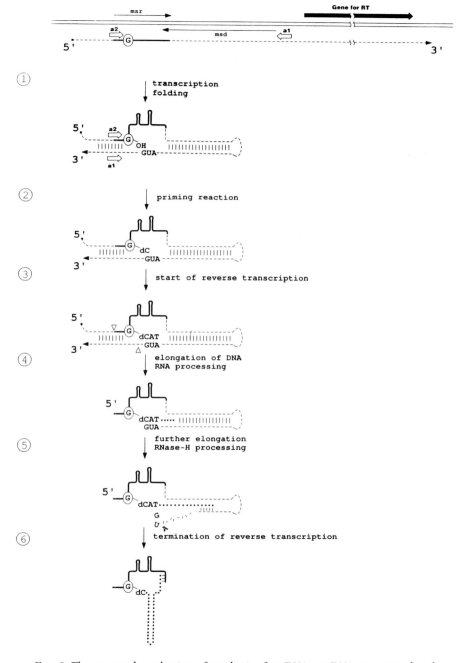

FIG. 6. The proposed mechanism of synthesis of msDNA. msDNA is proposed to be synthesized by reverse transcription (RT) from an RNA precursor that serves as both a primer and a template. See Section II,F for details.

and the 5' end of the first deoxyribonucleotide. From analysis of intermediate structures formed during the synthesis of Ec86 (of *E. coli* B) in an *in vitro* system (3), it was concluded that the formation of the linkage between RNA and DNA is an early event, most likely the first step in the synthesis of msDNA. However, it is unclear how these events occur. It is not known whether the associated RT can initiate the polymerization of DNA directly from the 2' OH of rG, since all known DNA polymerases require a 3' OH primer (33). It is possible that some other enzyme serves to prime the initiation of DNA synthesis, or a nonenzymatic activation of the 2' OH of the rG residue may occur by reactions similar to RNA self-splicing to produce a suitable primer. It is clear, however, that the 2' position of a specific rG is required to prime the synthesis of msDNA. For Mx162 of *M. xanthus*, it is residue 20 of the msRNA, as substitution of this rG with rA or rC blocks the synthesis of msDNA. In addition, a mutation in the RNA of Mx162 designed to favor priming at an alternative rG at position 24, by sequestering the 20th rG in a longer stem structure, greatly reduced the amount of msDNA made (32).

Based on intermediate structures observed in a permeabilized cell system developed to study the *in vitro* synthesis of the msDNA of *M. xanthus*, it was concluded that once elongation of DNA begins (step 4, Fig. 6), after the priming and initiation events, there is an RNA processing event (34). In the case of Mx162, RNA is removed at both the 5' end (75 bases) and the 3' end of the folded RNA. In addition, as elongation of the DNA strand continues along the RNA template, there is a concomitant removal of the RNA template within the growing DNA·RNA duplex by RNase-H activity (step 5). It is clear from the intermediate structures observed in the permeabilized cell system that RNase-H activity proceeds closely and in concert with polymerization of DNA by RT to digest away the RNA template in a 3'-to-5' direction. The RNase-H activity may be associated with the bacterial RT, as is the case for retroviral polymerases (28, 29). Certainly this appears to be likely for the Ec67-RT from *E. coli* strain Cl-1 (see Section II,D). However, other retron-encoded RTs, including those from *M. xanthus*, appear to lack an RNase-H domain. Thus, an additional retron-encoded protein may provide this function or it may come from a native RNase H encoded by the host cell.

For the Mx162 msDNA, elongation of the DNA strand continues along with the concomitant removal of the RNA template until termination at 162 deoxynucleotides, leaving a 77-base template RNA strand remaining with the molecule (step 6, Fig. 6). It is not clear how this precise termination of msDNA synthesis occurs *in vivo*. Experiments clearly show that when the msDNA is isolated (i.e., free of protein) from the host cell and then added to a reaction mixture containing a purified preparation of the msDNA-RT, the bacterial enzyme continues to extend the DNA strand (*in vitro*) until it reaches the branched rG residue (*3, 31*). It appears, then, that a factor(s) that normally stop synthesis of msDNA *in vivo* is lost or altered during purification. The termination signals may be a combination of secondary structures in the template RNA and complexed protein(s). Indeed, the discovery that the Ec67-RT is isolated as a large complex with its endogenous msDNA (*31*) may indicate that a large RNA–RT complex is required to ensure the proper folding and processing of the precursor RNA template as well as to supply the polymerase and RNase-H activities required to synthesize msDNA and provide the termination signals required to produce the msDNA molecule.

III. Origin of msDNA[2]

A. Prevalence and Diversity of msDNA

Five different msDNA-retron elements, two from *E. coli* and three from the myxobacteria (Fig. 1), have been studied in molecular detail; this review emphasizes the structures and features shared by all. However, there are many significant and interesting differences, particularly among the retrons found in the myxobacteria compared to those found in *E. coli*, which provide a clue to the possible origin and evolution of this unusual retroelement.

1. Myxobacteria

The first msDNA discovered, Mx162, was found in the *M. xanthus* laboratory strain DZF1. However, it was soon discovered that this same strain contains a second species of msDNA, designated Mx65 (*35*), roughly one-half the size of its larger co-resident, Mx162, and having an entirely different nucleotide sequence in both its RNA and DNA strands (Fig. 1). Mx65 msDNA is encoded by a separate retron element located at a different position on the DZF1 chromosome. The coding region for Mx65 is estimated to be at least 10 kb from the region coding for Mx162 (*35, 36*). Mx65 is also present at a lower copy number, estimated at about 100 copies per cell genome, compared with the more abundant Mx162 at about 500 copies (*35*). The RT required to synthesize Mx65 is substantially different from the Mx162-RT in aminoacid sequence and size (Fig. 4), but clearly more related to Mx162-RT than to the RTs from *E. coli* retrons.

Over 20 strains of *M. xanthus* have been examined for the presence of msDNA (*37*; B. C. Lampson, M. Inouye and S. Inouye, unpublished). These strains of *M. xanthus* came from either the collection of Dale Kaiser (Stanford, CA) or the collection of Hans Reichenbach (Braunschweig, Federal Republic of Germany) and were isolated from various locations throughout the United States and Europe. All of the *M. xanthus* strains examined appeared to harbor an msDNA essentially the same as the prototype, Mx162, based on size and Southern blot hybridizations (38). In addition, all strains cross-hybridize at high stringency to a probe equivalent to the region encoding the Mx162-RT, indicating that all of these strains appear to contain a similar, if not identical, retron element equivalent to the prototype Mx162. Preliminary experiments also indicate that most, but not all, of the *M. xanthus* strains appear to contain a second, small species similar to Mx65. It is also credible to conclude that the collection of *M. xanthus* isolates examined are, in fact, different strains, as they display considerable restriction fragment-length polymorphism in Southern blot hybridizations of their chromosomal DNA (B. C. Lampson, M. Inouye and S. Inouye, unpublished).

Many other myxobacteria contain msDNA (37). These include *Myxococcus coralloides, Cystobacter violaceus, Cystobacter ferrugineus, Nannocystis exedens,* and *S. aurantiaca.* The msDNA from *S. aurantiaca,* Sal63, has been cloned and sequenced (12) (Fig. 1). This msDNA is similar to Mx162, with 81% sequence homology between their DNA strands and 86% homology between their RNA strands.

2. *E. coli*

Analysis of many different *M. xanthus* strains reveals that every strain appears to harbor the same or a very similar msDNA-retron. This is in marked contrast to the msDNAs of *E. coli*, which differ markedly in their primary nucleotide sequences, and are present in only a small number of *E. coli* strains.

The common *E. coli* laboratory strain, K-12, does not contain an msDNA-retron element, as determined by ethidium bromide straining of msDNA, Southern blot hybridizations of chromosomal DNA with a number of msDNA probes, and the RT-extension method (7, 39). However, the serendipitous discovery of msDNA in another strain, *E. coli* B (3), prompted a search for msDNA among a wide diversity of *E. coli* strains (39). More than 100 *E. coli* isolates were collected from sick as well as healthy humans. These isolates were screened for the presence of msDNA, using the RT-extension method, which specifically labels the msDNA molecule with $[\alpha\text{-}^{32}P]dCTP$ by primer extension of the 3' end of msDNA using AMV-RT (see the description of the reaction in Section II,E). Among the 115 isolates screened, only seven (6%) contained msDNA. The msDNAs from the seven positive strains displayed little, if any, sequence homology, based on Southern blot hybridizations. Moreover, if the gene for the Ec67-RT is used as a probe against chromosomal DNA digests from the seven positive *E. coli* strains, only the original host strain, Cl-1, cross-hybridizes, indicating that the msDNA-associated RT genes also share little sequence similarity (39).

The usefulness of a random collection of isolates for making conclusions about the distribution of msDNA among natural populations of *E. coli* is limited, as these isolates are not genetically defined. Therefore, a standard reference collection of 72 *E. coli* strains, the ECOR collection (*40, 41*), was examined for the presence of msDNA. The ECOR collection broadly represents the genotypic diversity of natural *E. coli* populations, based on the electrophoretic analysis of a large number of metabolic enzymes (*41*). Preliminary examination of the 72 ECOR strains revealed only nine strains (13%) harboring an msDNA-retron element (P. Herzer, T. Whittam and S. Inouye, unpublished).

B. Codon Usage

A study of the codon usage for the msDNA-linked ORF encoding the RT revealed another interesting difference between the msDNA-retrons of *E. coli* and *M. xanthus*. The codon usage for the msDNA-RT genes of *M. xanthus* is very typical for this species, in contrast to the *E. coli* retrons, in which the codon usage for the msDNA-RT is significantly different from the general codon usage of *E. coli*. For example, the distribution of the six possible codons designating arginine in the Mx162-RT gene are compared with arginine codon usage for five other known *M. xanthus* proteins (Table I). The two most commonly used arginine codons are CGC or CGG in the Mx162-RT gene (~90%) and in the Mx65-RT gene (~86%) and are similarly represented among the arginine codons used in other known *M. xanthus* proteins (~80%) (*1, 36*). This is in contrast to the *E. coli* RT genes, in which the most commonly used arginine codons, AGA or AGG (~65% for the Ec67-RT and ~55% for the Ec86-RT), are very rarely found among 199 *E.*

TABLE I
ARGININE CODON USAGE[a]

Codon	M. xanthus			E. coli		
	Av[b]	Mx162-RT[c]	Mx65-RT[c]	Av[d]	Ec67-RT[c]	Ec86-RT[c]
CGU	13.0	6.7	5.1	50.3	9.7	18.2
CGC	64.1	55.6	40.7	37.9	3.2	9.1
CGA	0	2.2	8.5	3.9	9.7	9.1
CGG	15.2	33.3	44.1	5.1	12.9	9.1
AGA	3.3	0	0.0	1.7	41.9	36.4
AGG	4.3	2.2	1.7	1.0	22.6	18.2

[a]Arginine codon usage in msDNA-RT genes of *M. xanthus* is similar to usage in an average host-cell gene. In contrast, this usage in the msDNA-RT genes of *E. coli* is atypical compared to an average host-cell gene. This is discussed in Section III,B.

[b]Percentage average from five *M. xanthus* genes (*1*).

[c]Percentage calculated for each codon.

[d]Percentage average from 199 *E. coli* genes (*42*).

coli genes surveyed (2.7%) (*42*). In addition to arginine, most of the other amino acids show a similar representation of codon usage (*1, 36*). These codon-usage data imply that, unlike the retrons of *M. xanthus*, the *E. coli* RT genes are probably not native to this species, and were perhaps introduced into *E. coli* late in evolution.

C. Origin and Evolution of msDNA

msDNA is synthesized by reverse transcription; thus, the genetic element that codes for the production of msDNA can be considered the first prokaryotic member of a large and diverse group, the retroelements (Table II). RT was first discovered in the virions of animal retroviruses and is essential to their life cycle, converting the viral RNA genome into a double-stranded DNA copy that then integrates as a provirus into the chromosome of the infected cell (*43, 44*). Other viruses also require RT to replicate via an RNA intermediate. These include hepatitis B (*45*) and cauliflower mosaic virus (*46*). In addition, a large number of mobile elements, transposons, introns, pseudogenes, repetitive sequences, and plasmids from a variety of eukaryotic cells replicate or are believed to be generated by reverse transcription (*47, 48*).

Shortly after the discovery of retroviral RT, a number of reports appeared that described the purification of RT from *E. coli* and the synthesis of cDNA *in vitro* (*49–52*). However, the gene encoding this enzyme activity has not been determined, and it is not clear whether it is related to the msDNA-retron element, as the RT reported earlier was purified from *E. coli* K-12, which lacks an msDNA element. Among the different classes of retroelements (Table II), the element coding for the production of msDNA has been called a retron because of its seemingly more primitive form compared with

TABLE II
RETROELEMENT FAMILIES[a]

Type	Virion	Integrase	LTR	RT	Example
Retrovirus	+	+	+	+	RSV, HIV, MoMLV, Lenti
Pararetrovirus	+	−	+	+	Hepatitis B, cauliflower, mosaic
Retrotransposon	−	+	+	+	Ty, copia
Retroposon	−	+	−	+	SINES, LINES, introns, mt. plasmids
Retron	?	?	−	+	msDNA
Retrosequence	−	−	−	−	cDNA genes, pseudogenes

[a]Elements encoding RTs arose by reverse transcription and make up the different retroelement families. The prokaryote retroelement that produces msDNA is given the new class name "retron" because of its more primitive structure. See Section III,C. LTR, Long terminal repeat; RSV, Rous sarcoma virus; HIV, human immunodeficiency virus; MoMLV, Moloney murine leukemia virus.

retroviruses (it lacks long terminal repeats and perhaps virus-like particles). Also, it is unknown whether retrons contain an integrase function to promote the transfer of the element into a new host genome.

The discovery of msDNA and the retroelement that produces it in bacteria raises an interesting speculation about the origin of RT and retroviruses. Based on the distribution of msDNA and codon-usage data, the msDNA-RT gene of myxobacteria appears to be as old as other genes native to *M. xanthus*. It is thought that the myxobacteria, common soil organisms found in many diverse habitats around the world, evolved from their nearest bacterial relative about 2×10^9 years ago (8). This places the existence of the RT gene some time before the emergence of eukaryotic cells (1.5–0.9×10^9 years ago). Does the msDNA-RT system represent the ancestral RT gene from which eukaryotic retroelements and retroviruses arose? Temin (4) has further speculated that bacterial retrons, representing the most primitive RT element, evolved into "retroposons," which can transpose then into "retrotransposons," which have long terminal repeats, finally giving rise to retroviruses, which can produce virus particles.

Unlike the retrons of *M. xanthus*, *E. coli* msDNA systems occur rarely, are heterogeneous in nature, and have an atypical amino-acid codon usage, suggesting that retrons were transmitted to *E. coli* from some other source (2). Clearly, much more information about the structure, mode of replication and transmission, and occurrence in nature is needed to better understand the origin and evolution of msDNA.

IV. Function of msDNA

As this review attests, a great deal has been learned about the structure and synthesis of msDNA, but virtually nothing has been learned about its function in the host cell. Indeed, deletion mutations of the msDNA-retrons Mx162 and Mx65 which co-reside in *M. xanthus* strain DZF1 have been constructed to look for possible functions (25, 36). Deletions of both retrons from the host chromosome had no effect on cellular growth, motility, fruiting-body formation, spore formation, or germination. Likewise, the rare occurrence of retrons in *E. coli* strains argues against an essential function for msDNA in the biology of *E. coli*. However, given the present information about msDNA, we may speculate about possible functional roles for this unusual molecule.

The retrons of *E. coli* appear to have originated from some other, presumably bacterial, source and to have been transmitted to *E. coli* and inserted into the chromosome by a transposition-like mechanism. The msDNA molecule may have served a role in this process. For example, msDNA may serve as a primer to initiate the conversion of an RNA transcript of the retron element into a cDNA copy by the associated RT. The RT then synthesizes double-stranded cDNA, which could serve as the intermediate structure for transposition. Short DNA sequences complementary to the 3' end of Ec67 have been found at the terminal regions of the Ec67 retron, which could serve as primer (msDNA) binding sites.

Additionally, could the presence of RT and the abundant production of a hypervariable msDNA have some effect on the host cell? The suggestion has been made that msDNA might serve to prime the synthesis of a cDNA of a specific host gene, with subsequent gene conversion, provided that the host-gene mRNA contains a short sequence complementary to the 3' end of msDNA (2). Such an event could have a profound effect on the evolution of the bacterial genome, as the gene conversion (reverse transcription and integration) of an actively transcribed gene could induce a high degree of mutation because of the poor fidelity of DNA polymerization by RT (53–55), resulting in a new gene product able to perform new functions.

V. Summary

The msDNA-retron element represents the first prokaryotic member of the large and diverse retroelement family found in many eukaryotic genomes (Table II). This prokaryotic retroelement exists as a single copy element in the chromosome of two different bacterial groups: the common soil microbe *M. xanthus* and the enteric bacterium *E. coli*. It encodes an RT similar to the polymerases found in retroviruses, containing most of the strictly conserved amino acids found in all RTs. The RT is responsible for the production of an unusual extrachromosomal RNA–DNA molecule known as msDNA. Each composed of a short single strand of RNA and a short single strand of DNA, msDNAs vary considerably in their primary nucleotide sequences, but all share certain secondary structural features, including the unique 2',5' branch linkage that joins the 5' end of the DNA chain to the 2' position of an internal guanosine residue of the RNA strand. It is proposed that msDNA is synthesized by reverse transcription of a precursor RNA transcribed from a region of the retron containing the genes *msr* (encoding the RNA portion) and *msd* (encoding the DNA portion) and the ORF (encoding the RT). The precursor RNA transcript folds into a stable secondary structure that serves as both the primer and the template for the synthesis of msDNA.

The msDNA-retron elements of *E. coli* are found in less than 10% of all strains observed, are heterogeneous in nature, and have an atypical amino-acid codon usage for this species, suggesting that this element was transmitted to *E. coli* by some other source. The presence of directly repeated 26-base-pair sequences flanking the junctions of the Ec67-retron of *E. coli* also suggests that it may be a mobile element. However, the msDNA-retrons of *M. xanthus* appear to be as old as other genes native to this species, based on codon-usage data for the RT genes and the fact that every strain of *M.*

xanthus appears to have the same type of msDNA. If the msDNA-retron element originated with the myxobacteria, it would place the existence of retrons before the appearance of eukaryotic cells, suggesting that the bacterial element is perhaps the ancestral gene from which eukaryotic retroviruses and other retroelements evolved.

Many questions remain to be answered about msDNA, including: What function does msDNA have?; How is the branch structure synthesized?; How does synthesis of msDNA terminate *in vivo*?; Can the retron element encoding msDNA transpose to a new genome, and does msDNA have a role in this process?; and do msDNA and RT have any effect on the host cell? Further investigation of the msDNA-retron system will no doubt answer many of these questions and may provide a new tool to better understand the evolution of RT and retroelements and their effects on shaping the genomes of both eukaryotes and prokaryotes.[2]

ACKNOWLEDGMENTS

We thank Mei-Yin Hsu and Peter Herzer for their help in construction of the figures, and T. A. Webster for help with the aminoacid alignment. This work was supported by US Public Health Service (PHS) grant GM26843 and by a grant from Takara Shuzo Co., Ltd. B.C.L. was supported by PHS Research Fellowship grant F32GM11970-O1A1.

REFERENCES

1. S. Inouye, M.-Y. Hsu, S. Eagle and M. Inouye, *Cell* **56**, 709 (1989).
2. B. C. Lampson, J. Sun, M.-Y. Hsu, J. Vallejo-Ramirez, S. Inouye and M. Inouye, *Science* **243**, 1033 (1989).
3. D. Lim and W. K. Maas, *Cell* **56**, 891 (1989).
4. H. M. Temin, *Nature* **339**, 254 (1989).
5. H. E. Varmus, *Cell* **56**, 721 (1989).
6. D. Lim and W. K. Maas, *Mol. Microbiol.* **3**, 1141 (1989).
7. T. Yee, T. Furuichi, S. Inouye and M. Inouye, *Cell* **38**, 203 (1984).
8. D. Kaiser, *ARGen* **20**, 539 (1986).
9. L. J. Shimkets, *CRC Crit. Rev. Microbiol.* **14**, 195 (1987).
10. T. Yee and M. Inouye, *J. Bact.* **145**, 1257 (1981).
11. T. Furuichi, A. Dhundale, M. Inouye and S. Inouye, *Cell* **48**, 47 (1987).
12. A. Dhundale, Ph.D. thesis. State University of New York, Stony Brook, New York, 1987.
13. A. M. Maxam and W. Gilbert, in "Methods in Enzymology" (L. Grossman and K. Moldave, eds.), Vol. 65, p. 499. Academic Press, New York, 1980.
14. A. Dhundale, B. Lampson, T. Furuichi, M. Inouye and S. Inouye, *Cell* **51**, 1105 (1987).
15. T. Furuichi, S. Inouye and M. Inouye, *Cell* **48**, 55 (1987).
16. J. Arenas and J. Hurwitz, *JBC* **262**, 4274 (1987).
17. B. Ruskin and M. R. Green, *Science* **229**, 135 (1985).
18. R. A Padgett, P. J. Grabowski, M. M. Konarska, S. R. Seiler and P. A. Sharp, *ARB* **55**, 1119 (1986).
19. T. Kogoma, *J. Bact.* **166**, 361 (1986).
20. R. Karwan and U. Wintersberger, *JBC* **263**, 14970 (1988).
21. M. Viswanathan, M. Inouye and S. Inouye, *JBC* **264**, 13665 (1989).
22. S. Inouye, T. Furuichi, A. Dhundale and M. Inouye, *in* "Molecular Biology of RNA: New

Perspectives" (M. Inouye and B. S. Dudock, eds.), p. 271. Academic Press, San Diego, California, 1987.
23. N. D. F. Grindley and R. R. Reed, *ARB* **54**, 863 (1985).
24. N. L. Craig and N. Kleckner, in *"Escherichia coli* and *Salmonella typhimurium"* (F. C. Neidhardt, ed.), p. 1054. American Society for Microbiology, Washington, D.C., 1987.
25. A. Dhundale, T. Furuichi, M. Inouye and S. Inouye, *J. Bact.* **170**, 5620 (1988).
26. H. Toh, H. Hayashida and T. Miyata, *Nature* **305**, 827 (1983).
27. Y. Xiong and T. H. Eickbush, *Mol. Biol. Evol.* **5**, 675 (1988).
28. K. Moelling, D. P. Bolognesi, H. Bauer, W. Busen, H. W. Plassmann and P. Hausen, *Nature NB* **234**, 240 (1971).
29. M. S. Johnson, M. A. McClure, D.-F. Feng, J. Gray and R. F. Doolittle, *PNAS* **83**, 7648 (1986).
30. N. Tanese and S. P. Goff, *PNAS* **85**, 1777 (1988).
31. B. C. Lampson, M. Viswanathan, M. Inouye and S. Inouye, *JBC* **265**, 8490 (1990).
32. M.-Y. Hsu, S. Inouye and M. Inouye, *JBC* **264**, 6214 (1989).
33. N. Weiss, H. Teich, H. Varmus and J. Coffin, in *"RNA Tumor Viruses,"* Vol. 2, p. 385. CSH Lab, Cold Spring Harbor, New York, 1985.
34. B. C. Lampson, M. Inouye and S. Inouye, *Cell* **56**, 701 (1989).
35. A. Dhundale, M. Inouye and S. Inouye, *JBC* **263**, 9055 (1988).
36. S. Inouye, P. J. Herzer and M. Inouye, *PNAS*, **87**, 942 (1990).
37. A. Dhundale, T. Furuichi, S. Inouye and M. Inouye, *J. Bact.* **164**, 914 (1985).
38. E. M. Southern, *JMB* **98**, 503 1975).
39. J. Sun, P. J. Herzer, M. P. Weinstein, B. C. Lampson, M. Inouye and S. Inouye, *PNAS* **86**, 7208 (1989).
40. H. Ochman and R. K. Selander, *J. Bact.* **157**, 690 (1984).
41. R. K. Selander, D. A. Caugant and T. S. Whittam, in *"Escherichia coli* and *Salmonella typhimurium"* (F. C. Neidhardt, ed.), p. 1625. American Society for Microbiology, Washington, D.C., 1987.
42. T. Maruyama, T. Gojobori, S. Aota and T. Ikemura, *NARes* **14**, r151 (1986).
43. D. Baltimore, *Nature* **226**, 1209 (1970).
44. H. M. Temin and S. Mizutoni, *Nature* **226**, 1211 (1970).
45. C. Seeger, D. Ganem and H. E. Varmus, *Science* **232**, 477 (1986).
46. P. Pfeiffer and T. Hohn, *Cell* **33**, 781 (1983).
47. A. M. Weiner, P. L. Deininger and A. Efstratiadis, *ARB* **55**, 631 (1986).
48. J. D. Boeke and V. G. Corces, *Annu. Rev. Microbiol.* **43**, 403 (1989).
49. M. Beljanski, *C. R. Hebd. Seances Acad. Sci., Ser. D* **276**, 1625 (1973).
50. M. Beljanski and M. Beljanski, *Biochem. Genet.* **17**, 163 (1974).
51. T. P. Lushnikova, V. F. Podgornyi, N. P. Sedel'nikova, V. E. Chizhikov, V. V. Vlasov, N. N. Levina, A. G. Romashchenko and R. I. Salganik, *Mol. Biol.* **13**, 898 (1979).
52. N. V. Vorob'eva, V. L. T. Nebrat, V. A. Potapov, A. G. Romashchenko, R. I. Salganik and L. F. Yushkova, *Mol. Biol.* **17**, 770 (1983).
53. B. D. Preston, J. P. Bernard and L. A. Loeb, *Science* **242**, 1168 (1988).
54. J. D. Roberts, K. Bebenek and T. A. Kunkel, *Science* **242**, 1171 (1988).
55. J. Cairns, J. Overbaugh and S. Miller, *Nature* **335**, 142 (1988).

NOTE ADDED IN PROOF. Recent work indicates a link between some retrons of *E. coli* and known bacteriophages. The large segment of foreign DNA (34 kb) associated with the retron element that synthesizes msDNA Ec67 also appears to contain some genes homologous to the *E. coli* phage 186 (a relative of P2). It appears that a prophage-like element of 186 may have incorporated an msDNA retron into its genome. Some recent papers published or in press about msDNA are: P. J. Herzer, S. Inouye, M. Inouye and T. S. Whittam, *J. Bact.* **172**, in press (1990); M.-Y. Hsu, M. Inouye and S. Inouye, *PNAS*, in press (1990); Y. Xiong and T. H. Eickbush, *EMBO J.* **9**, 3353 (1990).

Vertebrate Protamine Genes and the Histone-to-Protamine Replacement Reaction

RAFAEL OLIVA*
AND GORDON H. DIXON†

*Unidad de Fisiologia
Grupo de Genética Molecular
Barcelona, Spain
†Department of Medical Biochemistry
Faculty of Medicine
University of Calgary
Calgary, Alberta, Canada T2N 4N1

25

Progress in Nucleic Acid Research
and Molecular Biology, Vol. 40

In contrast to the relative constancy of the complement of the five histones H1, H2A, H2B, H3, and H4, complexed with DNA in somatic chromatin of eukaryotes, an almost bewildering variety of basic proteins can be
extracted from the corresponding sperm nuclei of most animals and some
plants. In 1969, Bloch (1) compiled a catalog of sperm proteins and suggested
a classification into five classes of such proteins as follows:

Type 1: True protamines (small, arginine-rich)
Type 2: Stable protamines or keratinous protamines (arginine-rich, but
        also contain cysteine)
Type 3: Intermediate sperm basic proteins (contain histidine and/or
        lysine in addition to arginine
Type 4: Somatic-like histones
Type 5: No basic proteins detected in the nucleus of the mature sperm
        (ameboid in shape)

More detailed studies (2–6) have, in general, confirmed this classification. Subirana (2, 3) suggested an alternative classification by dividing sperm
proteins into protamines and sperm histones. Protamines are defined as
having a cysteine-plus-arginine composition of 45–80 mol% and a serine-
plus-threonine content of 10–25 mol%. This broader protamine class would
include Bloch's Types 1 and 2 plus some of the proteins in the intermediate
type 3 (e.g., "*Mytilus*-type" protamines). Subirana's other class is called
"sperm histones," but is divided into four subclasses of nuclear basic proteins, having (a) no detectable change in the family of very lysine-rich H1
histones; (b) slight changes in the family of H1 histones; (c) additional sperm-
specific basic proteins; and (d) considerable changes in histones H1 and
H2B.

There are detailed reviews of the whole range of sperm basic proteins (4,
5). Our discussion focuses on Bloch's classes Type 1 ("true" protamines) and
Type 2 ("stable" protamines), for which substantial molecular information is
now available. However, mention should be made of an additional class of
sperm protamines found in the sperm nuclei of certain flat fish in the order
Pleuronectiformes (7–9). These protamines are rich in arginine and serine,
but are very large (80,000–200,000 daltons) compared to the typical true and
stable protamines ranging from 5000 to 10,000 Da.

I. History

A. True Protamines

The first description of a true protamine, and, indeed, the naming of the
molecule, came from the pioneer studies by Miescher (10), more than a

century ago, on the nitrogenous base that he found complexed with the acidic "nuclein," later called deoxyribonucleic acid (DNA), in the sperm of the Rhine salmon (*Salmo salar*). Subsequent studies by Kossel in 1928 and 1929 (*11*) and by Felix in 1960 (*12*) established the polypeptide nature of protamines, but it was the meticulous application of the new separation and aminoacid sequencing methods that began the modern era of protamine research. In addition, the cytochemical visualization of protamines with the acidic dye Fast Green was developed into a rapid method for surveying the distribution of protamines in tissue sections (*13*). The pioneer studies by Ando's group are detailed in an excellent monograph by Ando *et al.*, (*14*), who used the classical methods of end-group analysis, proteolytic digestion, isolation, sequencing, and overlapping of the protamine peptides. The presence of several arginine tracts in each protamine with very similar sequences plus the limited variety of other amino acids made this approach technically difficult, but the deduced sequences for several fish protamines (Fig. 1) were proven substantially correct upon re-examination by automatic microsequencing (*15*) or by cloning of protamine cDNAs and genes (*16, 17*).

The other type of true protamine for which the aminoacid sequence was subsequently obtained was the chicken protamine (galline) (*18*), the initial sequencing also being performed by the classical method of overlapping peptide fragments. It should be noted that, historically, many protamines have been named by affixing the ending "-ine" either to the genus name, e.g., galline from *Gallus domesticus* or salmine from *Salmo*, or sometimes to the species name, e.g., iridine from *Salmo irideus*, an archaic name for *Salmo gairdnerii* [or, more properly, Onchorhynchus mykiss (see below)], the rainbow trout. However, this nomenclature is not consistently used today. We have recently sequenced the genes encoding the chicken protamine (*19*), and found that the predicted aminoacid sequence showed substantial differences from the sequence determined earlier (*18*). One explanation to account for these differences would be the possibility of the existence of different allelic variants of protamine in different poultry strains, so that Nakano *et al.* (*18*) would have sequenced one of these and Oliva and Dixon (*19*) another. However, a recent sequencing of 28 aminoacid residues at the amino terminus of galline confirm the order of amino acids predicted from the genes (*19*).

In addition, the fact that distinctive amino acids such as threonine or valine, present in chicken protamine polypeptides, are conserved in position in the aminoacid sequence of quail (*Coturnix japonica*, a second bird species) only if the sequence redetermined by Oliva and Dixon (*19*) is considered, makes the probability of different allelic variants in chicken much less likely.

Contrasting with the number of different protamines present in the salmonids, there is usually only a single component in birds (*19–21*). A further

	Protein sequences	cDNA	Genomic DNA
1a		pRTP43, pPc6b	
b		pRTP178	TP16,21
2a	CIII	pRTP59,pTp11	TP101
b		pRTP242,pTp8	TP15,17
c	Ia		
3a	II		
	Ib		
	CI		
	CIII	pTp4	TP14

Rainbow trout (Iridines)

Chum Salmon (Salmines)

Herring (Clupeines)

Tuna (Thynnines)

Pike (Esox lucius)

Sturine B (Caspian sturgeon)

Stelline A

remarkable feature of the bird protamines is their strong similarity, particularly in the amino-terminal region, to the stable protamine-P1 family of mammalian species (Fig. 3). However, as seen below, a major difference is the absence of cysteine residues, which are a constant feature of the "stable" mammalian P1 protamines, in bird protamines.

B. Stable or Cysteine-Containing Protamines

The essential characteristic of the "stable" protamines (also called "basic keratins" in 1) is the presence of six to nine cysteine residues per mole (see Fig. 3), which allow the formation of inter- and intradisulfide bridges in the protamine molecule. Such covalent disulfide bridges impart an additional degree of cross-linking and hence stability to the sperm chromatin in the mammalian sperm nucleus, which can only be disrupted and the protamine extracted following cleavage by treatment with high concentrations of thiol in the presence of strong denaturing agents. This type of protamine is present mainly in mammals (6, 22–24), but a protamine with similar properties may also be present in insect sperm (31). The first mammalian protamine sequenced was from bull (25). This was followed by that from boar, ram, human, stallion, goat, mouse, rat, and rabbit.

Figure 3 summarizes the presently available aminoacid sequences for the mammalian and bird protamines. There is a remarkable similarity among mammalian protamines and those of quail and chicken, although there is a complete absence of cysteine in the avian protamines.

All protamines are expressed at a late stage of spermatogenesis, a multistep differentiation process involving major changes in genetic activity and rearrangements of the chromatin structure by which the spermatogonia, the stem cells, undergo meiosis, producing haploid spermatids that further differentiate into spermatozoa (as described in Section VI and pictured in Fig. 16). The chromatin of spermatogonia, spermatocytes, or round spermatids has the typical nucleosome structure of any other somatic cell. However, during spermiogenesis, this nucleosome structure is lost in most species and replaced by a highly compact, genetically inactive nucleoprotamine complex

---

FIG. 1. Alignment of bony-fish protamines. The species name and primary protamine name are indicated on the left. Alternative names or matches to other sequenced protamines are indicated at the right, together with their origin (protein, cDNA, or genomic DNA). At the top, the presence of long arginine cluster (L+) or short positive regions (S+) and the presence of non-positive amino acids (●) is indicated. Gaps have been introduced to maximize similarity among protamines. Boxed regions indicate the non-positive residues. References are as follows: rainbow trout protamines (14–17, 37–43, 45), Chum salmon protamine (66), herring (14), tuna (277–280), pike (281), and sturgeon (282, 283). The nomenclature of the rainbow trout protamine sequence and their relationships with cloned cDNA or gene sequences (inset, "Other Names," top right) are discussed in 15.

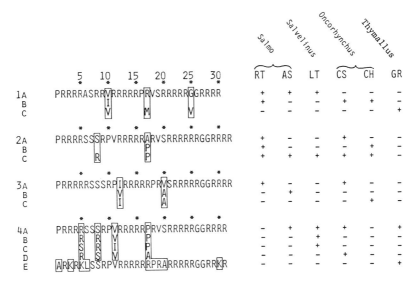

FIG. 2. Distribution of salmonid protamine aminoacid sequences among six salmonid species. Positions at which single aminoacid changes occur are boxed. The plus sign indicates that the protamine in that species was purified and sequenced and the minus sign indicates the absence of a protamine (42). RT, Rainbow trout; AS, Atlantic salmon; LT, lake trout; CS, Chinook salmon; CH, Chum salmon; GR, Arctic grayling.

(26–34). The implication of the aminoacid sequences in protamines for evolution and function is discussed in Sections IV, VI, and VIII.

II. Protamine Aminoacid Sequences

Figures 1–3 summarize the aminoacid sequences of the Type-1 and Type-2 protamines of vertebrates that have been reported. The sequences have been divided into groups, taking into account mainly the aminoacid similarities, rather than specific chemical properties. For example, quail and chicken protamines, which do not contain cysteines (and are Type-1 protamines), have been aligned with the cysteine-containing mammalian P1 family (Type-2) protamines (Fig. 3). In an attempt to classify all of the vertebrate Type-1 and -2 protamines in groups of marked aminoacid similarity and

FIG. 3. (A) Alignment of the aminoacid sequences of all mammalian protamines with those of avian species. Boxed regions indicate identities. Protamine protein, cDNA, or genomic sequences are from the following references: bull (6, 25, 49, 79, 80), ram (55), quail (20), chicken (19), mouse (69, 81), rat (54), rabbit (53), human (51, 58, 59, 83), stallion (52, 56), and boar (50, 78). (B) Alignment of mammalian P2 protamines. References are: mouse (57, 69), and human (59, 60, 88). (C) Alignment of dogfish protamines (85).

A Mammalian P1 - Avian Protamine Family

```
BULL      A R Y R C C L T H S G S R C R R R R R - - - - C R R R R R - V C C R - R - Y T V I R C T R Q - -
GOAT      A R Y R C C L T H S R S R C R R R R R - - - - C R R R R R - V C C R - R - Y T V V R C T R Q - -
RAM       A R Y R C C L T H S R S R C R R R R R - - - - C R R R R R - V C C R - R - Y T V V R C T R Q - -
QUAIL     A R Y R R T R T R S R S R R R R S - - - S R R R R Y G R S Y R S V G R R R R - R - Y G R R R R R R Y
CHICKEN   A R Y R R S R T R S R S P R S R R R R R - - S P R R R R Y G S A R R S R R S V G G R R R R - R - Y G S R R R R R Y
MOUSE     A R Y R C C R S K S R S R C - R R R R R C - - - C C R R R R R - C C R R - R - S Y T - I R C - K K Y
RAT       A R Y R C C R S K S R S R C - R R R R R C - - - C C R R R R R - C C R R - R - S Y T - I Y T - K K Y
RABBIT    V R Y R C C R S Q S R S R C - R R R R R C - - - R R R R R V R - - C C R R - R - I Y T - L R C - K R Y
HUMAN     A R Y R C C R S Q S R S R Y Y R Q R S - - R R R R S C T R R A M R C C R P R - R - Y R - P R C - R R H -
STALLION  A R Y R C C R S Q S Q S R R Q R S - - - R Q R R - R R R R R V R - V C C R - R - Y T V L R C R R R R -
BOAR      A R Y R C C R S H S R S R C - R P R R R R C - - R R R R C C P R R R R A V C C R - R - Y T V I R C R R -

CONSENSUS a R Y R c c t t h S r S r c - r R r r r c - - - - r R R R R c c r r r r - v c c R - R - Y t - R c r r r y
```

B Mammalian P2 - Protamines

```
HUMAN   R T H G G S H Y R R - R H C S R R R R L H R I H R R G H R S C R R R K R S C R H R R R H R R G C R - T R K R - - - - T R R H
MOUSE   R T H R G H H H H R R - R H C S R K R L H R I H Y R - R S C R R R R H S C R H R R R G C R S R R R R C R C R Y C R R H H
```

C Dogfish Protamines

```
Z1   G S C K P K K K Q A P - - C F L R R R H L R R L N V C K R D T S K T Y R R R H V R R L P K K R R R C
Z2   M K C G R K R R R R R R H A C K R K K K R - - - - A C K Q R S S - T I V R A H L V H R R A A R R - - C P
```

possibly sharing a homologous relationship, we have arranged them in the following four groups: bony fishes, cartilaginous fishes, mammalian P1–avian protamine family, and mammalian P2. However, no clear or specific aminoacid consensus is evident among these different groups, other than the common characteristics shared by all protamines, such as the presence of four or five arginine clusters and their overall aminoacid composition (Cys + Arg = 45–80% and Ser + Thr = 10–25%).

These substantial differences in size and aminoacid sequence may indicate different mechanisms for nucleosome disassembly during spermiogenesis and for nucleoprotamine formation; for example, chicken protamine is almost exactly twice as long as the fish protamines and is much more efficient in disassembling nucleosomes *in vitro* (33, 34). Consequently, different nucleoprotamine structures are likely to be present in the sperm nuclei of different species. Figure 4 shows two models proposed for the

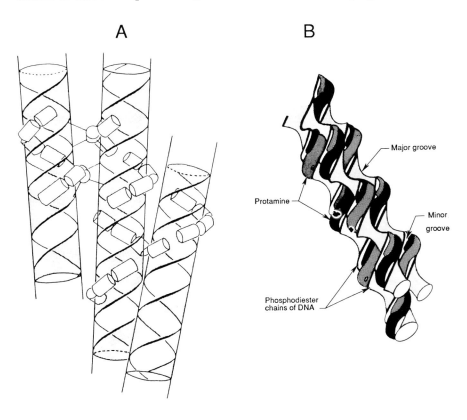

A   B

Major groove

Protamine

Minor groove

Phosphodiester chains of DNA

FIG. 4. Two models for the nucleoprotamine structure (35, 36).

structure of the nucleoprotamine (35, 36). The inability so far to detect an elementary unit in the structure of the nucleoprotamine as compared to the well-characterized structure of the nucleosome may be a consequence of the extremely high variability of the aminoacid sequence of protamines, which has made the determination of conserved structures difficult.

A. Bony-Fish Protamines

Figures 1 and 2 show an alignment of the presently available sequences of the bony-fish protamines. Overall, these protamines can be described as having four long arginine clusters (four to six arginines) and two short arginine clusters (one to three arginines) separated by a small number of characteristic residues such as serine, proline, or glycine/valine.

1. RAINBOW TROUT PROTAMINES

Several protamine aminoacid sequences from rainbow trout have been determined, using protein (15, 37), or deduced from cDNA (38, 39) or genomic sequences (40, 41). In each case, a set of one to four protamine aminoacid sequences was obtained, and each set usually had one or more unique members. These results, taken together, suggest considerable sequence variability, perhaps involving differences among individual fish or among separate geographic populations. Alternatively, the reported sequence differences may have been caused by the isolation of different subsets of a larger number of protamines possessed by all rainbow trout. To answer some of these questions, McKay et al. (15) purified all of the protamines separable by ion-exchange and reversed-phase chromatography, six in number, from a single testis, and completely sequenced all of them. The results are shown in Fig. 1 (top six sequences).

The six protamine sequences have been classified into three families according to their sequence similarities and differences. The family-1 and family-2 groups were suggested previously from cDNA sequencing studies (16). The sequence differences between these two families are best illustrated by comparing both the aminoacid and DNA sequences of protamines 1a and 2b (Figs. 1 and 2). By comparison with protamine 2b, protamine 1a has two fewer amino acids, apparently having lost codons 6 or 7 and 22 or 23 (to remove one serine and one arginine residue, respectively), and protamine 1a has two aminoacid substitutions, Ser → Ala at position 6 and Pro → Arg at position 9, each resulting from single-base changes in the corresponding codons. Protamine 3a is deemed sufficiently different from the family-2 sequences (e.g., protamine 2b) to warrant a separate group, because it has an apparent frame-shift in the middle region of its sequence caused by changes in the lengths of two of its tracts of arginine residues. No cDNA (38) or genomic DNA (40, 41) sequence has yet been found for this protamine.

This grouping also suggests that rainbow trout contains three, rather than two (40, 41), families of protamine genes.

Rainbow trout protamine aminoacid sequences obtained previously, using protein cDNA and genomic DNA sequencing methods, are also shown in Fig. 1 (sequences 7–13) and are also indicated by their names on the right side of Fig. 1 when there is a match to one of the six protein sequences.

The differences between these sets of sequences have several possible explanations. The trout used came from Japan (14, 37, 41, 43), Denmark (16, 40), the United States (40), and Canada (42), so there may be sequence differences among various geographic populations. Second, as starting material from more than one fish was often used, there may be sequence variants among individual fish in the same population. Third, each method used may have found only a subset of the total number of protamines present in all rainbow trout. Finally, there may be experimental errors.

Ando and Watanabe (37) determined the aminoacid sequences of three protamines from rainbow trout (S. irideus) by manual sequencing methods. Sequences Ia, II, and Ib differ from 2a, 2b, and 3a only in the lengths of some of the arginine tracts. Most notable is the sequence R–R–V–S instead of R–V–S in the middle section of each sequence. Sakai et al. (39) also used rainbow trout from Japan (referred to as S. gairdnerii), but found the sequence R–V–S in their protamines using cDNA sequencing methods. It is not clear whether S. irideus and S. gairdnerii are distinct species. In Canada, the species names gairdneri, gairdnerii, irideus, and several others have been used by different taxonomists for rainbow trout variants, which are now generally considered to be a single species called gairdneri (44). However, recently the rainbow trout has been renamed O. mykiss, placing it in the same genus as the Pacific salmons (274). The closely related cutthroat trout (S. clarki) is similarly renamed, Oncorhynchus clarki. We cannot unequivocally eliminate the possibility that Ando and Watanabe (37) used a different species; however, we consider it likely that sequences Ia, II, and Ib contain errors resulting from the extreme difficulties of purifying and sequencing these proteins using the methods available at that time.

Four of the five aminoacid sequences obtained by sequencing cDNAs are identical to four of the sequences determined from a single testis. The pTp4 sequence of Jenkins (45) closely resembles sequence 1b except that the two glycine residues near the carboxy-terminal end of the sequence are shifted by one position. Since this is the only rainbow trout sequence reported with this unusual Gly–Gly positioning, the existence of this unusual protamine requires confirmation. None of the cDNA sets contains sequences corresponding to sequence 2a or 3a. Since the protamine content of trout testis varies with the developmental age of the testis (46), the differences obtained by these cDNA methods and the isolation of less than complete sets of sequences probably reflects the mRNA population of the particular testes used in each case.

The absence of sequences 2a and 3a may indicate that these proteins are produced earlier in testis development, so that the corresponding mRNAs were present in very low levels in the more mature testes used in these studies. Two previous observations support this suggestion. Protamine peak C2 on CM-cellulose was larger than the C3 peak during the early stages of testis development (46). The less basic of the two protamine bands on poly-acrylamide gel electrophoresis (PAGE) in acid urea appeared earlier in testis development than the more basic protamine band (30). These observations indicate that at least some of protamine 2a, 2b, and 3a are produced early in testis development, so that there is some developmental regulation of the levels of particular protamines.

Three of the four aminoacid sequences obtained from genomic DNA sequencing match the three sequences in family 2. The fourth sequence, TP14, may represent an additional family-2 sequence; however, its expression as a polypeptide remains to be established by isolation and sequencing of the protein. The absence of sequences from families 1 and 3 can probably be attributed to the limitations of the methods used to construct the genomic library (16).

In conclusion, most of the protamine sequences reported for rainbow trout can be matched to one of the six sequences isolated from a single testis. The major cause of the differences among the sequences initially reported is likely to have been the isolation of different subsets of these six sequences. The available data clearly demonstrate that an individual rainbow trout can have at least six distinct protamines; however, whether all rainbow trout contain these same six protamines remains an open question. Perhaps the individual members of each protein family are the products of genetic alleles at one or two gene loci, so that other individual fish may have more or fewer members in each protein family.

2. OTHER SALMONID PROTAMINES

Figures 1 and 2 illustrate the extremely high similarity and, in some cases, identity between protamine components of the salmon and rainbow trout families. In Fig. 2, a comprehensive chart for all available salmonid sequences (42) is compared to the aminoacid sequences in rainbow trout. In the left part of Fig. 2, a listing of the different protamines with their nomenclature is shown. On the right side, the presence of the component in a particular species is shown by a plus sign, and its absence by a minus sign. It is interesting to note that the changes occur in a small number of positions; in addition, in many cases, the variant amino acids have common chemical properties (e.g., isoleucine to valine, alanine to proline, valine to alanine).

These hypervariable regions are likely to reflect domains of relatively less essential function as compared to the consensus regions.

3. OTHER BONY-FISH PROTAMINES

The closest member to the salmonid protamines for which the aminoacid sequence is now available is from pike (*Esox lucius*) (Fig. 1). The sequence similarity is consistent with its homologous relationship. Among the differences are the presence of an extra glycine at position 9, the substitution of the arginine in position 19 by lysine, and the substitution of valine for methionine at position 20. However, the extra glycine is a neutral amino acid, and lysine, like arginine is positively charged, so these changes are likely to have little effect on the structure of the nucleoprotamine. In order of aminoacid similarity, the next most similar protamines to those of trout are the clupeines (*14*) of Pacific herring.

Three different clupeines have been identified: YI, YII, and Z. Type YI is more conserved in the amino-terminal half of the molecule; the major change is the substitution of TT for the VS dipeptide. Also, one of the glycines of the dipeptide GG has been replaced by an alanine. This alanine is the only non-basic amino acid present in the carboxy-terminal domain of the YII and Z protamines. The main difference between YII and Z is the presence of an extra threonine or serine intercalated in the first consensus long arginine cluster. In tuna (thynnines), a marked amino acid similarity is still present. The only differences from the previous bony fishes are a proline-to-tyrosine change at position 17, and the substitution of the VS motif (or TT in YI herring) by an ST motif followed by two alanines. In addition, at the amino-terminal part of the molecule there is an extra E or Q in the same position (6) as the S in component Z of herring clupeine.

The most marked changes in the aminoacid sequence among this group of bony-fish protamine are found in the sturgeon (sturines). They have been included in this group because the amino terminus is notably similar to the preceding protamines in its general characteristics: an initial neutral amino acid followed by a long positively charged tract. The AST sequence matches quite well with A/S–S–S, and is also followed by a positive residue (a lysine in this case) as compared to one or two arginines in the rest of the protamines in this group. In the third consensus non-positive cluster, P V/I, has been substituted by LK or PQ. This is also followed by a long positive cluster. However, the rest of the molecule has little similarity to the consensus in this group.

4. OVERALL AMINOACID SIMILARITY OF BONY-FISH PROTAMINES

The amino-terminal residue of these protamines is always either a proline (24 out of 28) or an alanine (4 out of 28). This is also followed by a tetra-arginine cluster. Remarkably, all have a serine at position 9 or 10 (allowing for gaps). In many cases, it forms part of a di-serine or tri-serine motif. The primary hydroxyl group of serine is susceptible to phosphorylation, as has been shown in the rainbow trout (47), and the process of phosphorylation–dephosphorylation is known to be involved in modulating the binding of these molecules to DNA (183–185). Either a valine or an isoleucine residue is remarkably well-conserved at position 13, and is usually preceded by a proline and followed by a penta-arginine cluster and a second proline.

The carboxy-terminal portion is also well-conserved within this group, the consensus sequence being $PRVSR_6GGR_4$. In tuna, the glycine pair is replaced by two valines. Interestingly, these two valines are also present in a similar carboxy-terminal position in mammalian protamines (goat and ram) (55) (Fig. 3).

B. Mammalian P1–Avian Protamines

Classically, these two types of protamines (mammalian P1, on the one hand, and avian, on the other) would probably have been described separately; however, the recent redetermination (19) of the sequence for chicken protamine has revealed distinct aminoacid similarities that were not as well-marked when using the sequence previously determined (18). These marked similarities have been further strengthened by the recent determination of a second avian protamine sequence, from quail (20) (Fig. 3). Overall, these similarities allow the postulation of a homologous relationship between mammalian P1 and avian protamines.

Most of these molecules have a characteristic amino-terminal tetrapeptide sequence ARYR. The exception is rabbit (53), with a change of A to V at the first residue. However, because of the similar chemical properties of these two amino acids, this change is not likely to have a major effect on the structure of the nucleoprotamine. The sequence ARYR is followed by a conserved SRSR motif followed by a cluster of five to seven arginines. These sequences are also present in the marsupials opossum and wallaby (48). In addition, in this region at position 8, there is either a serine or a threonine, both being polar hydroxyl amino acids susceptible to phosphorylation.

It might be speculated that, upon phosphorylation, serine and threonine could form electrostatic links (as a result of the acquired negative charge from phosphate) with neighboring inter- or intramolecular cationic amino acids and therefore function like disulfide bonds. In fact, the cysteine positions in mammalian protamines are either substituted by serine or theonine in birds, or else those amino acids are near. The similarities at the carboxy terminus are less marked than at the amino terminus (Fig. 3A); however, the arginine clustering, the presence of the valine at position 44 (allowing for gaps in the alignment), the tyrosines at position 52, and the carboxy-terminal tyrosine follow a clearly conserved trend.

Despite many conserved sequences between mammalian and bird protamines, the presence of several cysteines in mammals leads to an essentially different mechanism for stabilization of the nucleoprotamine complex through the formation of disulfide bonds in the sperm nuclei (23, 35). The fact that cysteines are not conserved while other motifs (such as the amino-terminal tetrapeptide ARYR) are, may indicate a relatively less essential function of the cysteines as compared to the conserved aminoacid clusters. For example, cysteines might not be involved in the condensation process (this being accomplished by the consensus regions between mammals and birds), and would only take part in a final stabilization of the already condensed nucleoprotamine.

C. Mammalian P2 Protamines

In addition to the P1 mammalian protamines, the sperm nuclei of human and mouse contain an additional type of histidine-rich, cysteine-containing protamine named P2. These P2 protamines were first sequenced from human (88) and mouse (57) sperm. They are synthesized as a precursor (60, 61, 69, 82, 87) that, after a processing step leading to removal of a 43-residue leader sequence, gives rise to the final product. Figure 3B shows the alignment of the mouse P2 and human P2 mature polypeptides. The main compositional difference from the mammalian-P1/avian-protamine gene family is the presence of histidines, replacing 25–30% of the arginines. The molecules also show a positive aminoacid clustered domain structure. Frequent residues separating the positive clusters are cysteine, serine, and glycine. In particular, the motif SC is repeated three times along both molecules. Two additional positive aminoacid cluster-splitting sequences are GC and T/YC, respectively.

The occurrence of P2 among mammals is very unusual. In mouse and human sperm, it comprises 50–60% of the total protamine, but it has not been observed in other mammals (although there are low levels of P2 mRNA in rat and guinea pig) (82). It is difficult to be precise about the specific role of each type of protamine in the mammalian sperm nucleus. Because no P2 family has so far been identified in birds, it is tempting to speculate that the major protamine in mammals in terms of initial evolutionary appearance and function is P1, the P2 family appearing as a support type of molecule for determining sperm nuclear structure together with P1, or perhaps even related to the appearance of cysteines to allow cross-link formation.

D. Dogfish Protamines

Compared to the mammalian P2 protamine family, dogfish protamines (85) have a high lysine content. Like all other protamines, they are characterized by clusters of positive residues separated by neutral amino acids. Cysteines are also evenly spaced along the molecule. Z1 and Z2 have a low but significant similarity.

If there is a consensus between the sequences of all vertebrate pro-tamines, it is the common *positive aminoacid clustered structure*, and in addition, in the mammalian-P1/mammalian-P2/dogfish group, the even spacing of cysteine residues along the molecule.

III. Protamine Genes

A. Protamine Gene Sequence and Structure

The first protamine gene sequences determined (16) were those of rain-bow trout, and predicted coding sequences identical to family-2a, -2b, and -2c protamine polypeptides. The route to the cloning was by isolation of the frequent 6-S rainbow trout protamine mRNA from trout testis poly(A)-RNA (72) and its purification in milligram amounts (73). The identity of the mRNA was established by cell-free translation and partial RNA (74) and cDNA (38) sequence analyses. However, it was clear that while protamine mRNA could be separated into four distinct bands by gel electrophoresis (75, 76), each band was still sequentially heterogeneous. Therefore, it was necessary to prepare protamine cDNA libraries and to isolate and sequence individual clones. Five cDNA clones were sequenced in our laboratory (38), and others elsewhere (45). The coding regions predicted by these clones corresponded to polypeptides from families 1 and 2 (Figs. 1 and 2). Family-1 cDNAs predicted a total of 30 residues, with the sequence Ala–Ser–Arg at positions 6–8, while family-2 cDNAs had 32 residues total with the sequence Ser–Ser–Ser at positions 6–8, an additional proline at position 10, and an extra arginine in the third arginine tract between positions 20 and 26.

The sequences in the 3'-untranslated regions were highly conserved within each of the two families, but there were clear differences between families 1 and 2. The overall close similarities between family-1 and -2 cDNAs (and polypeptides) suggested that each had been derived from a common evolutionary precursor by gene duplication and subsequent inde-pendent divergence. The cDNA probes described above were used as probes to isolate genomic clones from a partial *Eco*RI library of rainbow trout DNA in λ Charon 4A. A total of 49 positive clones were isolated, and from these six different genes, all from family 2, were sequenced (16, 40).

Features of these trout genes (16, 40) were that they were intronless, they were not clustered in the same way as the trout histone genes (77), and they possessed well-defined and highly conserved TATA boxes and polyadenyla-tion signals. There were also other conserved 5' sequences, whose signifi-cance is discussed below (Section VI,D).

In the past 5 years, protamine genes have been cloned and sequenced from one other salmonid fish, the chum salmon (78); two birds, domestic chicken and Japanese quail (19, 20); and several mammals, including P1 protamines from bull (79, 80), mouse (69), and human (70). cDNA sequences are available for mouse (81), boar (82), and human P1 (83). The histidine-rich P2 protamine gene has also been cloned from mouse (69), and there is a cDNA for human P2 (60). Finally, a cDNA sequence has been determined for a dogfish protamine, scylliorhinine Z1 (85). Figure 5 summarizes the overall organization of the known protamine genes. The most striking feature is the distribution of the single intron, present in all of the mammalian genes, but absent from both salmonid fish and the bird genes. A second major difference is the presence of six to nine cysteine residues in the coding regions of the mammalian genes and a complete absence of cysteines in the salmonid fish and bird genes. The possible evolutionary origin of these major differences in gene structure is discussed in detail in Sections IV,A and IV,B).

Several major differences are apparent between the mammalian P1 and P2 protamines and their genes. As demonstrated in Fig. 6, dot-matrix comparisons of mouse and human P1 and P2 genes reveal no significant homology in their nucleotide sequences. However, alignments of their aminoacid sequences indicate a similarity score of 56% of mouse P1 and P2 and 56.3% for human P1 and P2 (57). This is significantly lower than the similarity score for either the pairs mouse and human P1s (68.8%) or mouse and human P2s (75.5%).

A second major difference between mammalian P1 and P2 genes is that the P2 gene encodes an additional 43-aminoacid sequence at the amino terminus (61), so that P2 is synthesized as a precursor (61, 82, 87) which is

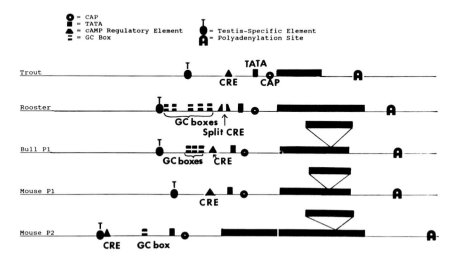

FIG. 5. Functional map of representative protamine genes, indicating the putative transcriptional regulatory elements.

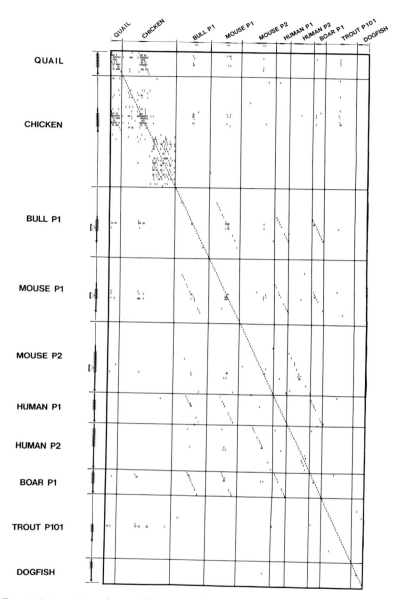

FIG. 6. Dot-matrix analysis of all the protamine gene sequences presently available. Twenty matches or more in a 32-nucleotide window are indicated as a dot. The arrow at the x or y axis indicates the scale size of the transcriptional unit. The shaded area indicates the coding region. The positions of known introns are indicated; however, intron sequences have not been included in the comparison. Sequences are from the following sources: quail (20), chicken (19), bull P1 (6, 25, 49, 79, 80), mouse P1 (69, 81), mouse P2 (57, 69), human P1 (51, 58, 83), human P2 (60, 88), boar P1 (50, 78), trout p101 (16), and dogfish (85).

post-transcriptionally processed by cleavage at a His–Arg bond at positions 43–44. Further processing must also occur at the amino terminus, as two distinct human P2 protamines, P2a and P2b, which differed by the absence of a tripeptide, Arg–Thr–His, from the larger protamine, P2a, have been isolated (88). Thus, a further cleavage of the His–Gly bond at positions 46–47 must have taken place. Therefore, one would predict that the P2 processing enzyme must have a specificity involving cleavage at the carboxyl side of histidine residues. The amino-terminal sequence of the mouse P2 precursor is unrelated to the mature P2 sequence, being much less basic. Although there are nine basic residues (six arginines and three histidines), these are largely neutralized by eight acidic residues (six glutamic acids and two aspartic acids), which do not normally occur in any of the mature P1 and P2 protamine polypeptides.

A search of the GenBank data base using the IFIND program (89, 101) revealed that the 5′ precursor segment shared significant nucleotide sequence similarity only with a segment of the Epstein–Barr viral genome, indicating the possibility that this sequence of viral origin may have become integrated into an ancestral P1-like gene to give rise to the P2 ancestor. In view of the limited distribution of P2 protamines—only in certain species of the mammalian orders of Rodentia and Primates—such an event would be predicted to have taken place at least 8×10^7 years ago at the time of the mammalian radiation (90, 101).

B. Copy Number of Protamine Genes

1. RAINBOW TROUT

It has been difficult to determine the copy number of protamine genes in the rainbow trout. Initial studies using cDNA probes (39, 84) suggested one or two copies of each of four to six protamine genes, accounting for a total of four to 12 copies. Subsequent copy-number determinations using a 920-bp BglII–BamHI probe indicated that as many as 150 genes could be present per haploid genome. However, it was later realized that the protamine genes are flanked by moderately repetitive DNA sequences (66). When a smaller probe comprising only the coding region was used, the copy number decreased to 15–20 (17). This information can be coupled to the determination of six individual polypeptide sequences classified into three different families from a single trout testis (15) as well as the data derived from the analysis of several other related genera in the suborder Salmonidae (42).

Protein sequencing revealed that families 1–3 are also represented in the related genera (Figs. 1 and 2) and an additional family, 4, not present in rainbow trout, is seen in several other species, including another member of the genus *Salmo*, the Atlantic salmon (*S. salar*). In some cases, e.g., protamines 1A and 1B, where there is a difference at a single position (position

10, Val ↔ Ile), the two forms can be regarded as alleles of a single gene. However, in other cases such as 1A and 1C, where there are two differences, or 1B and 1C, where there are three, it is likely that protamines are the product of separate non-allelic genes.

The conclusion is that protamine genes constitute a multigene family in the Salmonidae with a minimum of 15–20 members. However, it appears that in each species only a subset of the total gene family is expressed and that the particular subsets expressed in individual species can differ quite widely. At the moment, it is not possible to say whether the expressed subset is the only one present in the genome, or whether some members of the gene set are active and expressed, while others remain silent.

Comparative Southern blots of different species of Salmonidae with a rainbow trout protamine probe indicate considerable polymorphism among protamine genes, even in a series of individual rainbow trout, and certainly among different genera, indicating that the protamine genes occur in varying DNA contexts (65). Such a situation is likely to alter their expression, as, for example, if flanking enhancer sequences are present or absent. Measurements of the gene dosage by dot-blots of DNA from various Salmonidae with a rainbow trout protamine probe (65) (Table I) also indicate that there is fairly wide variation in the copy number.

TABLE I

DENSITOMETRIC SCANS OF DOT-BLOTS OF GENOMIC DNAs FROM VARIOUS FISH SPECIES[a]

	Relative signal	Standard deviation	Relative genome size	Relative signal/genome
Salmo gairdnerii	1.00	0.00	1.00	1.00
Salmo salar	1.01	0.15 (15)	1.30	1.31
Oncorhynchus keta	0.99	0.21 (21)	*1.00	0.99
Oncorhynchus kisutch	1.39	0.37 (27)	*1.00	1.39
Salvelinus namaycush	1.36	0.41 (30)	*1.25	1.70
Coregonus fera	0.80	0.12 (15)	1.18	0.94
Prosopium williamsonii	0.77	0.12 (16)	*1.18	0.91
Thymallus thymallus	0.90	0.34 (37)	0.75	0.68
Thymallus arcticus	0.93	0.23 (24)	*0.75	0.70
Clupea harengus	0.12	0.05 (50)	0.35	0.04
Clupea pallasii	0.15	0.08 (52)	0.35	0.04
Sprattus sprattus	0.16	0.07 (45)	0.39	0.06
Osmerus esperlanus	0.21	0.08 (37)	0.24	0.05
Lepisosteus osseus	0.07	0.04 (54)	*1.00	0.07
Perca flavescens	0.11	0.06 (60)	0.50	0.06
Hippoglossus hippoglossus	0.12	0.06 (52)	0.40	0.05
Cyprinus carpio	0.11	0.06 (60)	0.60	0.07

[a]The probe was an AvaII–HpaII fragment comprising the coding region of rainbow trout protamine gene p101 (16). Results are summarized from 65.

However, another factor comes into play, as there is such a rapid divergence of protamine gene nucleotide sequence even in forms whose protamines are similar in aminoacid sequence. A good example is provided by the protamine genes in the herrings (*Clupea harengus* and *Clupea pallasii*). Herring DNA hybridizes 1/25 as well to the rainbow trout probe as does the homologous rainbow trout DNA (65). This is despite the fact that the herring protamine aminoacid sequences are similar to the trout protamines (14). This rapid divergence in protamine gene DNA sequences can be confirmed by varying the stringency of the hybridization conditions. For example, in 10% formamide, 2× SSC, 1% SDS at 50°C, herring DNA hybridizes 80% as well as that of the homologous rainbow trout DNA, but in 50% formamide, the signal decreases to 4%.

This technique can also be used to compare protamine gene sequences in related salmonid species (65). For example, using the restriction enzyme *Hae*III, whose cutting sites, flanking the protamine genes, seem to be quite well-conserved, the two major bands in a genomic Southern blot of rainbow trout DNA are conserved in the closely related cutthroat trout (*S clarkii*), but are widely different in a third member of the genus, the Atlantic salmon (*S. salar*). The next most closely related salmonid genus, as judged by protamine gene restriction map similarity, is the Pacific salmon, *Oncorhynchus*, and two members of the genus, the Chum salmon (*O. keta*) and the Coho salmon (*O. kisutch*), each showing a single strong hybridizing band corresponding to one or the other of the two *S. gairdnerii* bands.

Later work (66) showed, in fact, that the protamine gene sequence of a cloned Chum salmon protamine gene was identical to that of one of the rainbow trout protamine-2 genes. Our findings with the protamine genes— that the rainbow trout gene is more closely related to the Pacific salmon genes (*O. keta* and *O. kisutch*) than to the Atlantic salmon (*S. salar*)—is in agreement with the work with salmonid mitochondrial DNA, which concluded (67) that the rainbow trout and the Coho (and Chinook) salmons diverged more recently from each other than from the other *Oncorhynchus* species. As noted above, the rainbow trout has recently been reassigned to the genus *Oncorhynchus* as *O. mykiss*. This is consistent with the similarities in the protamine genes of rainbow trout and Chum salmon and the clear differences from the Atlantic salmon (*S. salar*) noted by us (65, 66). The rapid divergence of protamine gene sequences and implications for protamine gene evolution are examined in more detail in sections IV,A and IV,B.

2. AVIAN

The situation with the rooster appears to be quite different. When a probe corresponding to the coding region was used, an extremely complex band pattern appeared (68), accounting in intensity for 50 to 200 copies per haploid genome, even at very high conditions of stringency (65% formamide,

50°C hybridizations, followed by 0.1× SSC, 85°C washes). When the stringency conditions are raised to the highest practical limit, or a non-repetitive, 5'-flanking probe is used instead, the band pattern reduces in complexity to one or two bands with an intensity equivalent to two copies per haploid genome. These two loci have been cloned and sequenced and are positioned in the center of a 40-kb cosmid clone. The two loci are separated by 4kb from each other (19). Despite a few nucleotide changes in the 5'- and 3'-untranslated regions of these genes, the coding region is identical in each, so that identical polypeptide sequences are encoded by both genes. The recent cloning of a cDNA for the quail (C. japonica) protamine (20) allowed the determination of a copy number for the protamine genes of this species, also of two. The sequence of the quail protamine cDNA shows several differences from the chicken genes in the coding region. This would imply that the duplication leading to the pair of identical chicken genes must have occurred in the chicken line more recently than the separation of the chicken and quail lines.

3. MAMMALIAN

The mammalian protamine genes mouse P1, mouse P2, and bull P1 all show a single copy per haploid genome (69, 70, 79, 87), and this copy number determination did not present as many problems as in the case of trout and chicken. In fact, the specificity of *in situ* hybridization has allowed the assignment of the mouse P1 and P2 genes to chromosome 16 (71) and of the human genes to chromosome 16 as well (70). It is noteworthy that the protamine genes are autosomal and not located on the Y chromosome. The high aminoacid sequence similarity of the mammalian-P1 protamine family to the avian genes, coupled with the presence of two copies in avian genes and a single copy in mammals, indicates either that the duplication in quail and chicken occurred after the separation of birds and mammals, or that mammals have maintained only one functional copy.

IV. Evolution of Protamine Genes

Protamines are certainly the most positively charged proteins found in nature (Lys + Arg = 45–80%) (3). Other proteins with domains nearly as basic as the protamines include several viral core proteins (91–93) and *Escherichia coli* protein P (94). The selection pressures that led to the appearance of protamines in evolution, their function, and their evolutionary pathways have been the subject of much speculation (1, 2, 6, 32, 95–100), but are not well-understood. Yet because of their extreme variability, the protamine genes provide an excellent model for the study of the origin of closely related species.

Such variability is even more marked at the DNA level, as many mutations are silent (particularly those affecting the third codon positions in the coding region, and as many of the changes are in the 5'- and 3'-distal regions of the genes). Therefore, the two molecular clocks—one measuring changes in aminoacid sequences, and the other, silent DNA changes—are complementary, the latter being useful for very fine tuning in closely related species in which no differences in the aminoacid sequences are present.

A. Detailed Protamine Gene Alignments

In the 5' region of the gene, the most obvious conserved motifs correspond to the TATA box and the CAP site (refer to Figs. 5 and 14). Also, the cAMP response element (CRE) is present in all protamine genes (21) as well as in the mouse transition protein 1 gene (146). There are several potential CREs in each of these genes, except in the chicken, one of them invariably being located at positions −48 to −57, the others ranging between positions −93 and −194 (21). We have found that the dinucleotide immediately following the second CRE half-site of the element is a C-A with a frequency 10 times higher (7 times in 12 potential CREs) than that expected randomly (0.7 times in 12 potential CREs). Similarly, we have found that the two bases preceding the TATA box are always pyrimidines, and that after the TATA box, a pair of Gs appears with high frequency (21). The CAP site of the protamine gene fits only partially with the consensus (YAYYYY). Weaker similarities include an oligopurine nucleotide region at position −47 and a conserved region (21) between the trout and mammalian P1 genes (position +13).

The most well-conserved domain of the coding region of the protamine genes is the amino-terminal portion. The first 22 bp are identical in mouse and bull P1, and most (16 out of 22) of these positions are conserved in chicken. Furthermore, there is a 16-bp region from 112 to 128 that is identical in chicken and bull P1 (21). The rest of the coding region shows weaker similarities and large gaps due to the marked differences in aminoacid length between the different protamines. It should also be noted that immediately downstream from the coding region, a duplicated sequence is present in the chicken gene that, if translated, would encode an additional cluster of arginines followed by another tyrosine and a termination codon. In the 3' region of the genes, the most conserved element is the polyadenylation signal AATAAA and to some extent its flanking nucleotides (21).

B. Dot-Matrix Analysis of Protamine Gene Sequences

A dot-matrix analysis (21) of all of the protamine gene sequences available so far is shown in Fig. 6. This type of comparison clearly indicates overall similarity, when present, as a diagonal succession of dots at the intersection of the corresponding genes. The most obvious relationships derived are those within the quail and chicken genes and within the bull P1, mouse P1, human P1, and boar P1 sequences. Also, the mouse P2 sequences display a strong similarity, evident as a well-marked diagonal line when compared with the human P2 sequences. The homologous regions between the members of the P1 family as well as those from the P2 family are limited to the transcriptional unit, the similarities being markedly reduced further upstream or downstream.

Another feature derived from Fig. 6 is the faint similarity of the chicken coding region with that of bull P1, mouse P1, and boar P1, which can be seen as a horizontal succession of dots in the dot-matrix. This type of similarity is because of a repeated motif widely spread along the chicken coding region, but present only in a limited region in the mammalian P1 protamine gene family. A second series of characteristics derived from Fig. 6 is the internal repeats, particularly in the chicken protamine gene. The coding region displays a "cross" shape, suggesting an internal duplication in sequence in this species. This property is also shared with the mouse P1 gene. Also, from examination of Fig. 6, it is obvious that the 3' region of the chicken gene is markedly repetitive.

Despite the great similarity among the members of the P1 family and within the P2 family, the P1 protamine family fails to share any marked similarity with the mouse P2 family, except for the short sequences, which are likely to represent the *cis*-acting elements required for the coordinate expression of genes during spermatogenesis and which indicate a distant common origin of the P1 and P2 families. Overall, these results are consistent with the proposed divergence of the mammalian P1 and P2 families about 8×10^7 years ago, prior to the divergence of primates and rodents at the time of the mammalian radiation (90, 101), which would have been followed by a much more recent divergence of the P1 gene family.

Little similarity in DNA exists between either the mammalian P1 or P2 families and the chicken protamine genes. However, unlike the limited similarity between the corresponding aminoacid sequences of the P1 and P2 mammalian protamines, the chicken protamine shows a remarkable aminoacid similarity to the mammalian P1 protamine sequences (Fig. 3A). Such a feature was already partially evident from the sequence (18) of the aminoterminal tetrapeptide ARYR. Using the recently redetermined protein sequence (identical to the sequence predicted from the genome (19) and similar to the predicted quail sequence), the avian–mammalian P1 similarities are even more marked and can be extended to the rest of the sequence. It is particularly interesting to note that, with the recently determined sequence, the only threonine found in rooster and quail protamines occupies the exact position of that in bull P1, goat, and ram, and the only valine found in rooster and quail occupies the exact position of that found in bull, boar, stallion, and ram (Fig. 3A).

Other significant conserved motifs have already been mentioned in Section II,B, and include the tripeptide SRS, the three following hepta-arginine clusters, and the two fairly well-conserved tyrosines at the carboxy-terminal end of chicken protamine. The most marked difference between the mammalian P1 and chicken protamines is the complete absence of cysteine residues in the latter. A possible link between bird protamines and the eutherian mammals may be found in two metatherian mammals, opossum and wallaby, which, as in the case of chicken and eutherian mammal P1's, contain the amino-terminal tetrapeptide ARYR, and as with chicken, contain no cysteine residues (48). In support of this view, we have found recently, by comparative Southern blotting, that the chicken protamine probe hybridizes to a distinct band in Southern blots of the metatherian mammalian DNA from wallaby and koala (see Section V,B and Figs. 7–9).

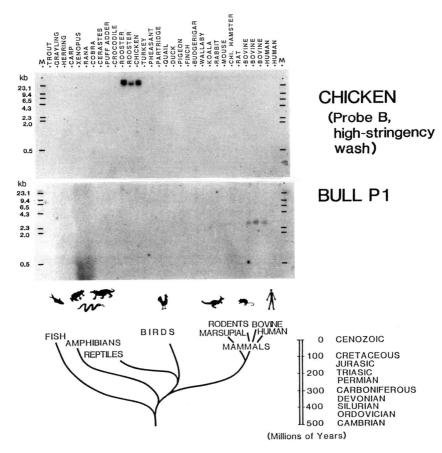

FIG. 7. Southern blots of *Eco*RI DNA digests of different vertebrate species probed with a chicken protamine probe B (see inset of Fig. 9 for the position of probe B) and a bovine protamine probe, and washed under high-stringency conditions (2×SSC, 1% SDS, 85°C for 20 min for the washes). M, Marker.

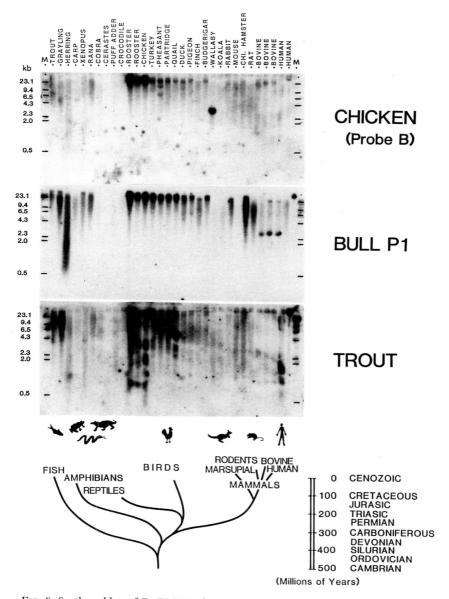

FIG. 8. Southern blots of *Eco*RI DNA digests of different vertebrate species probed with the chicken, bull, or trout protamine probes at medium conditions of hybridization stringency and washing (50% formamide, 1 M NaCl, 1% SDS, 0.15 mg/ml tRNA, 20 mM Tris at pH 7.0, at 45°C overnight for the hybridization, and 2×SSC, 1% SDS at 55°C for 30 min for the washes). M, Marker.

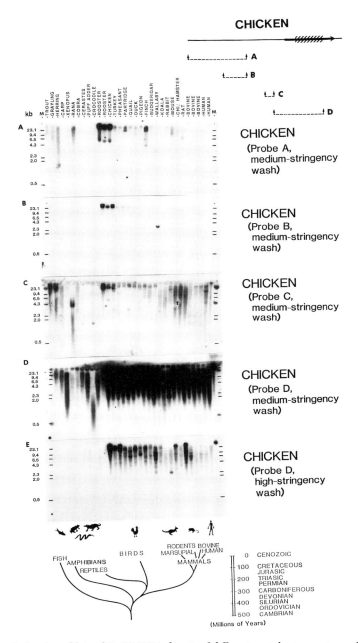

FIG 9. Southern blots of *Eco*RI DNA digests of different vertebrate species probed with different chicken protamine probes under different stringency conditions. Medium-stringency conditions are described in the legend to Fig. 8. High-stringency conditions are described in the legend to Fig. 7. The origin of the different chicken protamine probes is indicated in the upper right insert. M, Marker.

V. DNA–DNA Hybridization Studies

The comparison of DNA sequences by means of computer alignments (dot-matrix or pair-wise alignments) is the most sensitive way to determine their similarities (21) (Fig. 6). However, it can only be performed if the corresponding DNA or protein sequences are known. Therefore, in order to gain insight of the species for which the corresponding genes have not been cloned and sequenced, nor their protamines isolated or sequenced, an alternative approach has been to use a cloned and sequenced DNA as a probe in Southern blots of a battery of unknown DNAs. A correlation exists between the extent of the similarity of different DNA species and the strength with which they cross-hybridize, and therefore also with the intensity of the band generated in the corresponding Southern blot autoradiogram. The extent of hybridization also can be modulated by changing the experimental hybridization stringency conditions. At very high hybridization stringency, only those DNA species with identical or very strong nucleotide similarities to the labeled probe should appear on the Southern blots. At progressively lower hybridization stringency, additional DNA bands of decreasing similarity should appear.

In this section, we present a detailed study of the hybridization pattern of different protamine genes with 27 different vertebrate DNA species, covering the five main vertebrate classes: Pisces, Amphibia, Reptilia, Aves, and Mammalia. High-stringency/high-specificity Southern "zoo"-blots using the chicken protamine (top panel) and the bull protamine probes (bottom panel) are shown in Fig. 7. It is clear that under these conditions the hybridization signal is only detectable in the homologous DNA. A medium-stringency zoo-blot using the chicken, bull, and trout protamine gene probes is shown in Fig. 8. These results clearly indicate that protamine gene sequences are very variable throughout the phylogenetic tree. For example, using the rooster protamine probe, a pattern showing specific bands is present only in avian DNAs (covering five different orders: Anseriformes, Galliformes, Columbiformes, Psittaciformes, and Passeriformes), and in a marsupial (the wallaby).

With the bovine probe, there is reactivity with all avian DNAs, some mammals, amphibia, and fish, although the signal is in the form of a smear (except in the avian samples), which is suggestive of non-specific interaction or hybridization with a repetitive sequence. The trout probe shows a weak signal with herring DNA and no signal with carp, in accordance with previously reported data (65) and also with the absence of protamine polypeptides in carp sperm (102). This result could indicate that carp has never shared a protamine gene with the herring–salmonid line (thus arguing against the presence of a protamine precursor in these species) and would, therefore, support the horizontal transmission hypothesis (4, 17, 103). Alternatively, the selection pressures for keeping the herring–salmonid protamine genes active have resulted in sequences drifting in a different direction relative to that in carp, whose putative original protamine gene could have become non-functional.

The trout probe also shows a positive signal with some avian DNAs, human DNA, λ-DNA (as a marker), and much more weakly with an amphibian DNA from *Xenopus laevis*, in which a ~4-kb band is present). The limited hybridization of the protamine probes at low and medium stringency to a variety of DNAs becomes even more restricted at very high stringency (Fig. 7). As shown, the rooster protamine probe recognizes only the homologous hen or rooster DNA. Not even avian species phylogenetically close to the chicken, such as pheasant, partridge, quail, and turkey, all of which belong to the same order, Galliformes, show any detectable hybridization with the rooster protamine probe at this stringency (Fig. 7). Similarly, at this high stringency, the bovine probe only recognizes its own DNA (Fig. 7). A clear conclusion is that none of the species probed contains a protamine gene (or part of a gene) identical to that of another species; otherwise, a distinct band(s) would have been apparent even at very high stringency conditions.

Several questions may be raised at this point:

1. What is the homologous relationship, if any, among the protamine genes of the species examined?
2. Assuming a common ancestor, what similarities are conserved among the protamine genes, and what stringency conditions would reveal them?
3. What does a signal in the form of a smear mean?
4. What does it mean when a distinct band appears in a species relatively distant in the phylogenetic tree from that providing the probe?

A direct way to answer some of these questions is to compare the actual DNA sequences of the protamine genes of various species (this was the focus of the previous sections) and to relate the results of these comparisons to the pattern of hybridization present in the Southern blots (Figs. 7–9). A clear homologous relationship is shared at the DNA level by the members of the mammalian P1 protamine gene family (*21*). However, as can be seen in Fig. 8B, no single sharp band hybridizes in the mouse genomic DNA even at this average stringency condition. Also, in human and rat, there is only a smear. Therefore, DNA hybridization studies will show specific bands at this hybridization stringency condition only when the corresponding nucleotide sequences are substantially conserved (e.g., in the case of the mouse and bovine protamine genes, a similarity greater than a 72% nucleotide match in the coding region); even so, only weak signals can be expected. Polymorphic cleavage sites present in the target DNA may further reduce the signal. Decreasing the stringency conditions would certainly result in an increase of the signal, but it would also allow many other non-specific bands to appear.

A. What Does a Smeared Signal Designate?

The most likely interpretation is that there is a group of repetitive sequences spread along the genome which hybridize with some element of the probe. Whether this group of repetitive sequences and the probe have a homologous relationship cannot be established unless a direct DNA sequence comparison is available (see below).

B. What Is the Significance of a Distinct Band in the DNA of a Distantly Related Form?

The most obvious and interesting cases are those in which rooster protamine gene probe B hybridizes with a distinct band in the marsupials (metatherian mammals) wallaby and koala. This is also a difficult question to answer, since hybridization could be due either to a real sequence similarity characteristic of the protamine gene, or to the presence of a similar sequence either 5' or 3', perhaps with some general functional significance (e.g., a set of consensus binding sites for a *trans*-acting factor, but not protamine-gene specific). To clarify some of these questions, we have used a series of chicken protamine gene probes and have observed the hybridization patterns under various stringency conditions (Fig. 9).

Using a different type of 5' probe (A) extending farther 5' than the one described above in Fig. 8B, a slightly different pattern is seen (Fig. 9). The hybridization signal in different avian orders is still present; however, in this case, the zebrafinch (a Passeriform) and partridge (a Galliform) show a stronger signal (Fig. 9A). It is worth noting that the wallaby band is still present, although with a much weaker intensity. With a third 5' probe corresponding to a region closer to the gene than A or B (probe C in Fig. 9), a polymorphic site is present in rooster DNA (12th sample, Fig. 9C) and in hen. In the remainder of the avian DNAs, the signal has the characteristics of being specific. Figure 9D shows the results for the chicken protamine coding-region probe. Note the extremely high signal present at average stringency conditions in nearly all vertebrate DNAs. However, under high stringency conditions (Fig. 9E), none of the cold-blooded vertebrates shows any significant hybridization, whereas the warm-blooded vertebrates (birds and mammals) do. This is indicative of a marked difference in genome composition between cold-blooded and warm-blooded vertebrates.

There is a tendency in evolution for the $(C+G)$-content in genes to increase as the vertebrate temperature increases from cold-blooded to warm-blooded (104). Thus, the signals detected in the form of a smear (a series of overlapping bands) are likely to represent a non-specific increase in the (C+G)-content of the genome of these species. Consistent with the above hypothesis, the chicken protamine coding region probe used is extremely rich in (C+G) (88% in the coding region) (19). Interestingly, koala DNA (marsupial) shows a marked ~2-kb band that remains even under high stringency conditions (Fig. 9E), whereas the marked ~3-kb band that was present (Fig. 9B) with the 5' probe in wallaby DNA (marsupial) has disappeared. This may have several interpretations: (1) the hybridization is due to a random sequence match, or (2) it is indicative of a common ancestor for the marsupial P1 protamine genes and the avian genes. The fact that the pattern remains clearcut even at very high stringency supports the second possibility.

Evidence has also been presented to support the hypothesis of an avian/mammalian-P1-protamine gene line based on aminoacid sequence similarities. Therefore, the signal present at very high stringency in all avian and some mammalian DNAs, such as koala, rabbit, and Chinese hamster, has the characteristics of a specific pattern and opens the possibility of using the chicken probe to screen and isolate the protamine genes of these species. This conserved pattern at the DNA level in the coding region in all avian samples is consistent with the constancy of protamine polypeptide presence and size in different avian orders (105, 106).

Overall, DNA hybridization confirms the DNA and the aminoacid alignments, showing that protamine genes vary considerably in phylogeny, and that, as expected, this variability is much more marked at the DNA level than at the aminoacid level. This fact has the practical advantage that DNA sequence analysis can be used in a discriminating manner to establish phylogenetic relationships where the corresponding aminoacid sequences may be similar or identical. In addition, the Southern blot hybridization leading to the definition of restriction-fragment-length polymorphisms (RFLPs) is much faster and more convenient than sequencing a protein or cloning a gene. The regions flanking the chicken protamine genes are quite variable (RFLP analysis of chicken protamine genes reveals highly polymorphic flanking regions: R. Oliva, W. Connor, L. Walker and G. H. Dixon, unpublished), and polymorphic regions also flank the bovine genes (97). These polymorphisms flanking the protamine genes may be useful in tracking the migration and sexual habits of species, a subject on the leading edge of investigations in the field of natural selection (107, 108).

All of the above relationships have led us to reconsider the various hypotheses of vertebrate protamine gene evolution (Fig. 10). The two main hypotheses suggested are (1) an origin from a "basic pentapeptide core" that underwent a series of duplications to give rise to the present-day protamines (109), and (2) evolution from a histone or a histone-like protein (3, 4). The

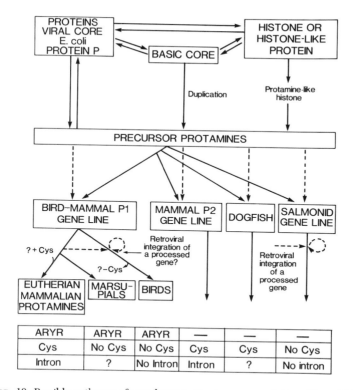

FIG. 10. Possible pathways of vertebrate protamine gene evolution. (From 21.)

basic pentapeptide core hypothesis has recently received support from comparisons of protamine gene sequences from trout, bull, and mouse with certain viral arginine-rich core protein sequences (101). The search for such potential "basic cores," including in the comparisons the potential basic core of the chicken gene, showed that the similarities at the nucleotide level were not as marked as those previously reported (20). This could simply reflect the markedly biased codon usage in the chicken protamine gene (toward the overwhelming use of C and G in "silent" positions) as compared to that of mammals and fish (in which there is approximately equal usage of the four nucleotides in silent positions).

This would be supported by the fact that, at the aminoacid level, the similarities are much more marked (20). However, caution must be used in concluding that these similarities indicate homology, since such similarities could also be explained simply by random matches due to the high arginine content of protamines and its repetitive distribution, since the presence of arginine blocks distributed along the coding region is a common property of the protamines (Figs. 1–3). At the DNA level, the repetitive nature of the coding region sequence for the chicken and mouse P1 protamine genes is also evident (Fig. 6). In addition, there is an oligonucleotide stretch present in multiple copies in the chicken protamine coding region that is also present in the mammalian P1 genes, and that can be seen as a horizontal succession of dots in the dot-matrix of the coding region for those protamines (Fig. 6). This could either be a consequence of the marked aminoacid similarity between avian and mammalian P1 protamines, or indicative of a series of partial duplications that occurred according to the basic core hypothesis.

Evidence that this duplication mechanism has operated, at least to some extent, comes from the fact that, overlapping the actual termination codon for chicken protamines, a sequence is present that, if translated, would encode an avian protamine with an additional arginine cluster followed by another tyrosine and a termination codon (20, 68). Alternatively, the present-day chicken protamine sequence might have arisen from a longer avian protamine gene through the mutation of an arginine codon (CGA) to the present-day termination codon (TGA). Also, there is a 94-bp sequence at the 3'-untranslated region of the human P2 protamine gene that duplicated with little divergence of sequence (20).

The hypothesis that evolution of protamines was from a histone or a histone-like protein is based on the fact that, in phylogeny, a whole spectrum of sperm nuclear proteins can be found, ranging from somatic-like histones to the mammalian, arginine-rich, cysteine-containing protamines (1–4, 86). Intriguing similarities are also found between viral core proteins and protamines (93, 101). Whether these reflect a common origin or an example of convergent evolution to serve a common function (namely, to condense DNA) remains to be established. As already pointed out, caution should also be exercised in deciding whether the fish and mammalian gene lines had a common precursor, since, besides their common chemical properties and repetitive nature, no clear specifically conserved aminoacid sequences can be found. The same would apply to the mammalian P1 and P2 families.

On the other hand, we think that the similarities between mammalian P1 and avian protamines (Fig. 3) are substantial enough to rule out the possibility of convergent evolution in this case. Assuming a common origin followed by species diversification and subsequent independent evolution, the present-day differences predict that the divergence of chicken and mammalian protamine genes would have happened 300 million years ago, when the separation between avian and mammalian precursors took place (110). The separation of the mammalian and bird protamine gene line would have been followed either by the appearance of cysteine residues in mammalian protamines or their loss in those of birds.

Several mechanisms by which cysteines could have originated starting from a cysteine-free protamine are possible. One of the more likely possibilities would be their generation from a CGC or CGT arginine codon, since this codon is the most abundant in protamine genes. In addition, CpGs are the major target of DNA methylation in eukaryotes, and it is known that 5-methyldeoxycytidine residues are unstable and tend to mutate to thymidine by deamination at position 5 (111, 112). Through this mechanism, CGC and CGT codons for arginine could readily mutate to the TGC and TGT codons for cysteine seen in present-day mammalian protamines.

Another of the striking features to emerge in a comparison of the structures of the protamine genes in vertebrates is that both fish and avian protamine genes are intronless, while those of mammals (both P1 and P2) contain a single intron at closely similar positions (Fig. 5). From the considerations of aminoacid and nucleotide similarities between mammalian P1 and bird protamines (Fig. 3), it seems likely that both are descended from a common precursor. The question is whether mammalian genes gained an intron, or the bird (and salmonid fish) genes lost an intron subsequent to their divergence from a common precursor.

It is difficult to be conclusive in this type of consideration, but the second possibility of intron loss in the bird (and also fish) lines seems the most likely, since the simplest way to explain the lack of introns in certain members of a gene family in which other members of the family do contain them is to consider the retroviral-integration hypothesis (17, 103, 113–118). Such a retroviral or "retroposon" mechanism could have operated both at the intra- or interspecies level. The latter would represent a case of horizontal transmission of genes in evolution.

Evidence to support this retroviral-integration mechanism to explain the lack of introns in the trout protamine genes has already been presented as a result of the presence of retroviral long terminal repeat (LTR)-like sequences flanking the genes (103) and the sporadic distribution of protamine genes in different orders of teleost fish (17), and because of the polymorphism of sequences flanking the protamine genes in the trout genome (65).

In avian species, the low copy number (two) of the chicken protamine gene (20) and the constancy of protamine presence and size among different avian orders (105, 106) argue against retroviral involvement in the evolution of bird protamines. However, the extremely high signal generated when the coding region of the chicken protamine gene is used as a probe under conditions of high stringency could be indicative of a high copy number of pseudoprotamine genes in bird genomes as well as in some mammals (Fig. 9E). Also, in the chicken protamine gene, no clear evidence of retroviral LTR regions flanking the gene has been found so far; however, this is not surprising, since the time lapse between the event rendering the protamine gene intronless and the present might have been sufficient to erase any evidence of a viral mechanism, apart from the lack of the intron itself.

Strong evidence for other testis-specific genes as recruited retroposons lies in a testis-specific phosphoglycerate kinase isozyme (PGK-2) (*118*) in which the PGK-2 gene has lost all 10 introns compared with the somatic PGK-1. Thus, while the homologous relationship between avian and mammalian protamine genes is fairly clear, it is more difficult at present to determine whether the avian genes appeared by horizontal transmission or by vertical divergence from a common precursor of both birds and mammals. More work is required to answer these questions, perhaps taking advantage of the "inside-out" polymerase chain reaction (PCR) techniques (*119*) applied to a wide variety of avian and mammalian species.

The important basic question—Why are protamine genes, in particular, and sperm nuclear proteins, in general, so extremely variable?—also remains. Is the extreme variability of sperm protein structure an advantage in developing sperm nuclei of differing morphology and function adapted to different modes of reproduction (e.g., external versus internal fertilization)? Or, is the function of the sperm nuclear proteins so non-specific that their structures are not conserved and thus subject to genetic drift? These questions are intimately interconnected with the question, what is the real function of sperm nuclear proteins? The different hypotheses on this point are the subject of discussion in Section VIII.

VI. Expression of Protamine Genes in Spermatogenesis

Spermatogenesis is a multistep differentiation process involving major changes in genetic activity and rearrangements of the chromatin structure by which the spermatogonia, the stem cells, undergo meiosis, producing haploid spermatids that further differentiate into spermatozoa (Figs. 11 and 16A). The metamorphosis of the round spermatids into spermatozoa is called spermiogenesis and is accompanied by a condensation of the DNA and a general cessation of transcription. In some species, such as trout, the process of spermatogenesis is quite synchronous, with the testis composed of a single

---

FIG. 11. (A) Photomicrographs showing the cellular composition and architecture of testes at three representative stages of development. Arrows indicate cells in mitosis or meiosis. In the adult testes (right), all stages of spermatogenesis may be found; meiotic and pre-meiotic cells appear close to the basal membrane. Round spermatids and elongated spermatids appear in clusters proximal to the tubular lumen. (B) Northern blot analysis of RNA isolated from testes at different stages of development and probed with a rooster protamine cDNA probe. A fraction (one-tenth to one-third) of each of the testes used for RNA isolation was removed and processed to determine, by optical microscopy, the cell composition and morphology. The cell composition of the typical stages of mitosis, meiosis, and spermiogenesis is shown in (A). Thirty micrograms

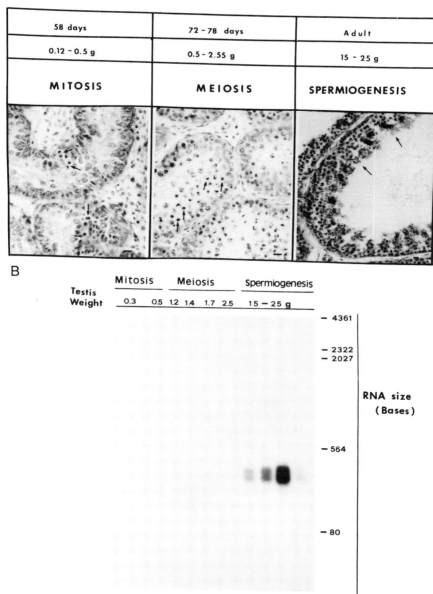

of total RNA was loaded on each lane, except in the last four lanes, where 8, 8, 30, and 4 μg were loaded, respectively. Hybridization with the rooster protamine cDNA probe was detected only in the RNA of the adult testis. (From 68.)

major cell type at each developmental stage (*120*), as is that in the winter flounder (*121*). In developing rooster testes, the spermatogenic cells are synchronous to some extent until the enter spermiogenesis (*122*). In the adult rooster testes, round and elongated spermatids are found together with meiotic and pre-meiotic cells. In mammals, waves of differentiating spermatogenic cells pass down each seminiferous tubule, so that, in the adult mammalian testes, all cellular stages are present simultaneously (*123*).

Another feature of testes cells is the existence of intercellular bridges between spermatogenic cells at the same state of differentiation and also an intimate relationship of these germ cells with the Sertoli cells (*123, 124*). The marked changes in gene activity and chromatin structure in developing sperm cells, together with the specialized patterns of cell to cell communication in the testis, make this system ideal for studying the developmental biology of terminal differentiation leading to a single cell type. In addition, the final stages of spermiogenesis allow a study of the regulation of post-transcriptional mechanisms such as translational control of mRNA expression in the absence of any endogenous transcription. The main questions that have been addressed using this model system are discussed in Sections VI,A–VI,D, which follow.

A. Timing of Expression of the Protamine Genes

The question of timing of expression has been approached in three different and complementary ways. The first method was an analysis of the amount of protamine mRNA in testis at different stages of development and its correlation with the distribution of distinct cell types. This method has been particularly applicable to the trout (*120, 125*) and to some extent to the rooster (*68*). The second method involved the separation of the different spermatogenic cells within a testis and their sorting into different cell pools followed by analysis of the protamine mRNA levels in each cell pool (*68, 120, 125, 126*). Finally, the expression of the protamine genes has been studied by the use of *in situ* hybridization using protamine cDNA or genomic probes (R. Oliva and G. H. Dixon, unpublished).

In the case of the rainbow trout protamine mRNA, the initial evidence, based on solution hybridization of RNA extracted from separated testis cells (*125, 126*), indicated the presence of low levels of protamine mRNA in premeiotic spermatocytes, but much larger amounts in post-meiotic spermatids. Recently, *in situ* hybridization with a biotinylated protamine riboprobe *126a* of trout testis sections has shown, in fact, that significant protamine mRNA levels can only be found in spermatid cells. The previous observations (*125, 126*) can probably be explained by contamination of the spermatocyte cell fraction by a small number of spermatids containing high levels of protamine mRNA.

In Fig. 11B the Northern blot analysis of testis at different stages of development illustrates the expression of the protamine mRNA in the roost-er. RNA was extracted from rooster testes at three different stages of matura-tion, separated by electrophoresis in denaturing formaldehyde gels, blotted to nylon membranes, and hybridized with the rooster protamine cDNA probe. The stage of development of each testis was judged by the age of the animal, the testis weight, and the histology of stained sections. At 58 days of age, the testes weighed 0.12–0.5 g and showed predominantly sper-matogonia in the proliferative stage with several mitoses (arrowed in the first panel of Fig. 11A). At 72–78 days, the testes weighed 0.5–2.55 g, and the sections showed typical pachytene spermatocytes with star-shaped meiotic figures (arrowed in the second panel of Fig. 11A). Finally, in adult roosters with 15- to 25-g testes, large numbers of round spermatids (lower arrow) and elongated spermatids (upper arrow) can be seen (in the third panel of Fig. 11A).

The Northern blots in Fig. 11B of RNA from testes at the mitotic, meiotic, and post-meiotic stages of development showed clearly that rooster protamine mRNA appears only in post-meiotic cells in the 15- to 25-g testis weight range. The analysis of the rooster protamine mRNA levels by North-ern blot analysis of sorted cell populations (68) as well as by *in situ* hybridiza-tion (R. Oliva and G. H. Dixon, unpublished) further confirm that the expression is post-meiotic. Similar studies in mammals demonstrate that protamine genes are also expressed in the haploid post-meiotic stages of spermatogenesis (*127, 131*).

B. Exchange of Expression Products through Intercellular Bridges Connecting Spermatids

One of the unique characteristics of a spermatid is its haploid genetic complement. On the other hand, the interconnecting bridges between sper-matids raise the possibility that these might allow exchange of the genetic products. Because chromosomal homologs segregate from one another dur-ing meiosis, spermatids are genetically different. Post-meiotic gene ex-pression could allow preferential transmission of certain alleles over others, which is thought to be important in the phenomenon of transmission rate distortion seen at the *t* locus in mice (*81, 133*). Experiments using transgenic technology show that, for a mouse-protamine-1/human-growth-hormone (hGH) construct, there is evidence of the exchange of the products of gene expression (mRNAs or hGH) through the cytoplasmic bridges connecting spermatids (*134*). Therefore, it is now clear that genetically haploid sper-matids can behave as if they are phenotypically diploid.

C. Protamine Gene Post-transcriptional Mechanisms

The first evidence for protamine gene post-transcriptional controlling mechanisms came from studies in the trout, in which the preparation of protamine poly(A)-mRNA showed a remarkable electrophoretic hetero-geneity. The different mRNA species were identified as arising from differences in the lengths of their poly(A) "tails" (76, 125, 126). There was also evidence of a progressive shortening of the poly(A) tail in later spermatids concomitant with the translation of the mRNA (76, 137). A similar phenomenon was observed later with mouse protamine-1 mRNA (127, 136) as well as in the rooster (Fig. 12) (68; R. Oliva and G. H. Dixon, unpublished). Figure 12 shows that the size heterogeneity in rooster protamine mRNA is due to a heterogeneity in the length of the poly(A) tail as determined by RNAse-H digestion of mRNA·oligo(dT) hybrids.

Despite much experimentation and speculation, the exact function of the poly(A) tail of mRNAs is still unclear (138–143). One hypothesis with some experimental support is that the poly(A) tail stabilizes mRNA molecules. This would be consistent with the fact that the total poly(A)$^-$ fraction of rooster testis RNA contains a very weak band of 345 nucleotides migrating in the same position (Fig. 12, small lower left arrow) as the RNAse-H product (band c in Fig. 12). The very small amount of this poly(A)$^-$ species would be consistent with its rapid degradation following removal of the poly(A).

There is also a series of faint bands (arrowed at left in Fig. 12) in the poly(A)$^-$ fraction migrating at approximately 560, 800, 900, and 1100 nucleotide lengths that may represent primary nuclear transcripts extending to variable distances 3' from the gene, which are subsequently cleaved and polyadenylated to the two mature poly(A)-mRNA species. In other cases, it has been shown that RNA polymerase II often transcribes well beyond the poly(A) site, and that these longer transcripts are then cleaved and polyadenylated (139, 142). Figure 13 portrays the known steps of protamine mRNA processing in spermatogenesis. It is likely that the larger protamine mRNA (470 ± 20 nucleotides) gives rise to the shorter mRNA (430 ± 20 nucleotides) by the removal of 40–45 adenylate residues, although the mechanism of conversion remains to be determined.

Rainbow trout protamine mRNA exists in two separate pools in trout testis cells (125, 137). In early spermatids, the majority of the mRNA is sequestered in a discrete mRNP particle in the cell supernatant (144, 145), while in later spermatids, protamine mRNP is associated with small polyribosomes, and an mRNP particle containing protamine mRNA can be dissociated by EDTA treatment (145). The length of the poly(A) tails in the cell supernatant mRNP particle is consistent with the idea that the length of the poly(A) decreases as translation of the mRNA proceeds.

A recent transgenic study (275) shows that 156 nucleotides of a mouse protamine-1 3'-untranslated-region sequence regulate temporal translational control and subcellular localization of a mouse protamine-1/hGH construct. Subcellular localization of the hGH protein product depended on the point in spermiogenesis when it was made.

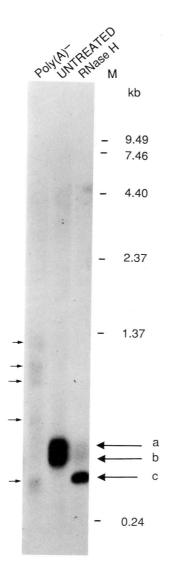

FIG. 12. Northern blot analysis of the RNase-H digestion of hybrids of chicken protamine mRNA with oligo(DT) (Lane labeled RNase H) and comparison with the untreated RNA and a poly(A)⁻ sample prepared from chicken testis. Blots were probed with the chicken protamine gene probe. The series of faint bands in the poly(A)⁻ sample probably represent intermediates in the processing of the primary transcript. The removal of the poly(A) tail by RNase H leads to the conversion of bands a and b to band c. An mRNA species with mobility similar to deadenylated band c may be seen in the poly(A)⁻ sample.

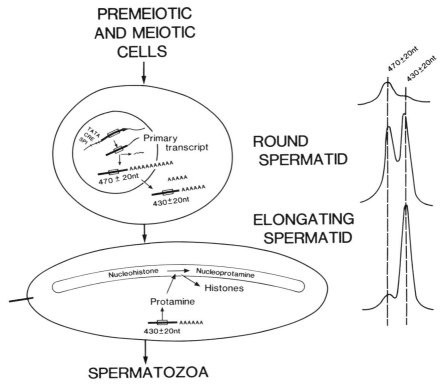

FIG. 13. Scheme indicating the known steps for protamine mRNA synthesis and processing. The diagram at the right corresponds to the relative changes in the protamine mRNA populations of cells separated at unit gravity (68), showing first the appearance of the 470 ± 20 nucleotide (nt) population, which is then processed to the 430 ± 20-nt population present in elongated spermatids.

D. Elements Regulating Protamine Gene Transcription

Figure 5 (in section III) summarizes the number and positions of all of the potential *cis*-acting elements found in the different protamine genes. Figure 14 illustrates in greater detail the alignments of the different *cis*-acting sequences. The TATA box, one of the most well-characterized *cis*-acting elements in most eukaryotic genes, is in all protamine genes described so far (21) and in the mouse transition protein (*TPI*) gene (146). This element is known to be important for the correct start of transcription of the gene (147–149) through the binding of transcription factors TFIIa and TFIId (150, 151). The distance between the TATA box and the initiation of transcription of the protamine genes (28–32 nucleotides) fits perfectly with the

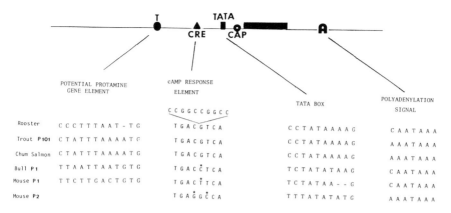

FIG. 14. Detailed sequence alignment of potential regulating elements of the protamine genes.

average distance in higher eukaryotes of 26 to 34. In all protamine genes, the first nucleotide of the transcript is an adenylate (A). The mouse *TP1* gene appears to have the most divergent CAP site, which instead starts with guanylate (G) (*146*).

The second well-conserved *cis*-acting element in all protamine genes corresponds to the palindromic sequence TGACGTCA (*152, 153*). This sequence usually referred to as a cAMP regulatory element (CRE), is considered essential for the biological activity of cAMP-regulated enhancers, and binds a *trans*-acting protein, CREB. Such an element is invariably present at positions −48 to −57 in all protamine genes studied so far, and is also seen in a mouse TP1 gene (*146*). We have found other potential CRE elements at positions −93 to −220 in all other protamine genes, except in that of chicken, which lacks further CRE elements. The elements of chicken, bull P1 (−220), mouse P1 (−170), mouse P2 (−54), and mouse P2 (−175) are split. However, the CREB protein is thought to bind as a dimer to the two half-sites (*152, 153*), so that it is likely that split CRE sequences may still be functional. There are other examples of CRE elements split by 5 bp (*153*) as well as *in vitro* experiments in which a region up to 10 bp is inserted between the two half-sites, only slightly modifying the activity of the element (*153*).

Since spermatogenesis is known to be dependent on gonadotropin control involving cAMP (*154–159*), such a regulatory signal might represent a link between a hormonal signal and the expression of sperm-specific genes. A further structural characteristic of the CREs found in the protamine genes is that the dinucleotide present immediately downstream from the element is frequently a C-A. We can speculate that such a dinucleotide could represent an extension of the CRE consensus core that might confer the necessary specificity for the coordinate expression of genes during spermatogenesis, since the CREs described so far in other genes not expressed in testis do not contain a C-A dinucleotide at this position (152, 153, 160, 161). Alternatively, the conserved C-A could indicate a common phylogenetic origin for the CRE element itself.

A family of DNA-binding proteins (TPBP1), purified 21,000-fold from a trout testis chromatin wash, with M_r's of 35,000–40,000, binds specifically to the CRE element of the trout protamine genes, as judged by DNAse-I protection footprinting, methylation interference, gel retardation, and South-Western blotting assays (270, 271). The level of TPBP1 proteins is much higher in testis than any other tissue and is developmentally regulated during spermatogenesis. From gel retardation or from South-Western blotting, there is a transition in mobility from a faster to a slower form of TPBP1 at the stage when early spermatids are predominant in the testis and the point at which protamine mRNA transcription is maximal. This slower species of TPBP1 appears to be the "active" form and converts to the faster form in mature spermatozoa after protamine mRNA transcription has ceased. From direct visualization of the complex *in vitro* by high-resolution electron-spectroscopic imaging, TPBP1 appears to bind to the CRE element as a dimer (P. D. Cannon, D. Bazett-Jones and G. H. Dixon, unpublished).

Neither the binding activity nor the mobility of TPBP1 appears to be affected markedly by *in vitro* phosphorylation, either by the cAMP-dependent kinase-A or kinase-C. It has not been possible so far to prove unequivocally that the binding of TPBP1 to the CRE element of the protamine gene is an essential event in the "turning-on" of protamine mRNA transcription, although it is a promising candidate for a regulatory role in protamine gene expression.

Among the differences between protamine genes, notice should be taken of the G-C boxes present in the rooster, mouse P2, and bull genes (Fig. 5). This type of element has been described as a transcriptional activator (162), although silencing functions have also been proposed (163). So far, no correlation can be drawn between the copy number of the protamine gene in the different species and the presence of this element, nor with a particular type of species-specific expression mechanism. However, its presence cannot be explained by random chance, so the determination of its function will have to wait until *in vitro* transcription assays are developed for each of those protamine genes.

At the 3' end of the gene, the polyadenylation signal is the only well-conserved motif (Fig. 14). Three to seven nucleotides downstream from this element, the T-G dinucleotide is present at a higher frequency than that expected at random (21). This element is known to be important for the correct cleavage and polyadenylation of the mRNA. None of the above elements is specific for protamine genes. Perhaps the flanking nucleotides that extend further than the elements themselves are responsible for modulating specific developmental expression. One example of such extended elements can be found in the CRE (see Section VI,D).

In a recent series of experiments, a transgene constructed from a mouse P1 protamine promoter linked to a mouse protamine coding region marked by the inclusion of an simian virus 40 (SV40) T antigen sequence was introduced into mouse embryos (164). Northern analysis of RNA from the progeny showed that expression of the marked protamine gene occurred only in the testis and at the correct developmental time. DNA sequences in the 2.4-kbp 5′ region of the mouse protamine promoter contained signals that controlled the tissue specificity and timing of protamine expression. Further deletion of the 5′ region from 2.4 to 0.88 kbp still allowed correct expression, but at reduced frequency, in the transgenic animals. Recent experiments show that the requisite signals for spermatid-specific expression of mouse protamine-1 gene lie in a shorter (0.46-kbp) 5′ region (285).

Specific spermatid expression of a different mouse protamine-1-derived transgene has also been demonstrated (128). A region of some common nucleotide similarity among all of the protamine genes at approximately −200 (Fig. 5, "testis-specific element" has been identified by homology comparisons (101). This region is absent in other genes and therefore could be regarded as a potential element regulating testis specificity of protamine gene expression; it could be the sequence controlling tissue-specific expression in the transgenic experiments (164). However, preliminary in vitro footprinting experiments have failed to show evidence of any regulatory protein binding in this region (P. D. Cannon, unpublished).

Recent studies (287) with in vitro transcription systems developed from mouse testis show that a post-puberal testis system has a uniquely low-temperature optimum of 20°C compared both with a pre-puberal mouse testis system and a HeLa cell lysate that have 30°C optima. Successive deletions in the promoter region of the mouse protamine P2 gene indicate that a region between −170 and −82 possesses a positive promoter function, but regions further upstream, when removed, increase in vitro transcription, thus indicating the presence of negative regulatory elements. Such elements may be important in suppressing protamine gene expression in tissues other than post-meiotic spermatids.

The mechanisms that control gene expression in spermatogenesis are of particular interest, as this is the process that prepares the male genome for fertilization and subsequent embryonic development. Evidence of imprinting during this process by DNA methylation has been presented (165–167), since a generalized DNA hypomethylation occurs during this process (*168, 169*).

VII. Transition of Nucleohistone to Nucleoprotamine in Spermiogenesis

A. Changes in Sperm Chromatin Structure

Spermiogenesis is a differentiation process by which the early spermatid (usually round in appearance) gives rise to the mature spermatozoan. The early spermatid appears to have most of the characteristics of any other somatic cell (with the major exception of being haploid), including a transcriptionally active nucleus in which the DNA is associated with histones in nucleosomes. During the process of spermiogenesis, the early round spermatid experiences a dramatic change, giving rise to a cell of markedly different morphology, each species having its specific sperm shape (*98*) (Fig. 15). The most common changes during spermiogenesis includes the loss of most (if not all) of the cytoplasm, often into "residual bodies," the growth of a motile sperm tail, and the development of a highly condensed nucleus with greatly diminished replicational, transcriptional, and repair activities. This condensation and biochemical inactivation of the DNA are accomplished in many species by the replacement of the histone complement of the nuclei by new sperm proteins (*4, 13*).

This replacement process constitutes one of the most remarkable changes in chromatin structure observed in eukaryotes. It occurs during spermiogenesis, when histones are removed from DNA and replaced by protamines (Fig. 16). An analogous process takes place during the transition from viral DNA, organized in nucleosomal complexes, to the highly condensed nucleoprotein cores present in mature virions (*93*). Not all species replace histones in the sperm nucleus. Examples of species that retain histones in the sperm are in bony fishes, such as carp (*102*), and invertebrates, such as *Holothuria* (*107*) and sea urchins (*171*). Species that completely replace histones in the sperm nucleus include birds (*19, 32, 68, 96, 105, 106*), trout, and other salmonid fish (*17, 27, 172, 173*) (Fig. 16). In mammals (humans, for example) most (85%) of the nucleosomal organization is replaced by a nucleoprotamine complex; 15% remains complexed with histones (*174*). Some mammals (rat, mouse, and ram) initially replace the nucleosomal organization by a set of intermediate proteins (transition proteins) before the final nucleoprotamine complex is formed (*22–24, 146*).

The remainder of this section focuses on those species that replace histones by protamines in the sperm nucleus. Those species that retain histones or histone-like basic proteins in the sperm nucleus have been reviewed (*4, 98*).

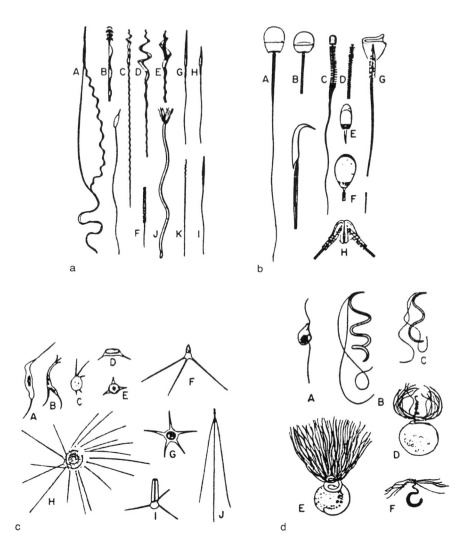

FIG. 15. Various spermatozoa (a) from animals: (A) beetle (*Copris*), (B) insect (*Calathus*), (C) bird (*Phyllopneuste*), (D) bird (*Muscicapa*), (E) bullfinch, (F) gull (*Larus*), (G–I) Tadorna, (J, K) snail (*Paludina*), and (L) snake (*Coluber*); (b) from mammals: (A, B) badger, (C, E) bat (*Vesperugo, Rhinolophus*), (F) pig, (G) opossum, (H) opossum, double spermatozoon, and (I) rat; (c) unusual spermatozoa: (A–C) crustacean (*Polyphemus*), (D, E) crab (*Dromia*), (F) *Ethusia*, (G) *Maja*, (H) *Inachus*, (I) lobster (*Homarus*), and (J) crab (*Porcellana*); and (d) from plants: (A) alga (*Fucus*), (B) liverwort (*Pellia*), (C) moss (*Sphagnum*), (D) *Marsilia*, (E) fern (*Angiopteris*), and (F) fern (*Phegopteris*). (Reproduced from 98.)

A
SPERMATOGENESIS

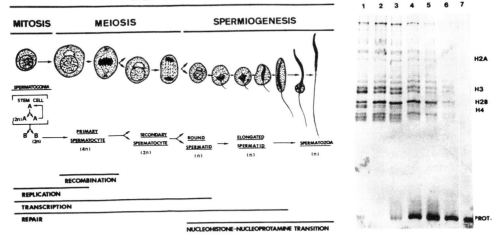

B

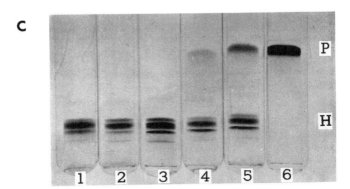

C

Fig. 16. (A) Correlation of the different stages of spermatogenesis with the molecular processes occurring at each stage (68). (B) Electrophoresis of nuclear proteins extracted from nuclei purified from rooster testis cells separated at unit gravity as described (68). Lane 1, Meiotic and pre-meiotic cells; lane 2, round spermatids; lanes 3–6, elongated spermatids at successive stages of elongation; lane 7, spermatozoa obtained from the vas deferens. (C) Electrophoresis of nuclear proteins from trout testis at different stages of development (1, immature testes; 2–5, testes at successive stages of development; 6, trout spermatozoa). (From 242.)

B. Protein Modifications during the Transition of Nucleohistone to Nucleoprotamine

A number of modifications most likely to have a priming or modulating function accompany the displacement of histones and the appearance of protamine during spermiogenesis. These include: the acetylation (27, 30, 33, 95, 102, 175–179), ubiquitinization (180), ADP-ribosylation (181, 182), phosphorylation (27, 46, 47, 95, 183–185), and methylation of histones (95, 186), and the phosphorylation (47, 184) and ADP-ribosylation of protamine (272). The best-documented as well as the most extensive of all of these during spermatogenesis are histone acetylation and protamine phosphorylation; these are emphasized below.

1. HISTONE ACETYLATION

The first type of histone acetylation discovered was that of the amino-terminal serine of histones H1, H2A, and H4 (188, 189). This type of modification takes place at the time of histone synthesis and is subject to little or no turnover. In contrast, the second type of histone acetylation (190–193) occurs at the lysine residues of the amino-terminal regions of the core nucleosomal histones H2A, H2B, H3, and H4 (27, 95, 175–177, 194), but not H1, and is subject to rapid induction and turnover.

Figure 17 illustrates this type of modification as well as the sites susceptible to acetylation in the different core histones. The positively charged amino-terminal "tail" domains of the histones are probably on the outside of the nucleosome, and thus free to interact with the negatively charged phosphoryl groups of the DNA. However, in the X-ray crystallographic studies of the nucleosome (195, 196), these amino-terminal tails are not definitely located in the crystals, and their precise structures cannot be determined. Since one of the effects of histone acetylation is to reduce the net negative charge of such histone tails, it has long been speculated that this could represent a way of changing histone–DNA interactions and therefore of modulating the structure of the chromatin. Histone acetylation has been correlated *in vivo* with transcription (194, 197–206) and DNA replication (95, 175–177, 183, 193, 207–211) and, as described in the present case, with the massive nucleosome disassembly and histone displacement that occur during spermiogenesis (27, 30, 34, 95, 102, 175–179, 212–215).

The different acetylated histone species can be resolved from each other by electrophoresis in starch gels (216) or Triton/acetic acid/urea PAGE (217). Figure 18 shows the separation of the acetylated histones extracted from the nuclei of cells at successive stages of spermiogenesis of trout (Fig. 18, frame A) and rooster (Fig. 18B, frame B). There is an obvious increase, particularly for H4, in the steady state of acetylation as spermiogenesis proceeds. This

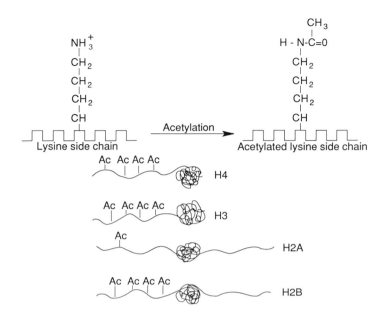

FIG. 17. Acetylation of lysines in histones H4, H3, H2A, and H2B. Acetylation reduces the net positive charge of the amino-terminal domain. (Reproduced from 96.)

marked increase in acetylation during spermiogenesis is universal in all species that replace histones by protamines, but is absent in those species that retain the full complement of histones in the sperm nuclei, such as carp (*102, 218*) and winter flounder (*7*). The timing and extent of histone hyper-acetylation in spermiogenesis have been described in detail for trout (*30, 102*), rooster (*33, 178*), and mammals (*179, 213–215*). Cuttlefish testes have also been described as being enriched in tri- and tetra-acetylated forms of histone H4 (*219*), although histone acetylation has not yet been analyzed at the different stages of spermiogenesis in this species. As can be seen in Fig. 18, the maximum level of histone hyper-acetylation coincides with the massive nucleosome disassembly and histone displacement as spermiogenesis proceeds.

FIG. 18. (A) Histones were isolated from six regions of a Staput separation of trout testis cells in a unit gravity gradient of bovine serum albumin (1–3%) using the Staput method with the larger, earlier cells (spermatogonia, spermatocytes) in fractions a–c and the smaller, more mature cells (spermatids) in fractions d–f. The substantial levels of protamine in fractions d–f have run off the gel in the 5–6 hr required to resolve the acetylated species of the histones. Histone bands are labeled and the acetylated species of H4 are indicated on the far right (numbers 0–4) as to the acetylated lysine residues present per molecule. (From *30*.). (B) Acetylation of histone H4 during rooster spermatogenesis. Frame A shows the Triton/acetic

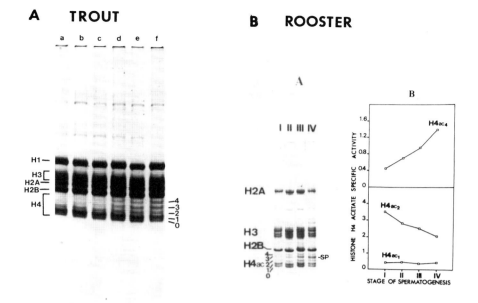

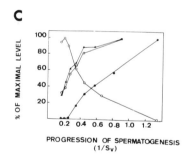

acid/urea gels of histones extracted from four stages of spermatogenesis as follows: (I) tetraploid primary spermatocytes; (II) small primary spermatocytes; secondary spermatocytes and spermatogonia; (III) early spermatids; (IV) elongated spermatids. Frame B shows the specific activities of histone H4 acetate calculated from the densitometer scans of the gels in (A). Monoacetyl H4 remains constant, diacetyl H4 decreases, and tetra-acetyl H4 increases markedly in both early and elongating spermatids. (From *178*.) (C) Changes in nuclear basic proteins at successive stages of rooster spermiogenesis. Quantitative changes in nuclear basic proteins, total histones (○) and protamine (●). The histone DNA ratio of 1 (w/w), determined in meiotic and pre-meiotic cells, is considered 100% nucleohistone. The arginine/nucleotide ratio of 0.8, determined in spermatozoa from the vas deferens, is referred to as 100% nucleoprotamine. Changes in the relative proportions of the acetylated forms of histone H4 are indicated as the ratio of triacetylated to monoacetylated H4 (▲); the ratio triacetylated to nonacetylated H4 (□).

The correlation of timing between hyper-acetylation and nucleosome disassembly suggests that this modification may serve to weaken the histone–DNA contacts in the nucleosome, thus exposing chromatin domains to protamine binding or priming the nucleosome for disassembly. Besides the marked increase in acetylation steady-state levels, there is a very high turnover of acetyl residues (comparable to that occurring during transcription) during the histone hyper-acetylation phase in the rooster (178). This raises the possibility that both hyper-acetylation and turnover could serve to expose sites in chromatin rapidly and reversibly and, by facilitating such "breathing," allow the binding of new chromosomal proteins to DNA. The functional consequences of histone H4 hyper-acetylation would then depend on the specific proteins bound to the DNA at each particular stage of the cell differentiation process.

As seen below (Section VII,B,4), experiments involving *in vitro* nucleosome disassembly by protamine competition are compatible with both hypotheses, namely, an increase in accessibility of chromatin to protamine binding and a lowered stability of individual nucleosomes as a consequence of histone acetylation.

2. PROTAMINE PHOSPHORYLATION

In the original observation of the involvement of protamine phosphorylation in spermiogenesis (47), it was noted that, in spermiogenesis, 75% of the protamine serine residues in early protamine stage testes was phosphorylated, while the protamine of mature sperm had only 5% of the serine residues phosphorylated. Experiments involving parallel uptake of [^{14}C]serine and inorganic [^{32}P]phosphate (26, 27, 95, 183–185, 220) indicated that all of the serine residues newly incorporated into protamine were phosphorylated.

Figure 19 illustrates the timing of protamine phosphorylation as spermiogenesis proceeds. It is clear that protamine binds to DNA in a phosphorylated state, and is subjected to dephosphorylation as the final nucleoprotamine complex is formed. Since the effect of serine phosphorylation is to confer a negative charge on the modified residues, it is thought that this modification serves the function of modulating the interaction of protamines with DNA and thus acts as a "plasticizer," allowing incorrect protamine–DNA complexes to resolve and reform. Once a correct nucleoprotamine complex becomes established, complete dephosphorylation of the protamines would increase the strength of the ionic interaction and further condense and stabilize the sperm nuclei.

An alternative hypothesis is that the negative charges of phosphoserine residues could serve as cross-linking points to other protamine molecules by establishing protein–protein electrostatic interactions with the positively charged arginine residues (221–224). Competition experiments *in vitro* have

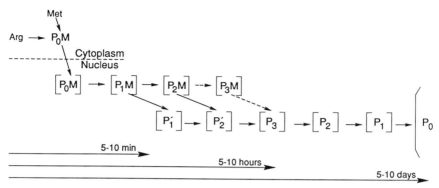

FIG. 19. The kinetic relationship of the different protamine species. Arginine and methionine are incorporated into nascent protamine (P_0M) in the cytoplasm. Protamine is rapidly transported into nucleus, where it binds to DNA. The P_0M from the cytoplasm becomes part of a larger P_0M pool in the nucleus. Protamine phosphokinases phosphorylate P_0M to P_1M and P_2M (and perhaps to P_3M). Simultaneously, methionine is removed from P_1M and P_2M to form P_1 and P_2. Phosphorylation of P_1 and P_2 continues to form P_3. Sequential dephosphorylation of P_3 eventually gives rise to P_0, the unmodified, or "mature," protamine characteristic of mature sperm. The brackets indicate "pools" of the various protamine species, and the arrows represent enzymatic removal of a molecule from one pool to another. The pool sizes of the nascent and methionine-containing species of protamine are small compared to the protamines from which methionine has been removed. Because of the size of the pools and the number of the protamine species, it takes about 5–10 min for labeled arginine to reach P_1M and P_2M, 5–10 hr to reach P_2 and P_3, and 5–10 days for labeled protamine to be completely phosphorylated and dephosphorylated to reach P_0. (From *183–185*.)

indeed demonstrated that the affinity of protamine for DNA is decreased by phosphorylation (*183–185, 220*). It has also been noted that protamine phosphorylation promotes the formation of large, ordered macromolecular complexes with DNA. The interpretation is that the serine phosphates serve to reduce electrostatic attraction between the interacting partners, thus permitting a thermodynamically controlled, ordered association (i.e., ·macrocomplex formation) that is not possible with unmodified protamines whose binding to DNA is too tight (*221–224*). Therefore, the controlled phosphorylation of protamine may be important in the correct binding of protamine to DNA, while the dephosphorylation of protamine is related to the controlled condensation of the spermatid chromatin (*183–185*). Protamine phosphorylation is likely to be a universal modulating element in nucleoprotamine formation, since it has also been described in mammals (*225, 226*), species having a remarkably different protamine sequence and structure (*21*).

3. UBIQUITINIZATION OF HISTONES

Ubiquitin is a small, globular, acidic protein present in eukaryotes (*227*) capable of forming covalent complexes with a variety of proteins (*228, 229,*

269). A major function of ubiquitin is the targeting of proteins in the cytoplasm to be degraded in an ATP-dependent process (230, 231).[1] Ubiquitin is covalently linked to histone H2A in the nuclei to form the protein A24. Ubiquitinated H2A is nevertheless assembled into nucleosomes and does not disrupt their structure, although it may prevent the formation of higher-order chromatin structures (232–234).

During chicken spermatogenesis, marked increases in ubiquitin and nuclear A24 occur (32, 180, 235). Ubiquitin is abundant in trout testes (236). So far, there is no evidence that ubiquitin serves to target histones for ATP-dependent proteolysis in the intact nucleosome. Instead, this modification may act together with histone hyper-acetylation to expose chromatin domains to the nucleoprotamine-forming machinery. However, following disassembly of the nucelohistone, ubiquitin may well be involved in the cytoplasmic ATP-dependent proteolysis of the displaced histones.

4. Transition of Nucleohistone to Nucleoprotamine *in Vitro*

Since the first attempts to reproduce the nucleohistone–nucleoprotamine transition *in vitro* (237–239), it has become apparent that under physiological salt and pH conditions, salmon-sperm protamine (salmine) is able to disassemble nucleosomal core particles only at concentrations several times higher (50% disassembly at an arginine/nucleotide ratio of 8) than those seen *in vivo* (arginine/nucleotide ratio = 0.8) (212, 222, 223, 240, 241). This relatively low efficiency of disassembly of nucleosomal core particles *in vitro* by the salmonid protamines, together with the detection of proteolytic products of histones in trout testes, led to the proposal that the displacement of histones from nucleosomes might be facilitated by the concerted action of a protease firmly associated with chromatin (172, 240, 242–245).

The finding that the rooster protamine, galline, whose length and number of arginine residues are both almost twice those of the fish protamines, can disassemble nucleosomal core particles *in vitro* at concentrations within the physiological range (212), suggested that this protamine might be directly involved in nucleosome disassembly during spermiogenesis. Squid and cuttlefish protamines (of similar length to galline) also can disassemble nucleosomal core particles *in vitro*, in the same range of protamine concentrations as galline (arginine/nucleotide ratio = 0.7–1.8). Furthermore, an artificially cross-linked salmine dimer (head-to-tail) has the ability of the large protamines of rooster, squid, and cuttlefish to disassemble nucleosomal core particles efficiently *in vitro* (34). These results are summarized in Fig. 20 and suggest that the size of the protamines must be the main

---

[1] See "The Ubiquitin Pathway for the Degradation of Intracellular Proteins," by A. Hershko and A. Ciechanover, in Volume 33 (1986) of this series. [Eds.]

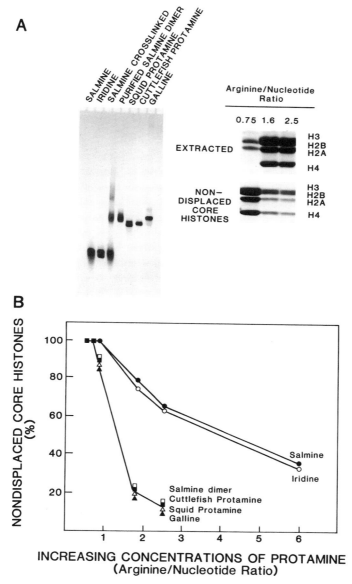

FIG. 20. Nucleosome disassembly *in vitro* by different protamines and an artificially cross-linked salmine dimer. (A, left) Acetic acid/urea/Triton 12% PAGE of the purified protamines, cross-linked salmine, and purified salmine dimer as shown. (A, right) An SDS 18% PAGE shows the extracted and non-extracted core histones at three different concentrations of squid protamine. (B) Nucleosome disassembly *in vitro* (butyrate-treated HeLa S3 core particles) by the protamines salmine (●), iridine (○), cuttlefish (■), squid (△), galline (▲), and the purified salmine dimer (□).

factor responsible for the differences in the disassembly efficiency between the salmonid protamines and the larger protamines from rooster, squid, and cuttlefish.

Such increased ability of the relatively large protamines from rooster, squid, and cuttlefish to disassemble nucleosomal core particles *in vitro* would explain how nucleosomes are disassembled *in vivo* during spermiogenesis in these species, but the question still remains as to how nucleosomes are disassembled during spermiogenesis in the salmonids. A factor that could lower the concentration of protamine necessary to disassemble nucleosomal core particles *in vitro* is histone hyper-acetylation. As mentioned, marked histone hyper-acetylation occurs in species that replace histones during spermiogenesis—in trout (*30, 102*), rat (*179, 213–215*), and rooster (*178, 212*)—but is absent in species that retain histones in the sperm nucleus (*7, 102, 218*).

Figure 21 illustrates the effect of histone hyper-acetylation on the nucleosome disassembly *in vitro* by protamine competition, using two different and complementary approaches. The first type of experiment (Fig. 21A) involves the treatment of intact isolated nuclei with protamine. After a period of incubation to allow the protamine to diffuse into the chromatin, the nuclei are pelleted and the histones present in the supernatant (displaced from the DNA as a consequence of protamine binding) and the histones remaining bound to DNA (in the pellet) are purified and analyzed. In the center of Fig. 21, two-dimensional electrophoresis (first dimension, Triton/acetic acid/urea PAGE; second dimension, sodium dodecyl sulfate–PAGE) of both fractions is shown, and the corresponding scans of the various hyper-acetylated species of histone H4 are shown at the bottom. It is obvious that there is marked enrichment of hyper-acetylated histone H4 species in the displaced supernatant fraction. This result could indicate either an in-

---

$\longrightarrow$

FIG. 21. Preferential disassembly of hyper-acetylated histones from nuclei or nucleosomes. (A) Two-dimensional electrophoresis (first dimension: Triton/urea/acetic acid PAGE; second dimension SDS–PAGE) of the nuclear proteins extracted (right) and residual (left) from nuclei using salmine (arginine : nucleotide = 20 : 1) as indicated by the scheme. At the bottom, the scans corresponding to the different acetylated or non-acetylated subspecies of histone H4 are shown. (B) Disassembly of the chicken erythrocyte core particles or hyper-acetylated core particles by the protamines galline or iridine. The top set shows that all of the DNA is in the pellet and none is in the supernatant in the range of arginine/nucleotide concentrations used. (Center) The proteins present in the pellet (left) and in the supernatant (right) in a disassembly experiment using galline. The bottom photograph shows the proteins present in the pellet (left) and in the supernatant (right) in a disassembly experiment using iridine. The graph at the bottom shows the extracted proteins (displaced histones) from chicken erythrocyte core particles (C) or hyper-acetylated core particles (H) using salmine or galline. The results are the average of several experiments.

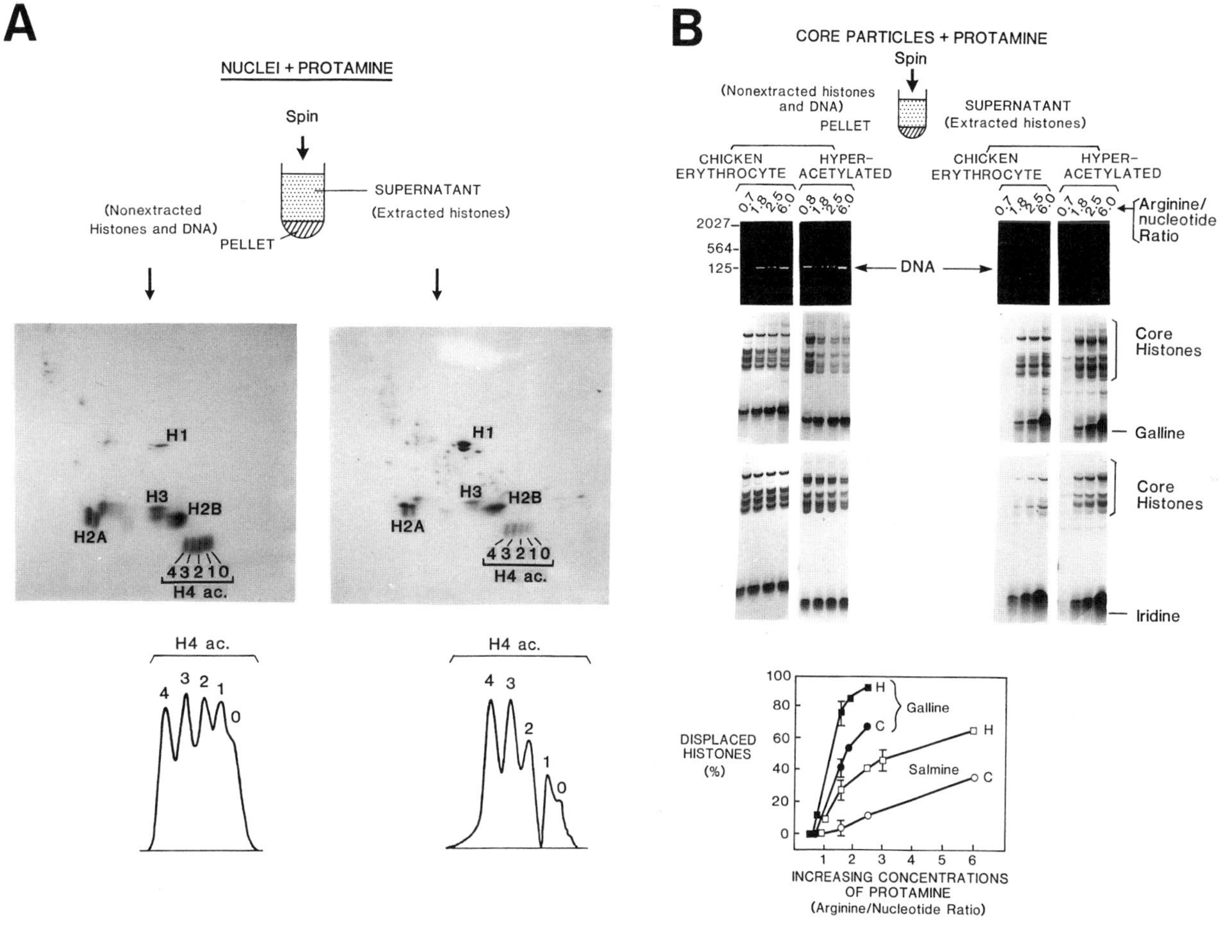

A

NUCLEI + PROTAMINE

Spin

SUPERNATANT (Extracted histones)

PELLET (Nonextracted Histones and DNA)

H1
H3   H2B
H2A
4 3 2 1 0   H4 ac.

H1
H3   H2B
H2A
4 3 2 1 0   H4 ac.

H4 ac.   4 3 2 1 0
H4 ac.   4 3 2 1 0

B

CORE PARTICLES + PROTAMINE

Spin

PELLET (Nonextracted histones and DNA)

SUPERNATANT (Extracted histones)

CHICKEN ERYTHROCYTE   HYPER-ACETYLATED

2027 —
564 —
125 —

DNA

Arginine/nucleotide Ratio

CHICKEN ERYTHROCYTE   HYPER-ACETYLATED

Core Histones   Galline

Core Histones   Iridine

DISPLACED HISTONES (%)

100
80
60
40
20
0

H   Galline
C

H   Salmine
C

1 2 3 4 5 6

INCREASING CONCENTRATIONS OF PROTAMINE (Arginine/Nucleotide Ratio)

creased accessibility, perhaps related to changes in the higher-order structure of those regions of chromatin within the nucleus containing a higher
level of hyper-acetylation, or an increased susceptibility of individual hyper-
acetylated nucleosomes to disassembly by protamine.

Consistent with this observation, an increase in the number of DNA
binding sites has been detected during rooster spermatogenesis (246) concomitant with histone hyper-acetylation (31, 212). In long, hyper-acetylated
chromatin domains of trout testes prepared by limited nuclease digestion
and observed by conventional transmission electron microscopy, smooth
regions devoid of nucleosomes are present (102). Rat spermatidal chromatin
undergoing hyper-acetylation and replacement by transition proteins also
shows a lowered stability to thermal denaturation (215). These results indicate either a decondensation of the 30-nm chromatin fiber, or a lowered
stability of individual nucleosomes.

To focus on the latter possibility, hyper-acetylated nucleosomal core particles were isolated and compared with control nucleosomes in their susceptibility to disassembly by protamine *in vitro* (Fig. 21B). Significant differences in the susceptibility to disassembly by protamines of the different
nucleosome pools were found. Chicken erythrocyte nucleosomal core particles with a low level of acetylation (average of 0.6 acetyl residues per histone
H4) appeared to be the most resistant to disassembly by protamines (not
shown). However, hyper-acetylated nucleosomal core particles obtained
from butyrate-treated HeLa cells (average of 2.2 acetyl residues per histone
H4) were disassembled with a higher efficiency than the control HeLa S3
nucleosomal core particles (an average of 1.2 acetyl residues per histone H4)
(Fig. 21B).

Direct visualization of nucleosomal core particles by electron-spectroscopic imaging (Fig. 22) has recently allowed an independent approach to
the effect of hyper-acetylation on nucleosome structure and stability (34,
286). The hyper-acetylated nucleosomes lost their round, compact shape and
became elongated (up to a length/width ratio of 3 when the acetylation level
reached 3.0 acetyl residues per histone H4). These differences were only
observed when the samples were bound to the electron-microscope support
film at low ionic strength. These results, together with other published data
on the effect of histone acetylation on the structure of the nucleosome, are
considered to mean that histone hyper-acetylation produces no marked disruption of the core particle per se. Nevertheless, intranucleosomal stabilizing forces are decreased, as judged by the lowered stability of the hyper-

FIG. 22. Direct analysis by electron-spectroscopic imaging (ESI) of different pools of core
particles containing increasing levels of histone acetylation. (Top four frames) Histograms of the
distribution in length-to-width ratio in different preparations of core particles whose source is
indicated at the top; Chicken erythrocyte cores; control: HeLa S3 core particles containing 1.2

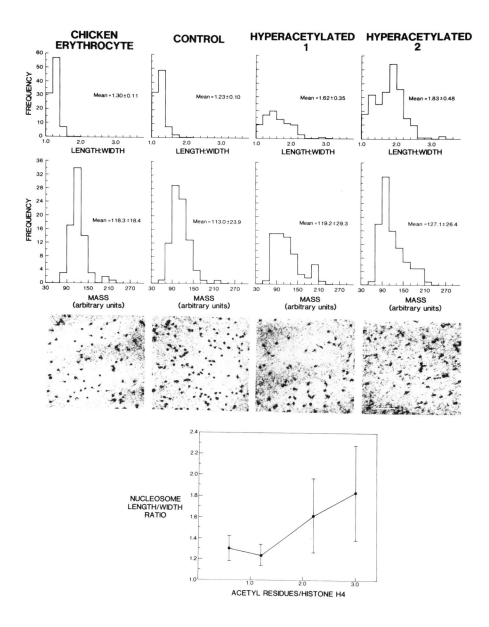

acetyl residues per histone H4; hyper-acetylated 1: butyrate-treated HeLa S3 core particles containing 2.2 acetyl residues per histone H4; hyper-acetylated 2: butyrate-treated HeLa S3 core particles containing 3.0 acetyl residues per histone H4. (Second four frames) Histograms of the mass distributions in the same preparations. (Third four frames) General view of the same preparations. (Bottom) Correlation between the extent of histone H4 acetylation in the different types of cores and the length-to-width ratio adopted by the specimens when bound to the carbon support film on electron-microscope grids at low ionic strength. (From 286.)

acetylated core under conditions of shearing stress, such as cationic competition for DNA binding (binding to the positively charged substrate on the electron-microscope grids or to the positively charged protamines).

In addition to histone hyper-acetylation, another factor that may be involved in nucleosome disassembly during spermiogenesis is the length of time that protamines are allowed to interact with the chromatin. As shown in Fig. 23, nucleosome disassembly by the protamines salmine or galline is time-dependent in a process that takes seconds to hours. Salmine shows a more marked time dependence than the longer protamine, galline, in nucleosome disassembly (Fig. 23). Although not necessarily a cause-and-effect relationship, this ability of the respective protamines to disassemble nucleosomal core particles *in vitro* correlates well with the time required for completion of spermiogenesis in both species, since spermiogenesis takes several weeks in the trout, but is much shorter (6 days) in the rooster. Therefore, since spermiogenesis in trout occurs over several weeks, the slow *in vitro* nucleosome disassembly process by salmine may be sufficient to allow complete displacement, thus supporting the hypothesis that a protamine-mediated displacement of the histones from DNA *in vivo* may take place in the salmonid fishes by a mechanism similar to that in rooster, squid, and cuttlefish.

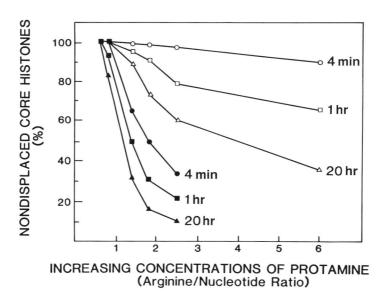

FIG. 23. Time dependency of the *in vitro* nucleosome disassembly process by the protamines salmine (○, □, △) and galline (●, ■, ▲) of butyrate-treated HeLa S3 core particles. (From *34*.)

Mention should also be made of the potential mechanisms leading to nucleosome disassembly and nucleoprotamine formation in mammals. Some of these species completely replace their histone complement by transition proteins (TPs) before the final cysteine-containing protamines appear (22–24, 146, 276). Rat testes TP's have DNA melting properties (251) as well as an ability, shown by circular dichroism and thermal denaturation (252), to decrease the compaction of the nucleosome core particle. Therefore, it is possible that TPs in mammals may function to disassemble nucleosomes in a way similar to that of the protamines in rooster and trout. The final replacement of TPs by protamines could then occur as a simple electrostatic competition mechanism. It is not at all clear, however, what functional reason underlies the two-stage process in mammals.

In vivo, there are likely to be several other factors, in addition to acetylation of the somatic histones, that could also affect the nucleohistone–nucleoprotamine transition, such as changes in DNA topology (247), topoisomerase activity (248), the presence of non-histone proteins (249, 250), the ionic environment (178), other chemical modifications of histone [such as ubiquitinization (180) or ADP-ribosylation (182)], plus protamine phosphorylation (183, 184, 242), some or all of which may play significant roles in the series of steps leading to an ordered nucleohistone–nucleoprotamine transition *in vivo*.

VIII. Function of the Protamines

Although we now possess considerable information about the structure, evolution, and expression of protamines, at both the protein and gene levels (17, 21, 82, 129, 130), the biological role of protamines in the sperm nucleus is still a matter of speculation.

The basic hypotheses proposed are (1) condensation of the nucleus and streamlining of the sperm, (2) condensation and protection of the genetic message, and (3) generation of an imprinted/blank state of the male genome prior to initiation of embryogenesis in the fertilized ovum.

Bloch (1) rejected the first two hypotheses with the argument that there did not seem to be a correlation in the different taxonomic groups between different aspects of sperm function and the type of sperm nuclear protein. He also proposed that the variability (non-conservation) of the sperm nuclear proteins reflected an evolutionary indifference to a relatively unimportant protein in an inert nucleus. However, recently, Kasinsky (4), by comparing the sperm basic proteins of related taxa on a systematic basis, showed that an evolutionary trend becomes apparent between the type of sperm basic protein (degree of basicity) and the biology of fertilization (sperm motility, condensation, and streamlining).

The condensing ability of the sperm proteins appears to be higher in species having internal fertilization, in which the sperm would require an efficient hydrodynamic shape to swim through the viscous environment of the female tract. Also, the size of the protamines is related to their ability to compete with the histones for DNA binding (34, 212). Therefore, if a selection for a greater DNA-compacting ability has taken place, this would have operated at both levels, increasing basicity and, to a certain extent, protamine size. It should be noted that selection pressures must be particularly intense on the "fitness" of an individual spermatozoon to survive in the external or internal environment prior to fertilization and to surmount all of the hurdles involved in successfully reaching, penetrating, and fertilizing of the ovum. In no other situation can Darwinian competition be more rigorous.

Subirana et al. (64) favoured the view that the basic proteins of sperm may have a protective function. However, the only effective mechanism for the protection of DNA is the ability to repair damage, and DNA repair mechanisms are notably absent in spermatozoa (253). In fact, the presence of sperm protein may, in some cases, enhance the damage to DNA caused by mutagens.

The third hypothesis for sperm protein function, that of imprinting (or erasing), has been reviewed by Risley (253). The generation of a "blank state," or "tabula rasa" in the male genomic DNA, which could be considered an extreme case of imprinting, would provide the egg with the opportunity to reprogram the male genetic complement (i.e., the sperm differentiation program might need to be erased before a new program for embryogenesis could be initiated). We prefer to consider an imprinted/blank state hypothesis, since both cases are compatible: the imprinting could be performed either by introducing DNA modifications or new structures in some parts of the genome, or by removing existing DNA modifications or structures. For example, protamines could compete with DNA regulatory binding proteins (trans-acting factors), important for spermatogenesis but not required during embryogenesis, by displacing them from the cis-acting sequences. Support for this imprinting/blank state hypothesis come from the fact that the maternal and paternal pronuclei are not equivalent in mouse embryos, the paternal pronuclei being important for the formation of extra-embryonic tissues, while the maternal pronucleus gives rise to the embryo itself (254, 255). The involvement of DNA methylation in imprinting the germinal cell line is already established (165–169).

The question of the function(s) of protamines in the sperm nucleus is by no means solved; it provides a challenge to understanding the origin and evolution of the protamine genes, how their post-meiotic expression might be controlled, and why their structures are so variable in phylogeny.

IX. Future Research in the Protamine Gene Field

A. Evolution

With the recent development of PCR technology (*119, 256, 257*), which enormously speeds up the determination of DNA sequences by bypassing classical cloning techniques, it should now be possible to determine the sequences of many more protamine genes. Up to the present, the rapid divergence of base sequences in protamine genes has precluded our ability to use a protamine probe from one species to isolate the gene from any but very closely related species (see Section IV). Because of the great variability of protamine genes, this will most likely have to be performed by "walking" from the protamine gene of one species to closely related ones (zoo-walking). Synthetic oligonucleotide primers can be used to obtain and determine the protamine gene sequence of a closely related species. By using the newly determined sequences to synthesize new primers, it should be possible to walk from the existing protamine sequences (mammals, birds, and fish) to a great number of other species.

B. Mechanisms of Nucleosome Disassembly and Nucleoprotamine Structure

The availability of a more extensive bank of protamine gene sequences will undoubtedly reveal the key consensus sequences among different groups of protamines. So far, there is little agreement on the structure of the nucleoprotamine (Fig. 4). Perhaps such a consensus in the structure of the nucleoprotamine does not exist, and several different basic nucleoprotamine structures may instead be present (fish, mammals, and birds). This question must, however, eventually be resolved by detailed X-ray crystallography of complexes of defined single-sequence protamines with defined-sequence DNA oligomers.

Evidence that the protamines themselves may be the main factor causing nucleosome disassembly and sperm nuclear compaction has already been provided (Section VII,B,4). However, more refined experiments are needed before the molecular details of the exact mechanism of disassembly can be defined. *In vitro* nucleosome disassembly experiments by protamines using reconstituted nucleosomes on closed circular DNA should be particularly promising, where all of the potential factors present in the nucleohistone–nucleoprotamine transition *in vivo* (e.g., acetylation, phosphorylation, DNA topology, non-histone proteins, and ionic state) could be tested individually or in conjunction. These experiments could be complemented with *in vivo* labeling experiments (perhaps with gold or biotin) to determine at the electron-microscope level the exact timing and migration of individual protamine and histone molecules.

C. Control of Gene Expression

PCR technology will also have a profound effect on the speed at which the understanding of the mechanisms of gene expression can be gained (258, 259). Particularly useful will be studies of the relationships among DNA methylation, binding proteins, expression of the protamine genes, and imprinting. The protamine gene will be a good model in the study of the mechanisms of post-transcriptional processing, since this is the only model in which endogenous transcription is physiologically blocked in the entire genome while active and massive rearrangements in the structure of the chromatin are taking place.

D. Potential Clinical Applications

1. PROTAMINE AS A HEPARIN ANTAGONIST

Protamine from salmon sperm has been widely used clinically during the last decades as a heparin antagonist. Subsequently, a great deal of information has been accumulated on the effect of protamine on hemodynamics and physiological parameters (260, 261). In some cases, protamine from salmon sperm causes an allergic reaction as a side effect (284). The potential use of either immobilized protamines or other synthetic polycations as a way of avoiding such negative immunological reactions should be considered.

2. STERILITY

Alterations in the ratio of the different protamine types have been observed in male patients affected by some types of sterility (262, 263). This observation should prove useful both at the diagnostic level and as a clue to elucidate the alterations underlying such sterility conditions. A different type of sterility is derived from the generation of antibodies against sperm, either homologous or heterologous. Protamine could be one of the proteins responsible for this type of sterility (264, 265). Specific reagents designed to quench the protamine antigenic determinants might be useful in the treatment of such autoimmune disease. Levels of protamine mRNA in various pathological conditions of the human testis have also been used to assess the functional status of germ cells versus non-germ testis cells (273).

3. PROTECTION OF THE DNA DURING SPERMATOGENESIS

Many cancer patients are being treated with drugs that damage DNA. Many of these patients recover; therefore, the possibility of having children arises. If the germinal cell line could be selectively protected during such anti-cancer treatments, the fertility of such patients and the possibility of genetic damage to their children could be minimized. A useful strategy might be to raise the levels of protective agents such as glutathione (266) in germ cells while anti-cancer treatments are taking place (253, 267, 268).

4. PROTAMINE EXPRESSION AS A SUPPRESSOR OF PROLIFERATION

The use of a controlled expression of protamine genes in cancer cells could lead to a block of proliferation due to the condensation of the DNA in the targeted cells. This approach could provide biological control free of the secondary effects produced by drugs or ionizing radiation.

ACKNOWLEDGMENTS

We thank Donna Hunt for the careful typing of this review. The work was supported by an Alberta Heritage Foundation for Medical Research fellowship to R.O. and a Medical Research Council term operating grant to G.H.D.

REFERENCES

1. D. P. Bloch, *Genetics, Suppl.* **61**, 93 (1969).
2. J. A. Subirana, *Biol. J. Linn. Soc.* **7** (Suppl. 1), (1975).
3. J. A. Subirana, *in* "Proceedings of the Fourth International Symposium on Spermatology" (J. Andre, ed.), pp. 197–213. Nijhoff, The Hague, The Netherlands, 1982.
4. H. E. Kasinsky, *in* "Histones and Other Basic Nuclear Proteins" (L. Hnilica, G. Stein and J. Stein, eds.). CRC Press, Boca Raton, Florida, 1989.
5. H. E. Kasinsky, M. Mann, M. Lemke and S.-Y. Huang, *NATO Adv. Study Inst. Ser.* **101**, 333 (1985).
6. J. P. Coelingh and T. H. Rozijn, *Biol J. Linn. Soc.* **7** (Suppl. 1), 245 (1975).
7. B. P. Kennedy and P. L. Davies, *JBC* **257**, 11160 (1982).
8. B. P. Kennedy and P. L. Davies, *JBC* **260**, 4338 (1985).
9. D. C. Young and P. L. Davies, *Biochem. Cell Biol.* **65**, 909, (1987).
10. F. Miescher, "Die Histochemischen und Physiologischen Arbeiten von Friedrich Miescher," 2 vols. Vogel, Leipzig, German Democratic Republic, 1987.
11. A. Kossel, "The Protamines and Histones," Longmans Green, London, 1928.
12. K. Felix, *Adv. Protein Chem.* **15**, 1 (1960).
13. M. Alfert, *J. Biophys. Biochem. Cytol.* **2**, 109 (1956).
14. T. Ando, M. Yamasaki and K. Suzuki, *in* "Protamines," pp. 52–53, 58–80. Springer-Verlag, Berlin, 1973.
15. D. J. McKay, B. S. Renaux and G. H. Dixon, *EJB* **158**, 361 (1986).
16. J. C. States, W. Connor, J. M. Aiken, L. Gedamu and G. H. Dixon, *NARes* **10**, 4551 (1982).
17. G. H. Dixon, J. M. Aiken, J. M. Jankowski, D. I. McKenzie, R. D. Moir and J. C. States, *NATO Adv. Study Inst. Ser.* **101**, 287 (1985).
18. M. Nakano, T. Tobita and T. Ando, *Int. J. Pep. Protein Res.* **8**, 565 (1976).
19. R. Oliva and G. H. Dixon, *JBC* **264**, 12472 (1989).
20. R. Oliva, R. Goren and G. H. Dixon, *JBC* **264**, 17627 (1989).
21. R. Oliva and G. H. Dixon, *J. Mol. Evol.* **30**, 333 (1990).
22. M. Loir and M. Lanneau, *Exp. Cell Res.* **115**, 231 (1978).
23. M. Loir and M. Lanneau, *J. Ultrastruct. Res.* **86**, 262 (1989).
24. R. Balhorn, S. Weston, C. Thomas and A. J. Wyrobek, *Exp. Cell Res.* **150**, 298 (1984).
25. J. P. Coelingh, C. H. Monfoort, T. H. Rozijn, J. A. Gevers Leuven, R. Schiphof, E. P. Steyn-Parve, G. Braunitzer, B. Schranck and A. Ruhfus, *BBA* **285**, 1 (1972).
26. G. H. Dixon, C. J. Ingles, B. Jergil, V. Ling and K. Marushige, *Can. Cancer Conf.* **8**, 76 (1969).
27. G. H. Dixon, *Acta Endocrinol. (Copenhagen), Suppl.* **168**, 128 (1972).
28. C. Mezquita and C. S. Teng, *BJ* **164**, 99 (1977).

29. C. Mezquita and C. S. Teng, *BJ* **170**, 203 (1977).
30. M. E. Christensen and G. H. Dixon, *Dev. Biol.* **93**, 404 (1982).
31. J. S. Kaye and R. McMaster-Kaye, *BBA* **696**, 44 (1982).
32. C. Mezquita, *NATO Adv. Study Inst. Ser.* **101**, 315 (1985).
33. R. Oliva and C. Mezquita, *Bchem* **25**, 6508 (1986).
34. R. Oliva, D. Bazett-Jones, C. Mezquita and G. H. Dixon, *JBC* **262**, 17016 (1987).
35. R. Balhorn, *J. Cell Biol.* **93**, 298 (1989).
36. R. W. Warrant and S.-H. Kim, *Nature* **271**, 130 (1978).
37. T. Ando and S. Watanabe, *Int. J. Pept. Protein Res.* **1**, 221 (1969).
38. L. Gedamu, W. A. Wosnick, W. Conner, D. C. Watson and G. H. Dixon, *NARes* **9**, 1463 (1981).
39. M. Sakai, Y. Fujii-Kuriyamu, T. Saito and M. Muramatsu, *J. Biochem.* **89**, 1863 (1981).
40. J. M. Aiken, D. McKenzie, H.-Z. Zhao, J. C. States and G. H. Dixon, *NARes* **11**, 4907 (1983).
41. K. Iwai and T. Ando, *in* "Methods in Enzymology" (C. H. W. Hirs, eds.), Vol. 11, p. 263. Academic Press, New York, 1967.
42. D. J. McKay, B. S. Renaux and G. H. Dixon, unpublished observations (1990).
43. K. Iwai, C. Nakahara and T. Ando, *J. Biochem.* **69**, 493 (1971).
44. W. B. Scott and E. J. Crossman, "Fresh Water Fishes of Canada," pp. 184–191. Fisheries Research Board of Canada, Ottawa, Ontario, Canada, 1973.
45. J. R. Jenkins, *Nature* **279**, 809 (1979).
46. V. Ling, B. Jergil and G. H. Dixon, *JBC* **246**, 1168 (1971).
47. C. J. Ingles and G. H. Dixon, *PNAS* **58**, 1011 (1967).
48. R. Balhorn, J. A. Mazrimas, M. Corzett, J. Cumming and B. Fadem, *J. Cell Biol.* **107**, 167a (1989).
49. J. A. Mazrimas, M. Corzett, C. Campos and R. Balhorn, *BBA* **872**, 11 (1986).
50. T. Tobita, H. Tsutsumi, A. Kato, H. Suzuki, M. Nomoto, M. Nakano and T. Ando, *BBA* **744**, 141 (1983).
51. H. Ammer, A. Henschen and C. H. Lee, *ZpChem* **367**, 515 (1986).
52. H. Ammer and A. Henschen, *ZpChem* **368**, 1619 (1987).
53. H. Ammer and A. Henschen, *FEBS Lett.* **242**, 111 (1988).
54. H. Ammer and A. Henschen, *ZpChem* **369**, 1301 (1988).
55. P. Sautiere, D. Belaiche, A. Martinage and M. Loir, *EJB* **144**, 121 (1984).
56. D. Belaiche, M. Loir, W. Kruggle and P. Sautiere, *BBA* **913**, 145 (1987).
57. A. R. Bellve, D. J. McKay, B. S. Renaux and G. H. Dixon, *Bchem* **27**, 2890 (1988).
58. D. J. McKay, B. S. Renaux and G. H. Dixon, *Biosci. Rep.* **5**, 383 (1985).
59. M. Gusse, P. Sautiere, D. Belaiche, A. Martinage, C. Roux, J. P. Dadoune and P. Chevalier, *BBA* **884**, 124 (1986).
60. L. Domenjoud, C. Fronia, F. Uhde and W. Engel, *NARes* **16**, 7733 (1988).
61. P. C. Yelick, R. Balhorn, P. A. Johnson, M. Corzett, J. A. Mazrimas, K. C. Kleene and N. B. Hecht, *MCBiol.* **7**, 2173 (1987).
62. M. Chauviere, A. Martinage, G. Briand, P. Sautiere and P. Chevallier, *EJB* **169**, 105 (1987).
63. M. Chauviere, A. Martinage, G. Briand, P. Sautiere and P. Chevallier, *EJB* **180**, 329 (1989).
64. J. A. Subirana, L. C. Puigjaner, J. Roca, R. Lopis and P. Suau, *Ciba Found. Symp.* **28**, 157 (1975).
65. R. D. Moir, "Structure of Several Multigene Families in Salmonid Families," Ph.D. thesis. University of Calgary, Calgary, Alberta, Canada, 1987.
66. R. D. Moir and G. H. Dixon, *J. Mol. Evol.* **27**, 8 (1988).

67. W. K. Thomas, R. E. Withler and A. T. Breckenbach, *Can. J. Zool.* **64**, 1058 (1986).
68. R. Oliva, J. Mezquita, C. Mezquita and G. H. Dixon, *Dev. Biol.* **125**, 332 (1988).
69. P. A. Johnson, J. J. Peschon, P. C. Yelick, R. D. Palmiter and N. B. Hecht, *BBA* **950**, 45 (1988).
70. S. A. Krawetz, M. H. Herfort, J. L. Hamerton, R. T. Pon and G. H. Dixon, *Genomics* **5**, 639 (1989).
71. N. B. Hecht, K. C. Kleene, P. C. Yelick, P. A. Johnson, D. D. Pravtoheva and F. H. Ruddle, *Somatic Cell Mol. Genet.* **12**, 203 (1986).
72. L. Gedamu and G. H. Dixon, *JBC* **251**, 1455 (1976).
73. L. Gedamu, K. Iatrou and G. H. Dixon, *BJ* **171** 589 (1977).
74. P. L. Davies, G. H. Dixon, A. Simoncsits and G. G. Brownlee, *NARes* **7**, 2323 (1979).
75. L. Gedamu and G. H. Dixon, *NARes* **6**, 3661 (1979).
76. K. Iatrou, L. Gedamu and G. H. Dixon, *Can. J. Biochem.* **57**, 945 (1979).
77. W. Connor, J. Mezquita, R. J. Winkfein, J. C. States and G. H. Dixon, *J. Mol. Evol.* **20**, 227 (1984).
78. W. M. Maier, I. Adham, V. Klem and W. Engel, *NARes* **16**, 11826 (1988).
79. S. A. Krawetz, W. Connor and G. H. Dixon, *JBC* **263**, 321 (1988).
80. C.-H. Lee, M. Ahmed, W. Hecht, N. B. Hecht and W. Engel, *ZpChem* **368**, 131 (1987).
81. K. C. Kleene, R. J. Distel and N. B. Hecht, *Bchem* **24**, 719 (1985).
82. N. B. Hecht, in "Histones and Other Basic Nuclear Proteins" (L. Hnilica, G. Stein and J. Stein, eds.). CRC Press, Boca Raton, Florida, 1989.
83. C. H. Lee, S. Hoyer-Fender and W. Engel, *NARes* **15**, 7639 (1987).
84. B. Levy-Wilson and G. H. Dixon, *JBC* **252**, 8062 (1977).
85. F. Berlot-Picard, G. Vojdani and J. Doly, *EJB* **160**, 305 (1986).
86. J. A. Subirana, C. Cozcolluela, J. Palau and M. Unzeta, *BBA* **317**, 369 (1983).
87. S. M. Elsevier, *Dev. Biol.* **90**, 1 (1982).
88. D. J. McKay, B. S. Renaux and G. H. Dixon, *EJB* **156**, 5 (1986).
89. Bionet IntelliGenetics, Inc., core programs SEQ, GENALIGN, FASTN and FASTP (1989).
90. W. M. Fitch and C. H. Langley, *FP* **35**, 2092 (1976).
91. F. Galibert, T. N. Chen and E. Mandart, *J. Virol.* **41**, 51 (1982).
92. C. Seeger, D. Ganem and H. E. Varmus, *J. Virol.* **51**, 367 (1984).
93. P. Alestrom, G. Akusjarvi, M. Iager, L. Yeh-kai and U. Pettersson, *JBC* **259**, 13980 (1984).
94. S. Altman, P. Model, G. H. Dixon and M. A. Wosnick, *Cell* **26**, 299 (1981).
95. G. H. Dixon, E. M. P. Candido, B. M. Honda, A. J. Louie, A. C. MacLeod and M. T. Sung, *Ciba Found. Symp.* **28**, 229 (1975).
96. C. Mezquita, in "Revisiones sobre Biologia Celular" (■. Barbera-Guillem, ed.), Vol. 5, pp. 1–137. Leioa-Vizcaya, Spain, 1985.
97. S. A. Krawetz, R. A. Bricker, W. Connor, R. B. Church and G. H. Dixon, *Theor. Appl. Genet.* **75**, 402 (1988).
98. D. Poccia, *Int. Rev. Cytol.* **105**, 1 (1986).
99. M. S. Risley, A. Miller and D. A. Burncrot, *Mutat. Res.* **203**, 125 (1988).
100. H. E. Kasinsky, M. Ann, S. Y. Huang, L. Fabrel, B. Coyle and E. W. Byrd, *J. Exp. Zool.* **143**, 137 (1987).
101. S. A Krawetz and G. H. Dixon, *J. Mol. Evol.* **27**, 291 (1988).
102. M. E. Christensen, J. B. Rattner and G. H. Dixon, *NARes* **12**, 4575 (1984).
103. J. M. Jankowski, J. C. States and G. H. Dixon, *J. Mol. Evol.* **23**, 1 (1986).
104. C. Bernardi, D. Mouchiroud, C. Gautier and G. Bernardi, *J. Mol. Evol.* **28**, 7 (1988).
105. M. Chiva. H. E. Kasinsky and J. A. Subirana, *FEBS Lett.* **215**, 237 (1987).
106. M. Chiva, H. E. Kasinsky, M. Mann and J. A. Subirana, *J. Exp. Zool.* **245**, 304 (1988).

107. D. Schluter, *Nature* **331**, 496 (1988).
108. M. R. Ball, S. Freeman, F. C. James, E. Bermingham and J. C. Avise, *PNAS* **85**, 1558 (1988).
109. J. A. Black and G. H. Dixon, *Nature* **216**, 152 (1967).
110. P. J. McLaughlin and M. O. Dayhoff, *in* "Atlas of Protein Sequence and Structure" (M. O. Dayhoff, ed.). National Biomedical Research Foundation, Silver Spring, Maryland, 1972.
111. C. Coulondre, J. H. Miller, P. J. Farabought and W. Gilbert, *Nature* **274**, 775 (1978).
112. A. P. Bird, *NARes* **8**, 1499 (1980).
113. A. M. Wiener, P. L. Deininger and A. Efstratiadis, *ARB* **55**, 631 (1986).
114. M. Marchioni and W. Gilbert, *Cell* **46**, 133 (1986).
115. F. Quigley, W. F. Martin and R. Cerf, *PNAS* **85**, 2672 (1988).
116. J. D. Hawkins, *NARes* **16**, 9893 (1988).
117. M. C. Shih, P. Heinrich and H. M. Goodman, *Science* **242**, 1164 (1988).
118. P. N. Boer, C. N. Adra, Y. F. Lau and M. W. McBurney, *MCBiol* **7**, 3107 (1987).
119. H. Ochman, J. W. Ajioka, D. Garza and D. C. Hartl, *in* "PCR Technology" (H. A. Ehrlich, ed.), pp. 105–111. Stockton, New York, 1989.
120. K. Iatrou, A. W. Spira and G. H. Dixon, *Dev. Biol.* **64**, 82 (1978).
121. B. P. Kennedy, L. W. Crim and P. L. Davies, *Exp. Cell Res.* **158**, 445 (1985).
122. J. D. S. Kumaran and C. W. Turner, *Poult. Sci.* **28**, 511 (1949).
123. M. Dym and D. W. Fawcett, *Biol. Reprod.* **4**, 195 (1971).
124. I. Zlotnik, *Q. J. Microsc. Sci.* **88**, 353 (1947).
125. K. Iatrou and G. H. Dixon, *Cell*, **10**, 433 (1977).
126. K. Iatrou and G. H. Dixon, *FP* **37**, 2526 (1978).
126a. N. A. Seniuk, W. G. Tatton, P. D. Cannon, A. T. Garber and G. H. Dixon, *Exp. Cell Res.*, submitted (1990).
127. N. B. Hecht, P. A. Bower, K. C. Kleene and R. J. Distel, *Differentiation* **29**, 189 (1985).
128. T. A. Stewart, N. B. Hecht, P. G. Hollingshead, P. A. Johnson, J. C. Leong and S. L. Pitts, *MCBiol* **8**, 1748 (1988).
129. N. B. Hecht, *Ann. N.Y. Acad. Sci.* **513**, 90 (1987).
130. N. B. Hecht, *in* "Experimental Approaches to Mammalian Embryonic Development" (J. Rossant and R. Pedersen, eds.) Cambridge Univ. Press, Cambridge, England, 1987.
131. P. Mali, M. Sandberg, E. Vuorio, P. C. Yelick, N. B. Hecht and M. Parviner, *J. Cell Biol.* **107**, 407 (1988).
132. D. Bennett, *Cell* **6**, 441 (1975).
133. R. D. Palmiter, T. M. Wilkie, H. Y. Chen and R. L. Brinster, *Cell* **36**, 869 (1985).
134. R. E. Braun, R. R. Behringer, J. J. Peschon, R. L. Brinster and R. D. Palmiter, *Nature* **337**, 373 (1989).
135. K. C. Kleene, R. J. Distel and N. B. Hecht, *Dev. Biol.* **98**, 455 (1983).
136. K. C. Kleene, R. J. Distel and N. B. Hecht, *Dev. Biol.* **105**, 71 (1984).
137. L. Gedamu, K. Iatrou and G. H. Dixon, *Cell* **10**, 443 (1977).
138. G. Brawerman, *CRC Crit. Rev. Biochem.* **10** 1 (1981).
139. M. L. Birnstiel, M. Busslinger and K. Strub, *Cell* **41**, 349 (1985).
140. D. J. Shapiro, J. E. Blume and D. A. Nielsen, *BioEssays* **6**, 221 (1987).
141. D. I. Friedman and J. Imperiale, *ARGen* **21**, 453 (1987).
142. T. Humphrey and N. J. Proudfoot, *Trends Genet.* **4**, 243 (1988).
143. J. Ross, *Sci. Am.* **260**, 48 (1989).
144. L. Gedamu, G. H. Dixon and P. L. Davies, *BChem* **16**, 1383 (1987).
145. G. D. Sinclair and G. H. Dixon, *BChem* **21**, 1869 (1982).
146. M. A. Heidaran, C. A. Kozak and W. S. Kistler, *Gene* **75**, 39 (1989).
147. D. J. Mathis and P. Chambon, *Nature* **290**, 310 (1981).
148. W. S. Dynan and R. Tjian, *Nature* **316**, 774 (1985).

149. K. Struhl, *Cell* **49**, 295 (1987).
150. N. Nakajima, M. Horikoshi and R. G. Roeder, *MCBiol.* **8**, 4028 (1988).
151. G. M. Hobson, M. T. Mitchell, G. R. Molloy, M. L. Pearson and P. A. Benfield, *NARes* **16**, 8925 (1988).
152. W. J. Roesler, G. R. Vandenbark and R. W. Hanson, *JBC* **263**, 9063 (1988).
153. J. S. Fink, M. Verhave, S. Kasper, T. Tsukada, G. Mandel and R. H. Goodman, *PNAS* **85**, 6662 (1988).
154. D. R. Idler, S. J. Hwang and L. S. Bazar, *Endocrinol. Res. Commun.* **2**, 199 (1975).
155. J. J. Heindel, R. Rothenberg, G. A. Robison and A. Steinberg, *J. Cyclic Nucleotide Res.* **1**, 69 (1975).
156. L. Eikvar, F. O. Levy, N. H. P. M. Jutte, J. Cervenka, T Yoganehan and V. Hansson, *Endocrinology (Baltimore)* **117**, 488 (1985).
157. R. Schultz and V. Blum, *Gen. Comp. Endocrinol.* **57**, 301 (1985).
158. C. W. Davenport and J. J. Heindel, *J. Androl.* **8**, 307 (1987).
159. O. Oyen, J. D. Scott, G. G. Cadd, G. S. McKnight, E. G. Krebs, U. Hansson and T. Jahnsen, *FEBS Lett.* **229**, 381 (1988).
160. J. P. Hoeffler, T. E. Meyer, Y. Yun, J. L. Lameson and J. F. Habenen, *Science* **242**, 1430 (1989).
161. J. A. Bokar, W. J. Roesler, G. R. Vandenbark, D. M. Kaetzel, R. W. Hanson and J. H. Nilson, *JBC* **263**, 19740 (1988).
162. S. P. Jackson and R. Tjian, *Cell* **55**, 125 (1988).
163. J. M. Jankowski and G. H. Dixon, *Biosci. Rep.* **7**, 955 (1987).
164. J. J. Peschon, R. R. Behringer, R. L. Brinster and R. D. Palmiter, *PNAS* **84**, 5316 (1987).
165. A. J. Silva and R. White, *Cell* **54**, 145 (1988).
166. J. L. Swain, T. A. Stewart and P. Leder, *Cell* **50**, 719 (1987).
167. J. L. Marx, *Science* **239**, 352 (1988).
168. M. Groudine and F. Conkin, *Science* **228**, 1061 (1985).
169. N. Rocamora and C. Mezquita, *FEBS Lett.* **2**, 415 (1989).
170. L. Cornudella and E. Rocha, *BChem* **18**, 3724 (1979).
171. P. Puigdomenech, M. C. Romero, J. Allan, P. Sautiere, V. Giancotti and C. Crane-Robinson, *BBA* **908**, 70 (1987).
172. K. Marushige and G. H. Dixon, *JBC* **246**, 5799 (1971).
173. G. H. Dixon and M. Smith, *This Series* **8**, 9 (1968).
174. J. M. Gatewood, G. R. Cook, R. Balhorn, E. M. Bradbury and C. W. Schmid, *Science* **236**, 962 (1987).
175. E. P. M. Candido and G. H. Dixon, *JBC* **246**, 3182 (1971).
176. E. P. M. Candido and G. H. Dixon, *PNAS* **69**, 1975 (1972).
177. E. P. M. Candido and G. H. Dixon, *JBC* **247**, 5506 (1972).
178. R. Oliva and C. Mezquita, *NARes* **10**, 8049 (1982).
179. S. R. Grimes, Jr., and N. Henderson, *ABB* **221**, 108 (1983).
180. N. Agell, M. Chiva and C. Mezquita, *FEBS Lett.* **155**, 209 (1983).
181. P. Quesada, B. Farina and R. Jones, *BBA* **1007**, 167, (1989).
182. M. Coromina and C. Mezquita, *JBC* **260**, 16269 (1985).
183. A. J. Louie and G. H. Dixon, *JBC* **247**, 7962 (1972).
184. A. J. Louie and G. H. Dixon, *Can. J. Biochem.* **52**, 536 (1974).
185. A. J. Louie, E. P. M. Candido and G. H. Dixon, *CSHSQB* **38**, 803 (1974).
186. B. M. Honda, E. P. M. Candido and G. H. Dixon, *JBC* **250**, 8681 (1975).
188. D. M. P. Phillips, in "Histone and Nucleohistones" (D. M. P. Phillips, ed.), p. 47. Plenum, New York, 1971.
189. R. J. DeLange and E. L. Smith, *ARB* **40**, 279 (1971).
190. V. G. Allfrey, R. Faulkner and A. E. Mirsky, *PNAS* **55**, 1182 (1964).

191. E. L. Gershey, G. Vidali and V. G. Allfrey, *JBC* **243**, 5018 (1968).

192. G. Vidali, L. E. Gershey and V. G. Allfrey, *JBC* **243**, 6361 (1968).

193. A. Ruiz-Carrillo, L. J. Waugh and V. G. Allfrey, *Science* **190**, 117 (1975).

194. D. Doenecke and D. Gallwitz, *MCBchem* **44**, 113 (1982).

195. J. T. Finch, Lutter, L. C. D. Rhodes, A. S. Brown, B. Rushton, M. Levitt and A. Klug, *Nature* **269**, 29 (1977).

196. T. J. Richmond, J. T. Finch, B. Rushton, D. Rhodes and A. Klug, *Nature* **311**, 532 (1984).

197. C. P. Prior, C. R. Cantor, E. M. Johnson, V. C. Littau and V. G. Allfrey, *Cell* **34**, 1003 (1983).

198. P. Loidl, A. Loidl, B. Puschendorf and P. Grobner, *Nature* **305**, 446 (1983).

199. P. Loidl, A. Loidl, B. Puschendorf and P. Grobner, *NARes* **12**, 5405 (1984).

200. P. Loidl and P. Grobner, *NARes* **14**, 3745 (1986).

201. V. G. Allfrey, *Annu. Eur. Mol. Biol. Organ. Symp.*, *Speakers' Abstr. 10th, Heidelberg, Federal Republic of Germany, September* (1984).

202. R. Reeves, *BBA* **782**, 343 (1984).

203. S. S. Chahal, M. R. Matthews and E. M. Bradbury, *Nature* **287**, 76 (1980).

204. J. H. Waterborg and H. R. Matthews, *Cell Biophys.* **5**, 265 (1983).

205. P. Allegra, R. Sterner, D. F. Clayton and V. G. Allfrey, *JMB* **196**, 379 (1987).

206. S. Hirose and Y. Suzuki, *PNAS* **85**, 718 (1988).

207. V. Jackson, A. Shires, N. Tanphaichitr and R. Chalkley, *JMB* **104**, 471 (1976).

208. S. A. M. Chambers and B. R. Shaw, *JBC*, 13458 (1984).

209. V. Giancotti, E. Russo, F. Cristini, G. Graziosi, F. Micali and C. Crane-Robinson, *BJ* **218**, 321 (1984).

210. C. D. Allis, L. G. Chicoine, R. Richman and I. G. Schulman, *PNAS* **82**, 8048 (1985).

211. L. G. Chicoine, I. G. Schulman, R. Richman, R. G. Cook and C. D. Allis, *JBC* **261**, 1071 (1986).

212. R. Oliva and C. Mezquita, *BChem* **25**, 6508 (1986).

213. S. R. Grimes, Jr., and N. Henderson, *Dev. Biol.* **101**, 516 (1984).

214. S. R. Grimes, Jr., and N. Henderson, *Exp. Cell Res.* **152**, 91 (1984).

215. S. R. Grimes, Jr., and P. G. Smart, *BBA* **824**, 128 (1985).

216. M. T. Sung and G. H. Dixon, *PNAS* **67**, 1616 (1970).

217. A. Zweidler, *Methods Cell Biol.* **17**, 223 (1978).

218. A. Ruiz-Carrillo and J. Palau, *Dev. Biol.* **35**, 115 (1973).

219. M. Couppez, A. Martin-Ponthieu and P. Sautiere, *JBC* **262**, 2854 (1987).

220. K. Marushige, V. Ling and G. H. Dixon, *JBC* **244** 5953 (1969).

221. J. Bode, *ABB* **228**, 364 (1984).

222. J. Bode, L. Willmitzer and K. Opatz, *EJB* **72**, 393 (1977).

223. J. Bode, K. Henco and E. Wingender, *EJB* **110**, 143 (1980).

224. J. Bode, M. M. Gomez-Lira and H. Schroter, *EJB* **130**, 437 (1983).

225. Y. Marushige and K. Marushige, *BBA* **518**, 440 (1978).

226. F. H. Pruslin, E. Imesch, R. Winston and T. C. Rodman, *Gamete Res.* **18**, 179 (1987).

227. G. Goldstein, M. Scheid, V. Hammerling, E. A. Boyse, D. H. Schlessing and H. D. Niall, *PNAS* **72**, 11 (1975).

228. I. A. Goldknopf and H. Bush, *in* "Cell Nucleus" (H. Busch, ed.), Vol. VI, Part C, pp. 149–180. Academic Press, New York, 1978.

229. M. H. P. West and W. M. Bonner, *NARes* **8**, 4671 (1980).

230. A. Ciechanover, H. Heller, S. Elias, A. L. Haas and A. Hershko, *PNAS* **77**, 1365 (1980).

231. A. Ciechanover, D. Finlay and A. Varshavsky, *J. Cell Biochem.* **24**, 27 (1984).

232. S. Matsui, B. K. Scon and A. A. Sandberg, *PNAS* **76**, 6386 (1979).

233. R. S. Wu, R. W. Kohn and W. M. Bonner, *JBC* **256**, 5916 (1981).

234. R. L. Seale, *NARes* **9**, 3151 (1981).
235. J. Mezquita, R. Oliva and C. Mezquita, *NARes* **15**, 9604 (1987).
236. D. C. Watson, B. Levy-Wilson and G. H. Dixon, *Nature* **276**, 196 (1978).
237. A. E. Mirsky and H. Ris, *J. Gen. Physiol.* **34**, 475 (1951).
238. K. Evans, P. Konigsberg and R. D. Cole, *ABB* **141**, 389 (1970).
239. D. R. van de Westhuyzen and C. Von Holt, *FEBS Lett.* **14**, 333 (1971).
240. T. K. Wong and K. Marushige, *BChem* **14**, 122 1975).
241. K. Marushige, Y. Marushige and T. K. Wong, *BChem* **15**, 2047 (1976).
242. K. Marushige and G. H. Dixon, *Dev. Biol.* **19**, 397 (1969).
243. G. H. Dixon, *Life Sci. Res. Rep.* **4**, 198 (1976).
244. K. Marushige, V. Ling and G. H. Dixon, *JBC* **244**, 5953 (1969).
245. Y. Marushige and K. Marushige, *BBA* **761**, 48 (1983).
246. C. Mezquita and C. S. Teng, *BJ* 170, 203 (1977).
247. M. S. Risley, S. Einheber and D. A. Bumcrot, *Chromosoma* **94**, 217 (1986).
248. J. Roca and C. Mezquita, *EMBO J.* **8**, 1855 (1989).
249. M. E. Christensen and G. H. Dixon, *JBC* **256**, 7549 (1981).
250. M. Chiva and C. Mezquita, *FEBS Lett.* **162**, 324 (1983).
251. J. Singh and M. R. S. Rao, *JBC* **262**, 734 (1987).
252. J. Singh and M. R. S. Rao, *Biochem. Int.* **17**, 701 (1988).
253. M. S. Risley, in "Chromosomes: Eukaryotic, Prokaryotic and Viral" (K. Adolph, ed.). CRC Press, Boca Raton, Florida, 1988.
254. J. McGrath and D. Solter, *Cell* **37**, 179 (1984).
255. M. A. H. Surani, S. C. Barton and M. L. Norris, *Nature* **308**, 548 (1984).
256. K. B. Mullis and F. A. Faloona, in "Methods in Enzymology" (R. Wu, ed.), Vol. 155, p. 335. Academic Press, San Diego, 1987.
257. T. J. White, N Arnheim and H. A. Erlich, *Trends Genet.* **5**, 185 (1989).
258. H. Saluz and J. P. Jost, *Nature* **338**, 277 (1989).
259. H. Saluz and J. P. Jost, *PNAS* **86**, 2602 (1987).
260. B. Lindblad, A. Borgstrom, T. W. Wakefield, W. M. Whitehouse and J. C. Standey, *Eur. J. Vasc. Surg.* **1**, 181 (1987).
261. K. A. Shastri, M. J. Philips, S. Raza, G. L. Logue and P. K. Rustagi, *Blood* **71**, 36 (1988).
262. D. Colleu, D. Lescoat, D. Boujard and D. Lelannov, *Arch. Androl.* **21**, 155 (1988).
263. R. Balhorn, S. Reed and N. Tanphaichitr, *Experientia* **44**, 52 (1988).
264. P. Primakoff, W. Lathrop, L. Woolman, A. Cowan and D. Myles, *Nature* **335**, 543 (1988).
265. T. C. Rodman, F. H. Pruslin, Y. Chauhan, S. E. To and R. Winston, *J. Exp. Med.* **167**, 1228 (1988).
266. A. Meister, *JBC* **263**, 17205 (1988).
267. K. S. Bentley and P. K. Working, *Mutat. Res.* **203**, 135 (1988).
268. L. Li, A. P. Seddon, A. Meister and M. S. Risley, *Biol. Reprod.* **40**, 317 (1989).
269. J. Atidia and R. G. Kulka, *FEBS Lett.* **142**, 72 (1982).
270. P. D. Cannon, Ph.D. thesis. University of Calgary, Calgary, Alberta, Canada, 1989.
271. P. D. Cannon and G. H. Dixon, in preparation (1990).
272. N. C. W. Wong and G. H. Dixon, unpublished observations.
273. S. A Krawetz, P. D. Cannon, R. Joshi and G. H. Dixon, *Mol. Cell. Probes* **3**, 109 (1989).
274. G. R. Smith and R. F. Stearley, *Fisheries* **14**, 4 (1989).
275. R. E. Braun, J. J. Peschon, R. R. Behringer, R. L. Brinster and R. D. Palmiter, *Genes Dev.* **3**, 793 (1989).
276. H. Luerssen, S. Hoyer-Fender and W. Engel, *NARes* **16**, 7723 (1988).
277. G. Bretzel, *ZpChem* **353**, 933 (1972).
278. G. Bretzel, *ZpChem* **353**, 1362 (1972).

279. G. Bretzel, *ZpChem* **354**, 312 (1973).
280. G. Bretzel, *ZpChem* **354**, 543 (1973).
281. W. Speckert, B. Kennedy, St. L. Daisley and P. L. Davies, *EJB* **136**, 283 (1983).
282. E. P. Yulikova, L. K. Evseenko, L. A. Baratova, L. P. Beryanova, V. K. Rybin and A. B. Silaev, *Bioorg. Chem.* **2**, 1613 (1976).
283. E. P. Yulikova, V. K. Rybin and A. B. Silaev, *Bioorg. Chem.* **5**, 5 (1979).
284. M. E. Weiss, D. Nyhan, Z. K. Peng, J. C. Horrow, E. Louerstein, C. Hirschman and N. F. Adkinson, *N. Engl. J. Med.* **320**, 886 (1989).
285. J. J. Peschon, R. R. Behringer, R. D. Palmiter and R. L. Brinster, *In* "1989 Testis Workshop N.Y. Acad. Sci." in press (1990).
286. R. Oliva, D. P. Bazett-Jones, L. Locklear and G. H. Dixon, *NARes* **18**, 2739 (1990).
287. D. Bunick, P. A. Johnson, T. R. Johnson and N. B. Hecht, *PNAS* **87**, 891 (1990).

Aminoacyl-tRNA Synthetase Family from Prokaryotes and Eukaryotes: Structural Domains and Their Implications

Marc Mirande

Laboratoire d'Enzymologie
Centre National de la Recherche
  Scientifique
91190 Gif-sur-Yvette, France

Aminoacyl-tRNA synthetases are ubiquitous enzymes that play a key role in protein synthesis. This family of 20 enzymes offers a suitable tool for the study of structure/function relationships for a class of proteins involving similar functions, yet with different substrate specificities. Extensive reviews report molecular and catalytic properties of aminoacyl-tRNA synthetases (1–4). One paradoxical feature of these enzymes is the wide variability in the number and size of their subunits. In bacterial cells, there are monomers, dimers, and tetramers with subunit M_r's of the protomers ranging from 37,000 to 108,000. One of the most puzzling questions concerns the aspects of tRNA recognition, extensively reviewed (4–6). The emergence of genetic engineering technology, the determination of the primary structures of several aminoacyl-tRNA synthetases (Table I), the site-directed mutagenesis of presumed essential amino acids (7, 8), and the high-resolution elucidation of the three-dimensional structure of two prokaryotic aminoacyl-tRNA synthetases (9–12) have provided deeper insight into the molecular features

95

Progress in Nucleic Acid Research
and Molecular Biology, Vol. 40

TABLE I
QUATERNARY STRUCTURES AND SUBUNIT MOLECULAR WEIGHTS OF AMINOACYL-tRNA SYNTHETASES[a]

Enzyme	Prokaryotes	Lower eukaryotes Cytoplasm	Lower eukaryotes Mitochondria	Higher eukaryotes,[b] cytoplasm
Cys	α(25) 54(25)	—	—	120(111)
Val	α(26) 108(27–29)	120(72)	α(45, 72) 126(73)	CX(112) 140(113) (α) [90]c(118) (α)
Ile	α(30) 105(31)	123(75)	—	CX(114) 139(115) (α)
Leu	α(32) 97(33)	126(77, 78)	α(79) 102(80–83)	CX(114) 129(116) (α)
Arg	α(34) 65(35)	73(84)	—	CX(114) 74(117)
Gln	α(36) 63(37)	93(85)	—	CX(114) 96(117)
Glu	α(38) 54(39, 40)	—	—	CX(114) 150(117)
Met	α2(41) 76(42, 43)	86(87)	α(88) 67(89)	CX(114) 108(117)
Asp	α2(44) 66[d]	63(91, 92)	75(47)	CX(114) 57(119)
Lys	α2(45) 58(46, 47)	68(93)	—	CX(114) 76(116) (α2)
Pro	α2(48) 47(48)	—	—	CX(114) 150[e]
Thr	α2(49) 74(50)	84(95)	54(96)	α2(120) 85(120)
Asn	α2(51) 53(52)	—	—	—
Ser	α2(53) 48(54)	53(98)	—	α2(121) 60(121)
His	α2(55) 47(56)	58(100)	α2(99, 100) 60(100)	α2(122) 57(123)
Tyr	α2(57) 47(58–60)	40(101)	α2(102) 60(103)	α2(124) 59(124)
Trp	α2(61) 37(62–64)	50(104)	42(105)	α2(125) 58(125)
Ala	α4(65) 96(66)	128(74)	—	α(126) 115(126)
Gly	α2β2(67) 77; 35(68)	80(106)	—	α2(127) 80(127)
Phe	α2β2(69) 87; 37(70, 71)	67; 57(108)	α2β2(109) 72; 55(110)	α2β2(128) 71; 63(128)

[a]Subunit molecular weights are indicated as $M_r \times 10^{-3}$ and are underlined when determined from completed primary sequences. Raised numbers in parentheses represent reference numbers.

[b]Aminoacyl-tRNA synthetases that associate within high-molecular-weight complexes are marked "CX"; quaternary structures of dissociated components are indicated in parentheses.

[c]Partial sequences.

[d]G. Eriani and J. Gangloff, personal communication.

[e]P. Kerjan and J. P. Waller, unpublished.

responsible for catalysis (8). In parallel, chemical or enzymatic modifications of tRNA (13), tRNA–protein cross-linking studies (5), and genetic experiments (14) have led to the identification of nucleotide residues necessary for proper and specific recognition by the cognate enzymes. Recent developments in redesigning tRNA molecules have allowed a better understanding of tRNA identity, that is, to identify the major recognition elements of some tRNAs (15–17).[1]

From an evolutionary point of view, the knowledge of primary structures for numerous aminoacyl-tRNA synthetases, including those for 18 enzymes from prokaryotes, has pointed out some common structural features arguing in favor of an extensive relationship among these enzymes. However, molecular and biochemical studies on eukaryotic aminoacyl-tRNA synthetases have delineated distinctive features acquired during evolution. The aim of this article is to focus on these evolutionary acquisitions in order to propose a comprehensive view concerning the possible physiological implications of the chain extensions that characterized lower as well as higher eukaryotic aminoacyl-tRNA synthetases, as compared to their prokaryotic counterparts.

I. From Prokaryotes to Higher Eukaryotes

A. General Features of Aminoacyl-tRNA Synthetases

Aminoacyl-tRNA synthetases are essential enzymes encountered in all living cells (4). They catalyze the esterification of one amino acid to the 3′ end of the corresponding tRNA. In most cases, aminoacylation of tRNAs is accomplished by 20 distinct aminoacyl-tRNA synthetases, one for each of the naturally occurring amino acids. This rule suffers one known exception in all Gram-positive microorganisms, such as *Bacillus subtilis* (18), and in the prokaryotic-like organelles of eukaryotic cells, yeast mitochondria (19), chloroplasts, and plant or animal mitochondria (20). Indeed, in the case of the aminoacylation of tRNA^{Glu} and tRNA^{Gln}, glutamyl-tRNA synthetase misacylates *in vivo* tRNA^{Gln} by the amino acid Glu, the formation of Gln–tRNA^{Gln} requiring a transamidation step of the intermediate Glu–tRNA^{Gln}. Accordingly, in *B. subtilis*, glutamyl-tRNA synthetase is the only enzyme that can aminoacylate tRNA^{Glu} as well as tRNA^{Gln}.

With the exception of formyl-methionine in bacteria, most of the aminoacid derivatives incorporated into proteins are thought to result from post-translational modifications (21). Noteworthy is the discovery of a 21st naturally occurring amino acid, that is, an amino acid inserted co-translationally.

---

[1] See Rogers and Söll, "Inaccuracy and the Recognition of tRNA" in Vol. 39 of this series. [Eds.]

Selenocysteine incorporation into *Escherichia coli* formate dehydrogenase (*22, 23*) and mammalian glutathione peroxidase (*24*) requires a natural suppressor tRNA[Ser] that recognizes a UGA codon. This tRNA species is aminoacylated with serine by seryl-tRNA synthetase, the pathway of conversion of the hydroxyl group of the serine residue to a selenol group remaining to be deciphered.

The 20 aminoacyl-tRNA synthetases from *E. coli*, and most of those from lower and higher eukaryotes, have been purified and characterized (references are listed in Table I). In prokaryotes, the complete primary sequences of 18 of them were determined via gene cloning and sequencing. They are all coded for by distinct and unique genes, with the exception of lysyl-tRNA synthetase, which is encoded by two genes: a constitutively expressed gene (*lysS*) and a heat-inducible gene (*lysU*), which have been mapped at 62.1 and 92 min, respectively, on the *E. coli* chromosome (*129, 130*). It is noteworthy that the *lysS* gene was first isolated as the *herC* gene (*46, 47*), a *herC180* mutation allowing the restoration of replication of a ColE1 mutant replicon.

From lower eukaryotes, 20 genes coding for cytoplasmic and/or mitochondrial aminoacyl-tRNA synthetases have been cloned and sequenced (Table I). All mitochondrial enzymes are encoded by nuclear genes. Genes encoding for cytoplasmic and mitochondrial aminoacyl-tRNA synthetases specific for the amino acids Ile, Leu, Gln, Met, Asp, Lys, Thr, Ser, Tyr, Trp, and Phe are structurally distinct, but only a single gene encodes the cytoplasmic and mitochondrial forms of the protein in the case of histidyl (*100*)- and valyl (*72, 73*)-tRNA synthetases. The two translation products arise from two classes of transcripts initiating at distinct in-frame AUG codons. An alteration of the first AUG codon leads to a *pet*[−] phenotype without affecting the level of the corresponding cytoplasmic enzymes.

It is noteworthy that the genes encoding *Saccharomyces cerevisiae* mitochondrial leucyl-tRNA synthetase (*80, 81*) and *Neurospora crassa* tyrosyl-tRNA synthetase (*103*) were first identified as the *NAM2* and *cyt-18* genes, respectively. These genes are involved in the splicing of the introns bI4 and aI4 of cytochrome *b* and subunit 1 of cytochrome oxidase mitochondrial genes from *Saccharomyces* and of intron 1 of the cytochrome *b* gene from *Neurospora*, respectively. The mitochondrial leucyl-tRNA synthetase gene from *S. cerevisiae* was independently isolated by its ability to complement respiration-deficient mutants unable to aminoacylate mitochondrial tRNA[Leu] (*82*). These enzymes are involved in protein synthesis and mRNA splicing, as demonstrated in the case of the Cyt-18 protein by partial purification of the corresponding gene product, which retains splicing and tyrosyl-tRNA synthetase activities (*102*).

Until now, the involvement of mitochondrial aminoacyl-tRNA synthetases in mRNA splicing remains a puzzling question. One can speculate that some tRNA-related structures displayed by the intron are recognized by the synthetase, which would act directly on the splicing activity or indirectly by stabilizing some RNA structure. In mammals, the involvement of tRNA-like structures in alternative splicing of a large mRNA transcript from genes of immunoglobulin heavy chains has been proposed (131). That an aminoacyl-tRNA synthetase, or a related molecule, can participate in molecular mechanisms other than tRNA aminoacylation is also suggested by the aminoacid sequence of the GCN2 gene product (132). In yeast, derepression of the general aminoacid control system, following aminoacid starvation, is mediated by the transcriptional activator GCN4 (133). Several *trans*-acting positive (GCN) and negative (GCD) factors control the expression of GCN4, at the translational level. The finding that the GCN2 protein displays an amino-terminal moiety homologous to catalytic domains of protein kinases and a carboxy-terminal moiety homologous to histidyl-tRNA synthetase suggests that this histidyl-tRNA synthetase derivative acts as a sensor for aminoacid availability (132).

Interestingly, the genes encoding aminoacyl-tRNA synthetases from lower eukaryotes are devoid of introns, with the notable exception of each of the three genes sequenced from *N. crassa*: the cytoplasmic leucyl-tRNA synthetase gene and the mitochondrial leucyl- and tyrosyl-tRNA synthetase genes that contain small introns of 62, 60, and 64 bp, respectively (78, 83, 103). In contrast, genomic sequences coding for aminoacyl-tRNA synthetases from higher eukaryotes are made of several exons flanked by large introns. However, our knowledge of aminoacyl-tRNA synthetases from higher eukaryotes, at the molecular level, is much less extensive than for those from prokaryotes and lower eukaryotes. Only two cDNA sequences encoding histidyl (123)- and aspartyl (119)-tRNA synthetases have been reported and the corresponding genomic sequences have been isolated (123; M. Lazard and M. Mirande, unpublished). The chromosomal gene for hamster histidyl-tRNA synthetase contains 13 exons and spans 18 kbp of the genome, whereas that corresponding to aspartyl-tRNA synthetase, divided into 16 exons, encompasses at least 40 kbp.

The knowledge of primary sequences of numerous aminoacyl-tRNA synthetases from various sources, together with the availability of cloned genes, has provided powerful tools and molecular bases for manipulation of synthetase genes in order to delineate the domain structure of these enzymes, and especially to point out specific features acquired during evolution from bacteria to mammals.

B. Structural Parameters of Aminoacyl-tRNA Synthetases

1. OLIGOMERIC STRUCTURES

From the biochemical data available to date, aminoacyl-tRNA synthetases can be divided into three classes according to their quaternary structures. As shown in Table I, prokaryotic enzymes occur as monomers, homologous dimers, or tetramers of the α_4 and $\alpha_2\beta_2$ types. As a general rule, this quaternary structure polymorphism is conserved for the eukaryotic enzymes. Furthermore, subunit structures of homologous enzymes have remained markedly unchanged during evolution from prokaryotes to lower eukaryotes with the exceptions, so far, of methionyl- ($\alpha_2 \rightarrow \alpha$), alanyl- ($\alpha_4 \rightarrow \alpha$), and glycyl- ($\alpha_2\beta_2 \rightarrow \alpha_2$) tRNA synthetases. The conservation in quaternary structures displayed by these enzymes is particularly exemplified by phenylalanyl-tRNA synthetase, which exists as a tetramer of the $\alpha_2\beta_2$ type in all species. In mammalian cells, aminoacyl-tRNA synthetases exhibit a more complex pattern of structural organization, with enzymes occurring as multi-enzyme complexes (10 of them marked "CX" in Table I) or as entities displaying quaternary structures identical to those observed for the corresponding enzymes from lower eukaryotes (134). The above consideration on the evolutionary conservation of quaternary structures applies also to individual aminoacyl-tRNA synthetases, when studied after dissociation from the high-molecular-weight complexes [valyl (α)-, isoleucyl (α)-, or leucyl (α)- and lysyl (α_2)-tRNA synthetases (115, 116, 135)].

In the case of the enzymes with an $\alpha_2\beta_2$ type structure, isolated α and β subunits of E. coli glycyl (136)- and phenylalanyl (137)-tRNA synthetases and yeast phenylalanyl-tRNA synthetase (138) are inactive in tRNA aminoacylation as well as in aminoacyl-adenylate formation. However, protein fusion experiments carried out on the α and β chains of E. coli glycyl-tRNA synthetase (139) indicate that an $\alpha_2\beta_2$ structure is not a prerequisite for the expression of catalytic activity. That a tetrameric organization is dispensable for catalysis is further exemplified by gene-deletion experiments conducted on the alaS gene from E. coli (140). A monomeric 461-aminoacid derivative of alanyl-tRNA synthetase (875 aminoacid residues for the native enzyme) is able to complement a chromosomal alaS5 mutant deficient for aminoacylation.

Likewise, the dimeric methionyl-tRNA synthetase from E. coli can be converted into a fully active monomer following limited proteolysis (141) that removes approximately 200 residues from the carboxy terminus (41). A series of carboxy-terminal-truncated methionyl-tRNA synthetases have been constructed by deletion experiments conducted on the cloned E. coli metG gene (142). Deletion of 129 residues from the carboxy terminus of the native enzyme generates a monomeric, fully active enzyme, as assessed by genetic complementation studies. Interestingly, yeast cytoplasmic (86) and mitochondrial (88) methionyl-tRNA synthetases are monomeric enzymes. They lack the carboxy-terminal domain responsible for dimerization of the E. coli enzyme (87, 89). However, the dimeric structure of aminoacyl-tRNA synthetases from the α_2 type is generally required for the expression of their catalytic activity.

Site-directed mutagenesis of Phe-164 of tyrosyl-tRNA synthetase of *B. stearothermophilus*, a residue located at the subunit interface of the dimeric enzyme, into Asp-164 leads to a fully active dimer that readily dissociates upon pH increase and enzyme dilution (*143*). The monomeric enzyme is inactive and does not bind tyrosine. *B. stearothermophilus* tyrosyl-tRNA synthetase displays half-of-the-sites activity (*144*). Several pieces of evidence suggest that the dimeric enzyme is intrinsically asymmetric in solution, even in the absence of substrates (*7, 145*), whereas the crystalline dimeric enzyme displays a symmetrical conformation (*146*). This asymmetry could explain the absolute requirement of dimerization for generating an active enzyme.

In addition, neutron scattering by *E. coli* tyrosyl-tRNA synthetase is consistent with the binding of one tRNA molecule per dimeric enzyme, with the CCA arm and the anticodon loop lying on different subunits (*147*). With the *B. stearothermophilus* enzyme, the tRNA interacts with the amino-terminal moiety of one subunit and the carboxy-terminal moiety of the other subunit (*148*). Accordingly, while methionyl-tRNA synthetase, a dimer made of large identical subunits, is active as a monomer and binds two molecules of tRNA per dimer (*149*), tyrosyl-tRNA synthetase, a dimer composed of small subunits, binds one molecule of tRNA per dimer and is active only as a dimer. However, among those aminoacyl-tRNA synthetases that have a dimeric structure, one or two tRNA binding sites have been found (*4*), irrespective of the subunit sizes of these enzymes. Thus, the proposal that dimeric aminoacyl-tRNA synthetases with large subunits can bind one molecule of tRNA per protomer and can function as monomers does not seem to be a general rule.

2. PRIMARY STRUCTURES: COMMON AND DISSIMILAR FEATURES

In addition to the diversity in quaternary structures displayed by this class of enzyme, large differences in subunit molecular weights are observed. The subunit masses of prokaryotic aminoacyl-tRNA synthetases range from 37 kDa for dimeric tryptophanyl-tRNA synthetase to 108 kDa for monomeric valyl-tRNA synthetase. As a general rule, it appears that aminoacyl-tRNA synthetases from eukaryotes have subunit masses significantly higher than those of homologous enzymes from prokaryotes (Table I), with the notable apparent exception of aspartyl-tRNA synthetase (discussed in the following section).

Numerous observations show that the chain extensions that characterize eukaryotic aminoacyl-tRNA synthetases are generally located at one extremity of the molecule, rather than as insertions within the catalytic domain. Controlled proteolysis of purified yeast lysyl (*93, 150*)- or aspartyl (*151*)-tRNA synthetases gives rise to truncated proteins that have lost an amino-terminal segment of the molecule without impairing their catalytic activities. Similarly, fully active, proteolytically modified forms of mammalian tryptophanyl (152)-, methionyl (153–155)-, lysyl (116)-, and arginyl (156)-tRNA synthetases were obtained. The corresponding truncated proteins have molecular weights similar to those of their prokaryotic counterparts. These dissection experiments point out the evolutionary conservation of a prokaryotic-like domain responsible for catalysis. The functional significance of the chain extension that characterizes eukaryotic aminoacyl-tRNA synthetases is discussed in the following sections.

Structural and functional similarities between catalytic domains of homologous aminoacyl-tRNA synthetases from prokaryotes and eukaryotes have been observed. For instance, native isoleucyl-tRNA synthetase and trypsin-modified monomeric methionyl-tRNA synthetase from sheep liver contain one zinc ion per polypeptide chain (115), the removal of which leads to inactive apoenzymes, as in the case of their prokaryotic counterparts (157). In addition, those enzymes that can efficiently catalyze Ap_4A synthesis in E. coli (158–160) are also able to synthesize this compound, when isolated from eukaryotic cells (160–162).

In the primary sequences determined by gene cloning and sequencing, several interesting features are noteworthy. There are no internal repeat sequences for either small or large polypeptide chains. Thus, the emergence of aminoacyl-tRNA synthetases harboring large polypeptide chains is not the result of duplication of some internal sequences. Internal deletions have been carried out on E. coli isoleucyl-tRNA synthetase (163), a monomeric enzyme with a large polypeptide chain. Comparison of primary sequences of E. coli methionyl- and isoleucyl-tRNA synthetases reveals significant homologies within a segment of their polypeptide chains (163) identified as the nucleotide binding domain of methionyl-tRNA synthetase (164). However, in isoleucyl-tRNA synthetase, a large internal sequence not found in methionyl-tRNA synthetase connects two parts of the nucleotide fold. Deletion of this segment does not impair isoleucyl-tRNA synthetase activity (163). This result suggests that aminoacyl-tRNA synthetases are made of functional pieces joined together by connective segments of variable sizes. Thus, subunit molecular-weight diversity can be accounted for, in part, by internal dispensable loops.

In E. coli methionyl (41, 141)- and alanyl (140)-tRNA synthetases, dispensable sequences, responsible for oligomerization have been identified in the carboxy-terminal extremities, as stated above. Alanyl-tRNA synthetase represses its own transcription by binding to a palindromic sequence flanking the alaS promoter (165). It has been proposed that tetrameric organization of this enzyme is required in this process (140). Similarly, it could be suggested that the amino-terminal extension found in the E. coli threonyl-tRNA synthetase (50), as compared to the yeast mitochondrial enzyme (96), is involved in autogenous translational control of *E. coli* threonyl-tRNA synthetase expression (*166*).

Primary structure comparisons reveal little homology between aminoacyl-tRNA synthetases with different aminoacid specificities; only small stretches of sequence similarities have been observed (*54, 167*). However, taking into account the extent of conserved sequences between different aminoacyl-tRNA synthetases, evolutionary linkages can be tentatively proposed. Significant structural homologies, distributed evenly throughout their primary structures, have been identified in glutamyl- and glutaminyl-tRNA synthetases (*39*), in methionyl-, leucyl-, isoleucyl-, and valyl-tRNA synthetases (*27–29, 33, 73, 82*), and in lysyl- and aspartyl-tRNA synthetases (*47*). These results suggest that, within these three families, enzymes have evolved from a common ancestral gene. In most cases, no immunological cross-reactivity was observed for heterologous aminoacyl-tRNA synthetases. However, antibodies directed against glycyl-tRNA synthetase inhibit the aminoacylation activity of phenylalanyl-tRNA synthetase (*168*), although homologies between the protein sequences from *E. coli* glycyl- and phenylalanyl-tRNA synthetases are quite limited.

Two characteristic sequences composed of four and five aminoacid residues, shared by numerous aminoacyl-tRNA synthetases, have been identified and their functional significance in part deciphered. The first of these, corresponding to the consensus sequence HIGH (His–Ile–Gly–His), was observed in the *E. coli* methionyl-, isoleucyl-, tyrosyl-, and glutaminyl-tRNA synthetases (*31*), and its occurrence, with some variations, was reported for several enzymes (*8*). It was always in the amino-terminal moiety of those enzymes that possess it. The two histidine residues are functionally relevant to the ATP binding site. Site-directed mutagenesis of these two residues from *B. stearothermophilus* tyrosyl-tRNA synthetase indicates that His-48 binds to the ribose of the nucleotide, whereas His-45 seems to be involved in the stabilization of the transition state by hydrogen-bonding to the γ-phosphoryl group of ATP (*7*).

Another small stretch of homology, a KMSKS (Lys–Met–Ser–Lys–Ser) sequence, identified by affinity-labeling experiments as the CCA binding site of tRNA in *E. coli* methionyl-tRNA synthetase (*169*), is highly conserved in these enzymes (*167*).Crystallographic data obtained on the monomeric, fully active fragment of trypsin-modified methionyl-tRNA synthetase (*10*) show that Lys-335 is in a loop located in the carboxy-terminal domain of the molecule, which lies on one side of the active site. Similarly, Lys-230 and Lys-233 from *B. stearothermophilus* tyrosyl-tRNA synthetase are found in a sequence pattern that shares some resemblance to the aminoacid sequence surrounding Lys-335 from *E. coli* methionyl-tRNA synthetase as well as lysine residues from *E. coli* tyrosyl-tRNA synthetase labeled by periodate-oxidized tRNA^{Tyr} (170). These two lysine residues are located within a loop displaying a structure too poorly ordered to allow unambiguous location in the crystal (171), but compatible with a model involving ε-NH$_2$ pointing toward the phosphates of ATP, in an induced-fit mechanism (172).

As shown in Fig. 1 for those aminoacyl-tRNA synthetases that contain the HIGH and KMSKS consensus sequences, the polarity NH$_2$ → HIGH → KMSKS → COOH is always conserved. This is the case for prokaryotic enzymes from E. coli, B. subtilis, B. stearothermophilus, B. caldotenax, and R. meliloti, for mitochondrial and cytoplasmic enzymes from the lower eukaryotes S. cerevisiae and N. crassa, and for mammalian enzymes from human cells (glutaminyl-tRNA synthetase) or from Chinese hamster ovary (CHO) cells [cDNA sequence from arginyl-tRNA synthetase (M. Lazard and M. Mirande, unpublished)]. As these two segments seem to be involved in the formation of the active site, this implies a common folding pattern for these enzymes, the carboxy-terminal moiety folding back upon the amino-terminal domain. The variation in the size of the segments located between these two consensus sequences can be due, in part, to the insertion of dispensable sequences, as reported above for E. coli isoleucyl-tRNA synthetase. In some aminoacyl-tRNA synthetases, no HIGH or KMSKS consensus sequences can be distinguished, but the presence of more distantly related sequences cannot be dismissed. Identification of the aminoacid residues implicated in ATP and CCA binding should clarify this point.

When homologous enzymes from various organisms are considered, more extensive primary-structure homologies can be observed. This is particularly striking for the aminoacid sequences of aminoacyl-tRNA synthetases from different prokaryotes. The primary structures of tryptophanyl- and tyrosyl-tRNA synthetases have been determined from three prokaryotic sources, including E. coli, B. stearothermophilus, and B. subtilis or B. caldotenax. Each is highly conserved (59, 60, 64). Only four aminoacid substitutions distinguish the tyrosyl-tRNA synthetases of B. stearothermophilus and B. caldotenax, two thermophilic strains (60). To a lesser extent, pro-

---

FIG. 1. Conservation of HIGH and KMSKS consensus sequences. (Left) Aminoacyl-tRNA synthetases that possess HIGH and KMSKS consensus sequences. The alignment is based on the position of the HIGH sequence, located in the amino-terminal part of the proteins. (Right) Aminoacid (a.a.) specificity of the enzyme, its source, and the HIGH and KMSKS consensus-sequence derivatives. Numbering corresponds to the position in the aminoacid sequence, deduced from the nucleotide sequence, taking into account the amino-terminal methionine. BSu, *Bacillus subtilis*; BSt, *Bacillus stearothermophilus*; EC, *Escherichia coli*; SCM, *Saccharomyces cerevisiae* mitochondria; BCa, *Bacillus caldotenax*; NCM, *Neurospora crassa* mitochondria; RM, *Rhizobium meliloti*; SCC, *Saccharomyces cerevisiae* cytoplasm; Hum, human HeLa S3 cells; NCC, *Neurospora crassa* cytoplasm. References for specific aminoacid sequences are given in Table I.

100 a.a.

NH₂ — COOH

Consensus

Enzyme	Source	▼ HIGH	◆ KMSKS
Trp	BSu	16-TLGN	193-KMSKS
Trp	BSt	15-TIGN	192-KMSKS
Trp	EC	17-TIGN	195-KMSKS
Trp	SCM	48-HLGN	244-KMSKS
Tyr	BSt	45-HIGH	230-KFGKT
Tyr	BCa	45-HIGN	230-KFGKT
Tyr	EC	48-HLGH	235-KFGKT
Tyr	NCM	110-HUGH	324-KFGKS
Glu	EC	16-HUGG	237-KLSKR
Glu	RM	19-HUGT	253-KLSKR
Arg	EC	129-HUGH	433-DLSKN
Gln	EC	41-HIGH	268-UMSKR
Gln	SCC	265-HIGH	495-ULSKR
Gln	Hum	44-HIGH	265-ULSKR
Met	EC	22-HLGH	333-KMSKS
Met	SCM	29-HLGH	341-KMSKS
Met	SCC	212-HLGN	525-KFSKS
Leu	EC	49-HMGH	619-KMSKS
Leu	SCM	63-HIGH	646-KMSKS
Leu	NCM	100-HLGH	697-KMSKS
Leu	NCC	91-HRGH	757-KMSKS
Ile	EC	65-HIGH	602-KMSKS
Ile	SCC	54-HYGH	603-KMSKS
Val	BSt	56-HLGH	525-KMSKS
Val	EC	49-HMGH	554-KMSKS
Val	SCC	151-HIGH	657-KMSKS

karyotic and lower eukaryotic homologous aminoacyl-tRNA synthetases display significant homologies, ranging from 28% of identities in the case of histidyl-tRNA synthetases to 46% for glutaminyl-tRNA synthetases. Two exceptions are leucyl-tRNA synthetase (78) and both subunits of phenylalanyl-tRNA synthetase (108), which display quite limited sequence similarities. Mitochondrial enzymes seem to be more closely related to their prokaryotic counterparts than to the corresponding cytoplasmic enzymes (89). In this connection, it must be noticed that *E. coli* tyrosyl-tRNA synthetase can substitute for *S. cerevisiae* mitochondrial tyrosyl-tRNA synthetase, provided that an amino-terminal sequence necessary for mitochondrial import is fused to the *E. coli* enzyme (173).

Cytoplasmic aspartyl- or histidyl-tRNA synthetases from *S. cerevisiae* display a higher similarity with their mammalian counterparts (52% and 44%, respectively) than with the corresponding bacterial enzymes (approximately 28%). However, the rule according to which yeast enzymes would be more closely related to their higher eukaryotic counterparts than to the bacterial ones is only tentative, due to our limited knowledge of the primary sequences of mammalian enzymes. The extent of structural relatedness has also been monitored by immunological approaches. Whereas immunological cross-reactivity was observed between aspartyl- or valyl-tRNA synthetases from yeast and rabbit liver (G. Bec and J. P. Waller, unpublished), no cross-reaction was visualized between yeast and sheep liver enzymes specific for lysine (174), methionine (175), or phenylalanine (128). In addition, bacterial and silkworm alanyl-tRNA synthetases share a common epitope in their catalytic domains (176), pointing out a distant relationship, in relation to more stringent evolutionary constraints related to the active site. A common epitope displayed by the prokaryotic and eukaryotic tryptophanyl-tRNA synthetases has been detected by a monoclonal antibody raised against the purified bovine enzyme (177).

The long-standing hypothesis of an initially restricted code requiring a limiting set of amino acids, tRNAs, and activating enzymes (178) is now generally accepted. It implies that during evolution, new aminoacyl-tRNA synthetases arose by modification of pre-existing enzymes. If such a consideration applies, one may suppose that enzymes specific for structurally related amino acids share some conserved regions (179). Because of some mechanistic specificities of the aminoacyl-tRNA synthetases, it was proposed that enzymes belonging to the XUX (for amino acids Leu, Ile, Val, Met, and Phe) and XCX (Ser, Pro, Thr, and Ala) codon groups evolved more recently than those of the XAX (Tyr, His, Gln, Asn, Lys, Asp, and Glu) and XGX (Cys, Trp, Arg, Ser, and Gly) families (180). A comparison of the primary sequences of those aminoacyl-tRNA synthetases whose sequences are presently known strengthens the idea according to which enzymes from the XUX family, on the one hand, and enzymes from the XAX family, on the other [Asn, Lys, Asp, and His (52)], were derived from a common ancestor, but provides only limited information for elaborating an evolutionary tree that includes all 20 enzymes. However, the finding that sequences related to the HIGH and KMSKS consensus sequences are also encountered in enzymes belonging to the XAX and XGX codon groups suggests that an extensive evolutionary relationship prevails in the aminoacyl-tRNA synthetase family.

C. Distinctive Features of Eukaryotic Aminoacyl-tRNA Synthetases

As stated above, eukaryotic aminoacyl-tRNA synthetases share significant common features with their prokaryotic counterparts. In particular, proteolytically derived, fully active forms of eukaryotic enzymes show extensive oligomeric and primary structure similarities with the corresponding bacterial enzymes, pointing out the conservation of a domain involved in catalysis. However, several differences distinguish eukaryotic enzymes from their prokaryotic analogs. In Table I, one can identify eukaryotic and prokaryotic enzymes by the invariably longer subunit molecular weights of the eukaryotic aminoacyl-tRNA synthetases. Taking this characteristic for granted, it can be inferred that the general polyanion binding property of the lower and higher eukaryotic enzymes (150, 181, 182), as well as the ability displayed by some higher eukaryotic enzymes to associate within high-molecular-weight complexes (134), are somehow related to these chain extensions. In the next two sections, the data pertaining to these evolutionary acquisitions are scrutinized in relation to the possible physiological significance of these findings.

II. Evolutionary Acquisition of Polyanion Binding Properties

A. Evidence for a Binding Domain

One characteristic feature of eukaryotic aminoacyl-tRNA synthetases is the ability to bind to polyanionic carriers under conditions in which the corresponding enzymes from E. coli do not. This general property was observed upon chromatography of a crude extract from rabbit reticulocytes on immobilized RNA (181) and of a crude extract from S. cerevisiae on immobilized heparin (150). A comparative study of aminoacyl-tRNA synthetases from S. cerevisiae and CHO cells was conducted (Fig. 2) to establish the more precise relative affinities of these enzymes for heparin–Ultrogel, under conditions in which none of the 20 enzymes from a crude extract of E. coli is retained (P. Kerjan and J. P. Waller, unpublished). Aminoacyl-tRNA synthetases from yeast have a strong affinity for this carrier, their elution requiring between 120 mM KCl for seryl-tRNA synthetase and 300 mM KCl for aspartyl- and glutamyl-tRNA synthetases. A similar binding was observed for the corresponding enzymes from CHO cells, although with decreased affinities. Only alanyl-tRNA synthetase was eluted in the flow-through fractions, possibly as a result of uncontrolled proteolysis.

It should be pointed out that in a recent study dealing with the purification of yeast mitochondrial methionyl-tRNA synthetase (88), a binding of several mitochondrial enzymes to immobilized heparin was observed. This result is unexpected because of the close relationship between prokaryotic and yeast mitochondrial aminoacyl-tRNA synthetases. However, the high magnesium concentrations (20 mM) in the equilibration buffer used in that study can promote the association of numerous proteins with polyanionic carriers (A. Wolfson, unpublished). Thus, to compare accurately the binding properties of yeast mitochondrial aminoacyl-tRNA synthetases with those of prokaryotic and yeast cytoplasmic enzymes, one must reexamine their behavior on heparin–Ultrogel in the same conditions as those used in other studies.

The structural features underlying this difference in behavior between eukaryotic and prokaryotic aminoacyl-tRNA synthetases begin to be understood. Several lines of evidence have led to the proposal that eukaryotic aminoacyl-tRNA synthetases have distinct domains, with the domain responsible for binding to polyanionic supports lying adjacent to the catalytic domain. This became clear from controlled proteolysis experiments carried out on homogeneous enzymes.

Yeast lysyl- and aspartyl-tRNA synthetases, in their native state, interact strongly with immobilized heparin (150, 151) (Fig. 2). To the contrary, it was shown that proteolytically modified forms of these enzymes (minus about 10% of their polypeptide chains but still active in both ATP–PP$_i$ exchange and tRNA aminoacylation, and retaining their dimeric structures) have a much lower affinity for this carrier, behaving like prokaryotic aminoacyl-tRNA synthetases. Similarly, homogeneous dimeric lysyl-tRNA synthetase from sheep liver (2 × 79,000), obtained upon dissociation from the high-molecular-weight complex of nine aminoacyl-tRNA synthetases, binds strongly to heparin–Ultrogel, but a proteolyzed form of this enzyme, a fully active dimer of 2 × 64,000, does not (116). This was interpreted as showing the existence of a distinct polycationic domain.

Threonyl-tRNA synthetase from rabbit reticulocytes can bind tRNA[Thr] as well as 16-S rRNA (183). However, while an excess of tRNA[Thr] efficiently removes rRNA from rRNA : enzyme complexes, rRNA does not dissociate tRNA[Thr] from tRNA[Thr] : enzyme complexes. In other words, tRNA in excess, through non-specific ionic interactions, can displace rRNA adsorbed to the polycationic domain, but rRNA cannot antagonize specific tRNA : enzyme interactions.

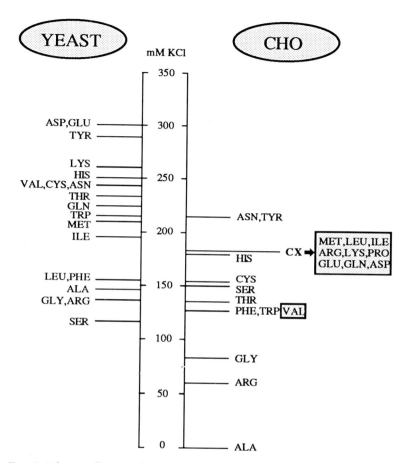

FIG. 2. Relative affinities of eukaryotic aminoacyl-tRNA synthetases for immobilized heparin. Crude extracts from yeast or Chinese hamster ovary (CHO) cells were applied on a column of heparin–Ultrogel equilibrated in 20 mM potassium phosphate, pH 7.2, 10 mM β-mercaptoethanol, 10% glycerol. After washing with the same buffer to ensure the removal of unbound proteins, elution was performed with a linear KCl gradient in the same buffer. All 20 aminoacyl-tRNA synthetases were assayed in the flow-through fractions and in the fractions obtained following KCl elution. No detectable yeast prolyl-tRNA synthetase activity was recovered. (Data from P. Kerjan and J. P. Waller, unpublished).

Also relevant to these considerations are studies dealing with the positioning of tRNA within its complexes with yeast aminoacyl-tRNA synthetase. Neutron-scattering studies show that, in a 1 : 1 complex of valyl-tRNA synthetase : tRNA^{Val}, the tRNA is intimately associated with the enzyme, lying closer to the center of mass of the complex than the protein (184). On the other hand, in a 1 : 1 complex with a non-cognate tRNA, the RNA lies farther away from the center of mass of the complex than the protein, and could interact with the polycationic domain.

Thus, a portion of the polypeptide chain, excisable by proteolysis, is responsible for the association of these eukaryotic aminoacyl-tRNA synthetases with polyanionic carriers. These results suggest that the chain extensions present in these eukaryotic enzymes, but absent from their prokaryotic analogs, are responsible for conferring polyanion binding properties upon them. This autonomous domain is distinct from the catalytic domain we refer to as the binding domain. As primary sequences for other enzymes became available, it was possible to generalize this observation to most, if not all, eukaryotic aminoacyl-tRNA synthetases, and to determine, at the molecular level, the structural elements involved in this binding property.

B. Structural Features of the Binding Domain

1. LOCATION OF THE BINDING DOMAIN

The primary structures of 11 aminoacyl-tRNA synthetases from both *E. coli* and *S. cerevisiae* cytoplasm are known. Except for phenylalanyl- and leucyl-tRNA synthetases, extensive homologies between the nine other homologous aminoacyl-tRNA synthetases from *E. coli* and yeast are made readily apparent by dot-matrix comparison of the corresponding primary sequences (Fig. 3). This dot-matrix representation indicates an amino-terminal extension of the polypeptide chain for yeast aminoacyl-tRNA synthetases specific for aspartic acid, glutamine, lysine, methionine, threonine, valine, and, to a lesser extent, histidine, and to a carboxy-terminal extension in yeast isoleucyl- and seryl-tRNA synthetases. Methionyl-tRNA synthetase from *E. coli* also has a carboxy-terminal extension corresponding to a domain involved in dimerization (*41, 141, 142*). Aspartyl-tRNA synthetase, a dimer made of identical subunits with molecular weights of 66,000 and 63,000 from *E. coli* and yeast, respectively, represents an exception to the rule that eukaryotic enzymes have longer polypeptide chains than their prokaryotic counterparts. The dot-matrix comparison shown in Fig. 3 gives a rational explanation to this apparent exception, namely, that the amino-terminal extension of about 100 amino acids present in the yeast enzyme is compensated by several internal deletions in its catalytic domain, as compared to the *E. coli* enzyme. It should be stressed that the point of cleavage of yeast lysyl (*93*)- and aspartyl (*151*)-tRNA synthetases by elastase and trypsin, respectively, which leads to the excision of the polycationic segment, is located just ahead of the fragment that is homologous to the corresponding *E. coli* enzyme.

On the basis of these primary sequence similarities, homologous enzymes can be aligned as shown in Fig. 4. The isoelectric points (pI's) calcu-

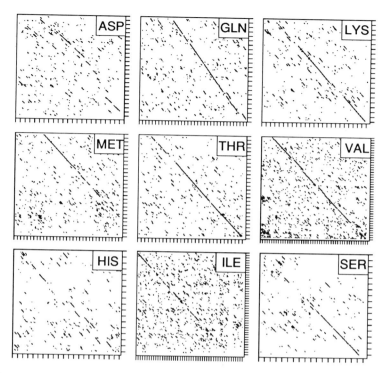

FIG. 3. Dot-matrix comparison of bacterial and yeast aminoacyl-tRNA synthetases. Primary sequences of homologous aminoacyl-tRNA synthetases from *Escherichia coli* and *Saccharomyces cerevisiae* were compared by using a matrix program that scores a dot for every homology, considering a window of 10 amino acids to display a homology score of 50%. Couples of enzymes are designated by their aminoacid specificity. Yeast and bacterial aminoacyl-tRNA synthetases are represented in the abscissa (residue 1 at left) and the ordinate (residue 1 at top), respectively. A gap between two dashes corresponds to a length of 25 amino acids. References for specific aminoacid sequences are given in Table I.

lated for the corresponding subunits are generally significantly more basic for the lower eukaryotic enzymes as compared to those of the prokaryotic counterparts, although the same calculation yields very similar p*I*'s when considering only the homologous portions of their polypeptide chains. Thus, the increase in p*I*'s observed for yeast enzymes is mainly due to the contribution of the chain extensions, which have remarkably basic p*I*'s, ranging from 7.55 in the case of methionyl-tRNA synthetase to 10.24 for lysyl-tRNA synthetase.

The short carboxy-terminal extension of yeast seryl-tRNA synthetase, composed of 13 amino acid residues, of which six are lysines, has a p*I* of

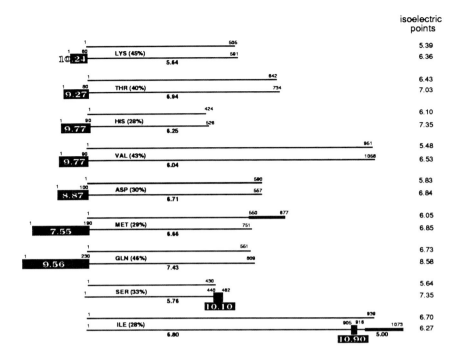

FIG. 4. Locations and net charges of the proposed binding domains. Alignment of homologous aminoacyl-tRNA synthetases is based on the Kanehisa (185) alignment program by weighting with the mutation data matrix of Dayhoff (186). Aminoacyl-tRNA synthetases are designated according to their aminoacid specificity, the polypeptide chain of yeast enzymes being schematized under that of their bacterial homologs ("1" refers to the amino-terminal methionine). The level of homology between conserved regions of their primary sequences (shown by thin lines) is indicated in parentheses. At right are theoretical isoelectric points for the full-length polypeptides. The polypeptide chain extensions are shown by solid bars, and their corresponding calculated isoelectric points are indicated. References for specific aminoacid sequences are given in Table I.

10.10. As an exception, the carboxy-terminal extension carried by *S. cerevisiae* isoleucyl-tRNA synthetase is composed primarily of acidic residues. However, around position 900 in its primary sequence, there is a cluster of lysine residues that is not found in the *E. coli* enzyme. In all cases, the polycationic character of these extensions is mainly due to the clustering of lysine (and arginine) residues (Fig. 5), rather than the absence of anionic residues.

Although the amino-terminal extension of yeast aspartyl-tRNA synthetase is responsible for its ability to bind to polyanionic carriers (151), its cationic character is less apparent because of several acidic residues located

DRSSC	30-S K K A L K K L Q K E Q E K Q R K K E E R A L-52
HRSSC	20-L K A S K A P K K G K L Q V S L K T P K G T K D -43
HRSHUM	36-A K L L K L K A Q L G P D E S K Q K F V L K T P K G T R D-64
IRSSC	894-E Y K A V A D W P D L G K K L K K D A K K V K D A-918
KRSSC	28-S K S E L K K R I K Q R Q V E A K K A A K K A A A Q P K P A S K K K T-62
MRSSC	8-D K S K K H P A H L Q L A N N L K I-25
	140-H S K F P E L P S K V H N A V A L A K K H V P R D S S S F K N I G A V K I Q A D L T V K P K D-186
QRSSC	17-E D K K V K E I V K N K K V S -31
	175-L K L L Q P K D E R D L I K K K T K N N E K K K T N S A K K S S-206
SRSSC	447-E L P K N S T S S K D K K K K N-462
TRSSC	12-V K K L S V N D S S N D A V K P N K K E N K K S K Q Q S-39
VRSSC	27-S P K T P K E I E K E K K K A E K L L K F A A K Q A K K N A A A T T G A S Q K K P K K K K E V E-74

FIG. 5. Aminoacid sequences of the lysine-rich regions found in the binding domains of eukaryotic aminoacyl-tRNA synthetases. Aminoacid sequences are derived from the nucleotide sequences of the corresponding cloned genes (references are listed in Table I). XRSSC and XRSHUM, Aminoacyl-tRNA synthetases specific for the amino acid X (one-letter symbol) from *Saccharomyces cerevisiae* cytoplasm (SC) or human cytoplasm (HUM).

in the vicinity of the basic ones. A similar situation is also encountered, to a lesser extent, for some other aminoacyl-tRNA synthetases, as shown in Fig. 5. Assuming that the results obtained for yeast lysyl- and aspartyl-tRNA synthetases—i.e., that their amino-terminal moieties are dispensable for catalysis, at least *in vitro*—are also true for other enzymes for which no similar data are available, it is reasonable to propose that these chain extensions account for the property displayed by all eukaryotic aminoacyl-tRNA synthetases: binding to polyanionic supports.

2. STRUCTURE OF THE BINDING DOMAIN

One intriguing feature of the aminoacid composition of the amino-terminal extension carried by aspartyl-tRNA synthetase from S. *cerevisiae* is the presence of several acidic residues located within its lysine-rich segment (Fig. 5). Moreover, whereas pI's determined experimentally are in the ranges of 5.9–7.0 and 5.6–5.9, respectively, for the native and truncated enzymes (151), the corresponding calculated values are similar, equal to 6.8 in both cases. The difference in behavior observed upon chromatography of the native and truncated enzymes on heparin–Ultrogel could be due to the clustering, in the folded protein, of the lysine residues within the amino-terminal domain of yeast aspartyl-tRNA synthease, in such a way that they allow anchorage of the native enzyme to the heparin matrix.

It is noteworthy that, when searching for potential secondary structures with various algorithms (187, 188), α-helical secondary structures can be predicted for the lysine-rich regions of the putative amino-terminal binding domains of yeast lysyl-, aspartyl-, threonyl-, and valyl-tRNA synthetases (93,

151). Likewise, using the same algorithms, residues Glu-894 to Ala-918 from yeast isoleucyl-tRNA synthetase have the propensity to fold into an α-helical structure. An interesting feature of these predicted α-helices is the segregation of lysine residues on one side of the helix. This anisotropic distribution and clustering of lysine residues are made clearly apparent on the helical net-diagram representations of the corresponding segments (Fig. 6). Such an anisotropic distribution of cationic residues within these binding domains, leading to a segregation of cationic and anionic residues, especially in yeast aspartyl-tRNA synthetase, may be optimally designed to generate a high-affinity site for polyanionic carriers.

In the lysine-rich domains of histidyl-, methionyl-, glutaminyl-, or seryl-tRNA synthetases, there is a lesser degree of confidence for secondary structure predictions. However, one can argue that the formation of a polyanion binding site may require more complex folding patterns, involving adjacent regions of the binding domain, that cannot be predicted easily by common algorithms. With regard to the possible significance of this lysine-rich domain as a biological interface, as discussed in Section IV, it would be of great interest to get more information on the three-dimensional conformation of these binding domains.

Crystals from dimeric, native aspartyl-tRNA synthetase from *S. cerevisiae* have been obtained (*190*), and their resolution is now in progress, together with the study of crystals from aspartyl-tRNA synthetase : tRNA^{Asp} complexes (*191, 192*). A preliminary account of this work (*191*), based on low-

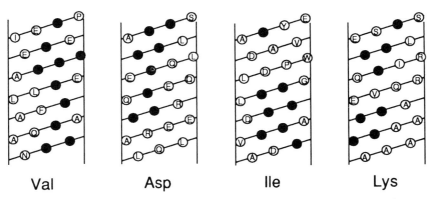

| Val | Asp | Ile | Lys |

FIG. 6. Predicted secondary structures for the lysine-rich clusters of the binding domains. Helical-net diagram (*189*) of the proposed α-helical structure of the region from residues P_{31}–N_{55} in valyl-tRNA synthetase, S_{30}–L_{54} in aspartyl-tRNA synthetase, E_{894}–A_{918} in isoleucyl-tRNA synthetase, and S_{28}–A_{52} in lysyl-tRNA synthetase, from *Saccharomyces cerevisiae* cytoplasm. Lysine residues are indicated by black circles. References for specific aminoacid sequences are given in Table I.

resolution crystallographic data, reveals that the two tRNA molecules bound to the dimeric enzyme are located on one side of the protein. If the propensity to associate *in vitro* to polyanionic supports also applies *in vivo*, one may speculate that the binding domains are located on the opposite side of the molecule, allowing the attachment of the enzyme to polyanionic components of the cytoplasm without impairing interactions of tRNA and protein.

C. Are Binding Domains Dispensable *in Vivo?*

To test for the absolute requirement of these binding domains *in vivo*, constructs carrying deletions in the amino-terminal extensions of yeast glutaminyl-, methionyl-, or lysyl-tRNA synthetases have been used to transform yeast cells defective for the corresponding wild-type alleles.

Derivatives of *GLN4* carrying internal deletions in the large amino-terminal extension borne by glutaminyl-tRNA synthetase, constructed on a multicopy plasmid, complement a *GLN4* disrupted allele in a haploid strain that is not viable in the absence of a functional, plasmid-borne *GLN4* allele (*193*). Several interesting features are noteworthy. (1) Frame-shift mutations constructed in the 5'-end coding region of the transcript (i.e., located within the amino-terminal extension) do not complement a chromosomal null allele, thus indicating that translation initiation does not occur downstream from this chain extension. (2) All of the in-frame deletions examined involved the region encompassing the first 128 codons of *GLN4*, which precedes the lysine-rich segment indicated in Fig. 5. Hence, these deletions do not directly address the function of the polycationic region of the amino-terminal extension. (3) Even so, while the level of mRNA corresponding to multicopy, plasmid-borne *GLN4* derivatives is much higher than that observed in a wild-type strain carrying a single-copy gene, the steady-state level of glutaminyl-tRNA synthetase activity, assayed *in vitro*, was not significantly elevated. This result suggests that the truncated gene products are less stable *in vivo* than is the native, full-length enzyme. However, in the absence of immunological quantification of the corresponding gene products, other possibilities cannot be excluded. In particular, one could argue that the shortened amino-terminal extension cannot be folded as in the native domain, thereby interfering with the tRNA-aminoacylation reaction.

Deletions in yeast cytoplasmic methionyl-tRNA synthetase, encompassing up to the complete amino-terminal extension, were constructed in an *MES1* allele carried by a multicopy plasmid (*194*). These constructs were used to transform a mutant yeast strain with a temperature-sensitive methionyl-tRNA synthetase corresponding to the chromosomal *mes1* mutation. A multicopy, plasmid-borne *MES1* derivative lacking its amino-terminal domain can complement the *mes1* mutation.

In another set of experiments, a *KRS1* derivative, encoding a truncated lysyl-tRNA synthetase missing the amino-terminal extension, was used to replace the wild-type *KRS1* allele by a one-step disruption procedure (R. Martinez and M. Mirande, unpublished). The growth rate of the strain carrying a single copy of the *KRS1* gene product was slightly impaired. This approach was designed to test the behavior of yeast cells expressing an amount of a truncated enzyme similar to that of the native enzyme in a wild-type cell. However, the truncated lysyl-tRNA synthetase is expressed at a level much higher than that of the wild-type enzyme, because of translational regulation events. As in the case of glutaminyl-tRNA synthetase, low levels of lysyl-tRNA synthetase activity were detected *in vitro*, as compared to the level of the protein determined by immunotitration, suggesting an *in vivo* instability of the truncated enzyme.

These experiments show that the binding domains are dispensable *in vivo*, at least under conditions in which the truncated aminoacyl-tRNA synthetases are expressed in large amounts. However, taking into account that most, if not all, eukaryotic aminoacyl-tRNA synthetases share a similar domain, it would be surprising if its occurrence had no functional meaning. If the cationic polypeptide extensions are implicated in cellular compartmentalization, as discussed in Section IV, one may argue that overexpression of a truncated enzyme will allow palliation of this requirement.

III. Complexes of Aminoacyl-tRNA Synthetases in Higher Eukaryotes

A. Synthetase Composition of the Complexes

1. TYPICAL SIZE DISTRIBUTION OF MAMMALIAN AMINOACYL-tRNA SYNTHETASES

One distinctive feature that characterizes the aminoacyl-tRNA synthetases of higher eukaryotes is the occurrence of high-molecular-weight forms of these enzymes that behave as entities much larger than the α, α_2, or $\alpha_2\beta_2$ species encountered in crude extracts from lower eukaryotes or prokaryotes. The particulate behavior of some of these enzymes was made apparent by size fractionation of crude extracts of mammalian cells or tissues on sucrose gradient (*195–200*) or gel-filtration media (*114, 196, 201, 202*). A typical gel-filtration behavior of mammalian aminoacyl-tRNA synthetases is shown in Fig. 7.

According to their apparent molecular weights, these enzymes fall into two classes. Those in class I invariably behave as do their lower eukaryotic counterparts, that is, as enzymes with oligomeric structures of the α_2 or $\alpha_2\beta_2$ type. In class I are the synthetases specific for phenylalanine, alanine, as-

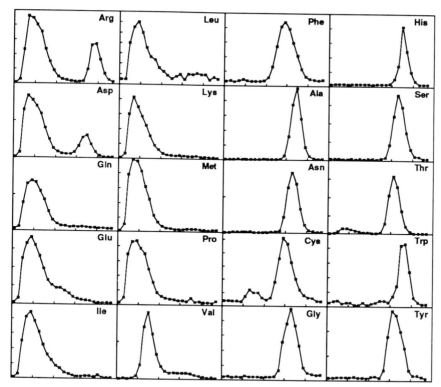

FIG. 7. Size distribution of mammalian aminoacyl-tRNA synthetases. A crude extract from exponentially growing Chinese hamster ovary cells was submitted to gel filtration on a Biogel A-5m column. Experimental conditions are as described in *114*. Fractions were assayed for each of the 20 aminoacyl-tRNA synthetases, designated by their specific amino acids.

paragine, cysteine, glycine, histidine, serine, threonine, tryptophan, and tyrosine. Class II includes the other 10, which display apparent molecular weights of about 1.0×10^6. Among them are the nine synthetases specific for arginine, aspartic acid, glutamine, glutamic acid, isoleucine, leucine, lysine, methionine, and proline, which co-elute as an entity of 1.2×10^6, and valyl-tRNA synthetase, which displays a significantly lower molecular weight of about 0.7×10^6.

Two particular features should be noticed. First, among class I enzymes, cysteinyl- and threonyl-tRNA synthetases also display a small fraction eluting as high-molecular-weight entities. Whether this represents an artifact due to self-aggregation or is their actual native state is not known. Second, among class II enzymes, arginyl- and aspartyl-tRNA synthetases are recovered as high-molecular-weight entities (representing about 75% of the total activity recovered) as well as α_2-type entities.

Essentially similar results were obtained from crude extracts of CHO cells (114, 195, 200), rat mammary gland (196), rabbit reticulocytes (197), mouse liver (197), mouse embryo (197), Friend leukemia cells (197), HeLa cells (197), human placenta (198), rat skeletal muscle (199), Ehrlich ascites cells (201), and beef liver (202), thus pointing out the general occurrence of complexes containing aminoacyl-tRNA synthetases in mammalian cells. In addition to the above studies, in which most, if not all, aminoacyl-tRNA synthetases were assayed, partial characterization of these enzymes from calf brain (203), from the nematode *Ascaris suum* (204), from Yoshida ascites hepatomas (205), and from *Drosophila* (206) also revealed the presence of high-molecular-weight entities. However, in several of these studies, multiple forms of the class II enzymes were described. In light of recent achievements in the purification and characterization of these complexes, the apparent heterogeneity observed in most of the above reports may be ascribed to proteolytic cleavage, which generates truncated but active forms of these enzymes, as described below.

2. A MULTIENZYME COMPLEX CONTAINING NINE AMINOACYL-tRNA SYNTHETASES

The elution patterns presented in Fig. 7 show that nine aminoacyl-tRNA synthetases co-elute as entities of M_r about 1.2×10^6. The most recent achievements in purification and characterization of these enzymes show that they are tightly associated within a single particle amenable to purification by conventional procedures (114, 207, 208). However, there are many conflicting reports concerning the aminoacyl-tRNA synthetase composition of this multienzyme complex (see 209 and 210 for compilations).

Purified complexes have been isolated from various sources in several laboratories (Table II). Five to nine aminoacyl-tRNA synthetases occur in the purified fraction despite the remarkably similar polypeptide patterns displayed by most of these complexes upon electrophoresis on polyacrylamide gels in the presence of sodium dodecyl sulfate. The archetype of a purified multienzyme complex is shown in Fig. 8. It includes 11 polypeptides with masses ranging from 18 to 150 kDa. The nine synthetases specific for proline, glutamic acid, isoleucine, leucine, methionine, glutamine, lysine, arginine, and aspartic acid are in the purified fraction (114, 207, 208). Together, these results suggest that each of these enzymes is present in all of the purified complexes listed in Table II, at least in an inactive state.

One exception is prolyl-tRNA synthetase that has been recently assigned to the polypeptide of M_r 150,000 from the complex of rabbit liver (P. Kerjan and J. P. Waller, unpublished). This polypeptide was also assigned to glu-

TABLE II
Aminoacyl-tRNA Synthetases Co-purified as a Multienzyme Complex[a]

Source	Pro	Glu	Ile	Leu	Met	Gln	Lys	Arg	Asp	Reference
Rat liver			+	+	+	+	+			(211)
Rat liver			+	+	+		+	+		(212)
Rat liver			+	+	+	+	+	+		(213)
Rat liver	+		+	+	+	+	+	+	+	(207)
Rabbit liver		+	+	+	+	+	+	+		(214)
Rabbit liver		+	+	+	+	+	+	+		(215)
Rabbit reticulocytes		+	+	+	+		+	+		(216)
Rabbit reticulocytes		+	+	+	+	+	+	+		(214)
Rabbit reticulocytes		+	+	+	+	+	+	+	+	(217)
Human placenta		+	+	+	+	+	+	+		(198)
Sheep liver		+	+	+	+	+	+	+		(218)
Sheep liver		+	+	+	+	+	+	+	+	(115)
Sheep spleen		+	+	+	+	+	+	+		(214)
Chinese hamster ovary cells	+	+	+	+	+	+	+	+	+	(114)
Murine erythroleukemia cells	+	+	+	+	+	+	+	+	+	(208)

[a] Aminoacyl-tRNA synthetases are designated by their aminoacid specificity. Only complexes purified to homogeneity, as judged by electrophoresis on polyacrylamide gels in the presence of sodium dodecyl sulfate, are indicated. +, Occurrences of specific aminoacyl-tRNA synthetases.

Molecular weight	Identity	Specific activity	Molar ratio
150,000	Glutamyl-, Prolyl-tRNA synthetases	34, 29	1-2
139,000	Isoleucyl-tRNA synthetase	50	1
129,000	Leucyl-tRNA synthetase	36	1
108,000	Methionyl-tRNA synthetase	70	1
96,000	Glutaminyl-tRNA synthetase	19	1
76,000	Lysyl-tRNA synthetase	133	3-4
74,000	Arginyl-tRNA synthetase	167	2-3
57,000	Aspartyl-tRNA synthetase	44	2
43,000	Unknown	-	1
38,000	Unknown	-	1
(18,000)	Unknown	-	n.d.

FIG. 8. "Identity card" of the multienzyme complex containing nine aminoacyl-tRNA synthetases. The polypeptide composition of the multisynthetase complex from Chinese hamster ovary cells (114) is shown at left. Molecular weights, molar ratios, and isoelectric points of the polypeptide components were determined on the homologous complex from rabbit liver (154). Assignment of each of the nine aminoacyl-tRNA synthetases to individual polypeptides has been described elsewhere (117). Specific activities of the corresponding enzymes from Chinese hamster ovary cells are expressed as nanomoles of aminoacyl-tRNA formed at 25°C per minute and per milligram of protein (114). n.d., Not determined.

tamyl-tRNA synthetase (117). In the sheep liver complex, glutamyl-tRNA synthetase was assigned to the polypeptide of M_r 85,000 and no prolyl-tRNA synthetase activity and no M_r 150,000 polypeptide were detected (114, 115, 117). A slightly modified purification procedure, designed to reduce uncontrolled proteolysis, yielded a complex from sheep liver that does contain an M_r 150,000 polypeptide and does display prolyl-tRNA synthetase activity (P. Kerjan and J. P. Waller, unpublished).

This result and many other reports (153–156, 219, 220) have pointed out the involvement of proteolytic events in generating artifactual free forms of some of these enzymes. In this connection, to isolate the most native form of this complex, freezing and thawing of cells or tissues must also be avoided, as demonstrated by the isolation of low-molecular-weight species of these enzymes, starting from frozen tissues (219, 221). This can be attributed to proteolysis during the grinding and thawing of the frozen tissues prior to suspension in a buffer containing protease inhibitors. Thus, the presence of free forms of arginyl- and aspartyl-tRNA synthetases in extracts from CHO cells (114) (Fig. 7) or rat liver (156, 207, 222) could be ascribed to artifactual proteolysis.

The free form of rat liver arginyl-tRNA synthetase, purified to homogeneity, is a monomer of M_r 60,000, as compared to 73,000 for its complexed counterpart (156). These two forms share common epitopes (156, 207). In extracts from rabbit liver, very low amounts of the free forms of arginyl- and aspartyl-tRNA synthetases are detected (156), suggesting that even if they do exist in rat liver in vivo, their physiological significance is unlikely to be of major importance.

That the 11 polypeptide components of these complexes, and therefore these nine aminoacyl-tRNA synthetases, are physically associated within the same particle was demonstrated by immunological approaches conducted on crude extracts from metabolically [^{35}S]methionine-labeled CHO cells (114) or on the purified complex from sheep liver (174). In both cases, immunoprecipitates obtained following incubation with antibodies directed to the complex or to its isolated methionyl- or lysyl-tRNA synthetase components contain each of the 11 polypeptides.

The identification of the aminoacyl-tRNA synthetase components within individual polypeptides of this complex was carried out by various approaches: partial renaturation of polypeptides isolated on polyacrylamide gels (117, 156); immunotitration of synthetase activities with antibodies raised against the electrophoretically separated polypeptide components (117); immunoblotting using antibodies directed to proteolytically modified free forms of these enzymes (154); affinity labeling with oxidized tRNA (233); and purification of individual enzymes, in their native state, after partial dissociation from the complex (115, 116, 224).

All of the aminoacyl-tRNA synthetase multienzyme complexes purified so far contain, in addition to the synthetase components, three polypeptides of M_r 43,000, 38,000, and 18,000, of presently unknown function. These do not react with the antibodies to aminoacyl-tRNA synthetase components and thus are unlikely to correspond to proteolytic fragments of the synthetases (207). The function(s) of these three polypeptides remains to be discovered. Several protein components have been tentatively reported to be associated with these aminoacyl-tRNA synthetases. Co-purification of S-adenosyl-L-methionine : tRNA methyltransferase (225, 226) and tRNA sulfurtransferase (227), of elongation factors (228) or of casein kinase I (229) activities with these aminoacyl-tRNA synthetases has been reported. However, no compelling evidence for association has been presented.

3. VALYL-tRNA SYNTHETASE IS ASSOCIATED
   WITH ELONGATION FACTOR EF-1

Valyl-tRNA synthetase from prokaryotes and lower eukaryotes is a monomer with a large polypeptide chain (Table I). The enzyme from a crude
extract of mammalian cells has an apparent native M_r of about 700,000 (Fig.
7). The valyl-tRNA synthetase of high molecular weight is the only form of
that enzyme detected. No other aminoacyl-tRNA synthetase co-elutes with
valyl-tRNA synthetase, suggesting either the formation of a homotypic complex containing only valyl-tRNA synthetase or the association of non-syn-
thetase components with it.

Valyl-tRNA synthetase from rabbit liver was purified to homogeneity as a
heterotypic complex containing four polypeptides of M_r 140,000, 50,000,
35,000, and 27,000 (112, 113) and as a monomeric form displaying an M_r of
about 130,000, generated by uncontrolled proteolysis (230). The polypeptide
of M_r 140,000 from the high-molecular-weight complex was assigned to valyl-
tRNA synthetase by the immunoblotting procedure using antibodies directed against the corresponding yeast enzyme (113). The other polypeptide
components of the complex were identified as those from the heavy form of
the eukaryotic elongation factor eEF-1H (113, 231). It was shown that the
purified complex can substitute for EF-1α in an assay for poly(U)-dependent
synthesis of polyphenylalanine (113, 231). It should be noted that the fraction of elongation factor EF-1α associated within the complex containing
valyl-tRNA synthetase represents approximately 1% of the cellular amount
of this factor. The possible physiological significance of this association is
discussed in the following sections.

B. Hydrophobic Interactions and Multienzyme Assembly

1. DISSOCIATION OF THE COMPLEXES

The high-molecular-weight complex containing nine aminoacyl-tRNA
synthetases, henceforth referred to as the multisynthetase complex, is very
resistant to dissociation. Upon gel filtration of the purified complex in high
concentrations of salt, such as 0.2 M potassium phosphate (232) or 1 M NaCl
(233), no dissociation occurs. However, in 1 M NaCl plus a non-ionic detergent, or a chaotropic salt such as thiocyanate, a partial but significant
breakdown of the multisynthetase complex is observed (233). In accordance
with these findings is the observation that hydrophobic-interaction chromatography leads to partial dissociation of this complex. Some of the aminoacyl-tRNA synthetase components may subsequently be isolated as free
enzymes (116, 224, 234). However, the complete disruption of the multisynthetase complex into its individual components, in their native states, has

not yet been reported. Hydrophobic interactions have been proposed to play a prominent role in complex formation (*134, 235*).

For the complex containing valyl-tRNA synthetase, a partial dissociation can occur upon chromatography on heparin–Sepharose or upon gel filtration in the presence of 0.3 M KCl (*112*). Valyl-tRNA synthetase has been isolated as a free enzyme following incubation of the complex in the presence of 0.5 M thiocyanate (*135*), conditions that only partially dissociate the multi-synthetase complex (233). Thus, the valyl-tRNA synthetase complex is more fragile than the multisynthetase complex, but hydrophobic interactions are also involved in complex formation.

2. EVIDENCE FOR A HYDROPHOBIC DOMAIN

That hydrophobic interactions play a prominent role in the formation of these high-molecular-weight structures in higher eukaryotes has been more accurately demonstrated by the characterization of aminoacyl-tRNA synthetases isolated from the complexes in their native state. Isolation of leucyl- and lysyl-tRNA synthetases from the multisynthetase complex of sheep liver was accomplished upon hydrophobic-interaction chromatography on hexyl-agarose (*116*). Valyl-tRNA synthetase was separated from EF-1H after chromatography on hydroxylapatite in the presence of 0.5 M NaSCN (*135*). Isoleucyl-tRNA synthetase, very resistant to proteolysis, was purified to homogeneity following controlled trypsinolysis of the multisynthetase complex from sheep liver (*115*). The oligomeric structures of the free, native forms of these enzymes are identical to those of the corresponding enzymes from lower eukaryotes, of the α type for isoleucyl-, leucyl-, and valyl-tRNA synthetases, and of the α_2 type for lysyl-tRNA synthetase. In all cases, addition of non-ionic detergents was required to prevent progressive loss of activities.

It was reported in the preceding section that all 20 enzymes from lower eukaryotes as well as class I and class II aminoacyl-tRNA synthetases from higher eukaryotes can bind to polyanionic carriers (Fig. 2). The four mammalian enzymes derived from the high-molecular-weight complexes also bind to polyanionic supports (*115, 116, 135*). On the other hand, while mammalian isoleucyl (*115*)-, leucyl (*116*)-, lysyl (*116*)-, and valyl (*135*)-tRNA synthetases strongly interact with hydrophobic supports, the yeast enzymes do not, indicating that they have acquired hydrophobic properties.

In sheep liver lysyl-tRNA synthetase, it was found that proteolytic conversion of the native dimer of $2 \times 79,000$ to a fully active dimer of $2 \times 64,000$ leads to loss of both the hydrophobic and polyanion binding properties. In addition, mammalian methionyl-tRNA synthetase, which is tightly associated within the multienzyme complex and has so far resisted dissociation under non-denaturing conditions, can be converted to a fully active monomeric form of M_r about 68,000 by a limited tryptic digestion that removes about one-third of the corresponding native polypeptide (115, 153–155, 219). The truncated monomeric enzyme, similar in size to the monomeric methionyl-tRNA synthetase of M_r 64,000 from E. coli, does not display hydrophobic properties (115) and has lost its ability to associate with other components of the multisynthetase complex (154).

Relevant to these findings are the observations that all of the free forms of the class II enzymes characterized to date, arising through controlled proteolysis or uncontrolled or presumed endogenous proteolysis, or which are believed to correspond to naturally occurring low-molecular-weight forms, invariably possess subunit molecular weights significantly lower than those of the corresponding enzymes associated within complexes (155, 156, 207, 236, 237). Moreover, when tested, they behave as non-hydrophobic proteins (156, 236, 238).

Together, these observations clearly establish that aminoacyl-tRNA synthetases from higher eukaryotes that are encountered in high-molecular-weight complexes possess a hydrophobic domain necessary for their association into stable structures. On the contrary, class I mammalian aminoacyl-tRNA synthetases do not display hydrophobic properties. For instance, homogeneous tryptophanyl-tRNA synthetase from beef pancreas does not bind to phenyl-Sepharose under conditions in which the purified leucyl-tRNA synthetase component derived from the multisynthetase complex of sheep liver is strongly retained (116). The lack of a hydrophobic domain for class I enzymes provides a rational explanation for their isolation as free enzymes.

Molecular cloning of mammalian aminoacyl-tRNA synthetase genes encoding two class I enzymes [histidyl (123)- and threonyl (239)-tRNA synthetases] and two class II enzymes [aspartyl (119)- and glutaminyl (118)-tRNA synthetases] was reported. The complete nucleotide sequences of the corresponding cDNAs were determined for CHO and human histidyl-tRNA synthetases (123) and for aspartyl-tRNA synthetase from rats (119) and humans (240). From the comparison for aspartyl-tRNA synthetase from E. coli (G. Eriani and J. Gangloff, personal communication), S. cerevisiae (91), and rat liver (119), several interesting features are noteworthy.

The aminoacid sequences of the yeast and mammalian enzymes display significant homologies with that from E. coli. There are amino-terminal extensions of about 80 and 30 amino acids in the yeast and mammalian enzymes, respectively. The polypeptide extension from the yeast enzyme is related to the polyanionic binding property displayed by this enzyme, as discussed above. The shorter amino-terminal extension of the mammalian enzyme remains markedly hydrophilic (119). However, alignment of the homologous amino-terminal regions of the yeast, rat, and human enzymes, as shown in Fig. 9, suggests that the corresponding region of the mammalian

```
31-K K A L K K L Q K E Q E K  ORKKEERALQLEAERE  A R E K K A A A E D T A K D N Y G K L P L-80
 1-M P S A N A S R K G Q E K                       P R E I V D A A E D Y A K E R Y G V S S M-34
 1-M P S A   T Q R K S Q E K                       P R E I M D A A E D Y A K E R Y G I S S M-33
```

FIG. 9. Alignment of the homologous regions from the amino-terminal extensions displayed by aspartyl-tRNA synthetases from *Saccharomyces cerevisiae* (top), rats (middle), and humans (bottom), as compared to the *Escherichia coli* enzyme. Identical residues are boxed. Shown in boldface are lysine residues from the yeast enzyme and the corresponding hydrophobic residues from the mammalian enzymes. The cluster of charged residues, inserted in the yeast enzyme, is underlined.

enzyme is implicated in complex formation. Residues Gln-44 to Glu-59 in the yeast enzyme, comprising a cluster of charged residues (2 lysines + 3 arginines + 5 glutamic acids), are absent from the mammalian enzymes. Furthermore, in both rat and human aspartyl-tRNA synthetases, hydrophobic residues substitute for six lysine residues located at positions 21, 32, 36, 63, 64, and 77 in the yeast enzyme. This difference in aminoacid composition may account for the hydrophobic properties presented above as responsible for complex formation.

Knowledge of the positioning of these residues into the three-dimensional structure of this amino-terminal domain would be of prime interest. It has been postulated that this domain can be folded into an amphiphilic α-helix displaying an average hydrophobic moment of 0.42 per residue (240). However, secondary structure predictions carried out on rat or human aspartyl-tRNA synthetases with the algorithms of Chou and Fasman (188) or Garnier *et al.* (187) differ significantly. Thus, that this domain is actually implicated in complex formation must be confirmed by other approaches, such as site-directed mutagenesis of presumed essential aminoacid residues or determination of the amino-terminal sequences corresponding to complexed and free forms of this enzyme. Indeed, it should be kept in mind that a low-molecular-weight form of this enzyme was described. Its origin is not known. Although it could be generated through uncontrolled proteolysis of the complexed form of this enzyme, the possibility that it is encoded by a separate gene cannot be excluded. The cDNA sequences reported in both studies (119, 240) provide no compelling evidence in favor of the isolation of a full-length species, encoding the associated enzyme. For rat liver arginyl-tRNA synthetase, it has been argued that a basic amino-terminal extension is required in its association within the multisynthetase complex (241). Determination of the primary sequence of this enzyme should prove useful to establish molecular features involved in complex formation, by comparison with the data obtained on mammalian aspartyl-tRNA synthetase.

Finally, the mode of association of the nine aminoacyl-tRNA synthetases within the multisynthetase complex remains a puzzling question. It has been proposed that one or several of the three unidentified components of the complex may be involved in mediating complex formation (117). Many reports have discussed the presence of lipids co-eluting with the complex (220, 242, 243), but their physical association with aminoacyl-tRNA synthetases has not yet been proven. One other feature of these aminoacyl-tRNA synthetases is that they may contain carbohydrates (244). All of these observations could well be relevant to the mode of assembly of these enzymes, but no compelling evidence has been presented.

C. Functional Significance of the Synthetase Complexes

All of the data reported to date support a structural model in which each of the aminoacyl-tRNA synthetases in the multisynthetase complex includes a hydrophobic domain, responsible for complex formation, contiguous to its catalytic domain. Several lines of evidence clearly establish that association of these enzymes within the high-molecular-weight complex is not a prerequisite for the expression of their catalytic function, at least in vitro. As already discussed above, controlled proteolysis of the purified complex yields active, free forms of several of these enzymes. In the case of methionyl (155, 245)-, lysyl (245)-, and arginyl (156)-tRNA synthetases, proteolytically modified forms of these enzymes have kinetic parameters essentially similar to those of the corresponding native, associated enzymes. Moreover, identical catalytic properties are observed for the free and associated forms of native isoleucyl (115)- and lysyl (213)-tRNA synthetases, indicating that the hydrophobic and catalytic domains are functionally independent.

In addition, aminoacylation catalyzed by any of the associated enzymes is unaffected by the concomitant functioning of the other aminoacyl-tRNA synthetases, no dissociation of the complex occurring under conditions prevailing in the tRNA aminoacylation assay (245). This result implies that the aminoacyl-tRNA synthetase components of this complex are spatially organized so that their functional domains are freely accessible to their substrates. Considering the size of a tRNA molecule, about 75 Å in length, the shape of the multisynthetase complex is likely to be fairly open, the component enzymes being sterically individualized. Preliminary electron-microscope studies do agree with this prediction (208, 211, 215, 246). This type of structural organization can be connected with the finding that mild proteolysis leads to the removal of the hydrophobic domain, which suggests that the inter-domain region is rather exposed.

Any model of the organization of the complex must also be compatible with the fact that, following a 2-fold specific overexpression of methionyl-tRNA synthetase upon methionine restriction of CHO cells, the multisynthetase complex can accommodate one additional polypeptide without affecting its stability (247). However, this result might be atypical. Indeed, none of the other eight aminoacyl-tRNA synthetases associated within the multisynthetase complex could be derepressed, as assessed by tRNA aminoacylation assays, upon cognate amino acid starvation (247). Regulation of ribosomal protein gene expression in eukaryotes is, in part, under the control of post-translational events (248). Since unassembled ribosomal proteins are unstable, it is believed that protein turnover palliates imbalanced ribosomal protein synthesis. In this connection, as it is unlikely that aminoacyl-tRNA synthetases, harboring a hydrophobic domain, could be present as free entities within the cell, one may speculate that regulation of their expression could be, at least in part, controlled by similar mechanisms. That the multisynthetase complex could be endowed with a post-translational regulation function should be investigated.

Despite intensive investigations during the past few years, the functional significance of the association of mammalian aminoacyl-tRNA synthetases as multienzyme complexes remains obscure. It was proposed that this complex contains tRNA-modifying enzymes and therefore prevents miscoding (249), but neither the actual association of tRNA methyltransferase or tRNA sulfurtransferase has been demonstrated nor has the coupling between modification and aminoacylation of the corresponding tRNAs been established. The demonstration that the multisynthetase complex exists within the cell as a discrete, physiological entity suggests that it may have a specific function. Clearly, to get more insight into such a putative function, it would be of prime interest to determine the function of the three unidentified components of M_r 43,000, 38,000, and 18,000 which are always found tightly associated with the synthetase components.

In the case of the complex containing valyl-tRNA synthetase, it may be speculated that its association with EF-1 is functionally relevant. The tRNA aminoacylation reaction can be well accomplished *in vitro* by the monomeric enzyme, dissociated from the complex (135). Thus, the associated state is not required for its catalytic activity. However, association of this enzyme with EF-1α suggests that an adequate supply of valyl-tRNA^{Val} for translation requires a coupling between aminoacylation and ternary complex formation with EF-1α : GTP. Pertinent to this hypothesis is the finding that, in *E. coli*, valyl-tRNA^{Val} displays the lowest affinity for EF-Tu : GTP, as compared to the other aminoacyl-tRNAs (250). In *E. coli*, this low affinity is compensated by a higher copy number of valyl-tRNA^{Val} (250). Assuming that valyl-tRNA^{Val} also displays, in mammalian cells, a low affinity for EF-1α : GTP, a coupling mechanism could be a prerequisite for a proper translational efficiency of valyl-tRNA^{Val}.

One other characteristic of aminoacyl-tRNA synthetase complexes that deserves mention is that they associate with the cytoskeletal framework of mammalian cells (251, 252). As discussed in the following section, the polyanion binding property displayed, *in vitro*, by eukaryotic aminoacyl-tRNA synthetases might be the reflection of an *in vivo* dynamic association with components of the translational machinery. In this connection, the finding that seryl-tRNA synthetase, representative of the class I enzymes, is not retained within the cytoskeletal fraction of detergent-extracted cells, whereas 44% of the multisynthetase complex is recovered with the detergent-insoluble components, could be relevant to the multiple binding domains exposed by the complex and/or the lower diffusibility of a high-molecular-weight structure. From the class I enzymes, only phenylalanyl-tRNA synthetase associates with components of the cytoskeletal fraction. This might be related to its pronounced tendency to associate, *in vitro*, with ribosomes (*128, 175, 253*), a property that could be ascribed to its unusual cationic net charge [pI = 8.0 (*128*)]. With regard to the hypothesis of a spatial organization of the translational machinery, through fragile electrostatic interactions, it is conceivable that the formation of multienzyme complexes would help to stabilize the loose network.

IV. A View of the Biosynthetic Machinery in Eukaryotic Cells

The cytoplasm of higher eukaryotic cells is highly organized, comprising a dynamic three-dimensional network made of various filamentous systems, including microfilaments, intermediate filaments, and microtubules, referred to as the cytoskeleton. Many reports indicate that this extensive proteinaceous matrix could serve as a support for organizing the protein biosynthesis machinery within the cell. Findings related to this hypothesis are presented in this section.

Biochemical characterization of the cytoskeletal framework was conducted following detergent extraction of cultured cells under conditions designed to preserve its integrity (*254, 255*). Following extraction of HeLa cells under conditions in which 75% of the cellular proteins are recovered in the soluble fraction, all of the polyribosomes remain associated with the cytoskeletal framework (*256*). Moreover, several lines of evidence suggest that mRNA binding to the cytoskeleton is an absolute requirement for translation. Indeed, it was shown that viral mRNAs are translated only when associated with the cytoskeleton, after infection of HeLa cells with vesicular stomatitis virus (*256*) or poliovirus (*257*), of human KB cells with adenovirus (*258*), or monkey CV-1 cells with poliovirus (*259*), or of Ehrlich ascites tumor cells with vaccinia virus (*260*). In addition, infections by poliovirus or adenovirus, which induce the more drastic cytopathic effects, lead to the removal of host mRNAs from the cytoskeletal framework (*257–259*).

The sensitivity of eukaryotic cells to drugs known to disturb the cytoskeletal framework also suggests the involvement of the cytoskeleton in polyribosome binding. Incubation of cells with cytochalasin B, a drug acting on the integrity of microfilaments and thus altering filamentous networks and cell morphology, releases mRNA from the cytoskeletal framework (254, 261, 262). The level of inhibition of protein synthesis is directly proportional to the extent of released mRNA (261). These observations point to a strong relationship between the cytoskeletal framework and the formation of "active" mRNA. Due to extensive interconnection between the different filamentous systems, it is not possible to ensure that mRNA binding is solely mediated by the actin cytoskeleton. Cytochalasin B is not, per se, an inhibitor of translation, since this drug has no effect on protein synthesis in reticulocytes (261), cells displaying little cytostructure, with a presumed soluble protein synthesis machinery. Cytochalasin B has no effect on the class of membrane-bound polyribosomes, that is, polyribosomes attached to the membranes of the endoplasmic reticulum. However, also in this case, the integrity of one of the components of the cytoskeletal framework, the microtubules, appears necessary to ensure translation of these membrane-bound polyribosomes (263). Depolymerization of microtubules results in the slow retraction of the endoplasmic reticulum (264).

These observations strongly suggest that the efficiency of the protein-synthesis process is dependent on a three-dimensional organization of the cytoplasm. Furthermore, spatial distribution of specific mRNAs was observed. Intracellular localization of messages for actin, vimentin, tubulin, and histones was followed by *in situ* hybridization with labeled cDNA probes. It turns out that (1) poly(A)$^+$-mRNA is homogeneously distributed throughout the cytoplasm (265); (2) tubulin mRNA is distributed throughout the cytoplasm (265) but displays a preferential perinuclear localization (266); (3) vimentin mRNA is preferentially localized near the nucleus, where intermediate filaments are most concentrated (265, 266); (4) actin mRNA is more abundant in cell extremities, especially in the lamellipodia of motile cells, which contain high concentrations of microfilaments (265–267); (5) histone mRNA is not localized near the nucleus (267). Spatial distribution of histone and actin mRNAs was also observed in the cytoskeletal framework of ascidian eggs (268).

Together, these data lead to the following observations. Polyribosomes are not free in the cytoplasm, but are bound to components of the cytoskeletal framework, including the endoplasmic reticulum. Moreover, in some instances, there is a precise spatial distribution of specific mRNAs in relation to the site of utilization of their corresponding proteins. Compartmentalization of mRNAs is particularly suited in the case of mRNAs specific for myosin heavy chains (269) or spectrin (270), proteins that are co-translationally assembled into the cytoskeleton. If protein synthesis in eukaryotic cells requires cellular organization of mRNAs, the finding that some specific mRNAs are spatially organized suggests that there is a corresponding spatial distribution of the components of the translational machinery. Thus, we must consider that all of these components have evolved in such a way that they could be compartmentalized in the vicinity of the polyribosomes. In addition, as no isoenzymes were described for aminoacyl-tRNA synthetases and other components involved in translation, the same entity must be able to be distributed in the various locations where mRNAs are found, implying the existence of a common target.

In agreement with the first of these assumptions, numerous data have suggested that components of the translational machinery from eukaryotic cells are able to associate with the cytoskeletal framework. Following detergent extraction of cultured cells, a significant amount of translation-initiation factors and aminoacyl-tRNA synthetases are recovered in the detergent-insoluble fraction: the cytoskeletal framework. This propensity to associate with components of the cytoskeleton was observed for cap-binding proteins (271), initiation factor eIF-2α (272), various other initiation factors (273), and some aminoacyl-tRNA synthetases (251, 252). This binding propensity is so high that all components of the protein biosynthesis machinery can be isolated from a crude extract of rabbit reticulocytes by affinity chromatography on heparin–Sepharose 4B (274). Thus, the polyanion-binding property displayed by eukaryotic aminoacyl-tRNA synthetases is not a feature specific to this class of enzymes. In particular, purified eukaryotic elongation factors eEF-1 and eEF-2 are RNA-binding proteins, whereas prokaryotic elongation factors EF-Tu and EF-G are not (275).

All eukaryotic elongation factors EF-1α whose primary sequences are known possess carboxy-terminal extensions composed of about 20 amino acid residues, as compared to their prokaryotic counterparts (Fig. 10). This chain extension carries a cluster of seven lysine residues, likely to be responsible for the polyanion-binding property. However, the involvement of this carboxy-terminal cationic extension in the ability to bind to polyanions has not yet been tested experimentally. Purified EF-2 also interacts non-specifically with RNA (286), although no obvious binding site can be seen from simple examination of its primary sequence (287).

The association of polyribosomes and components involved in translation with the cytoskeletal fraction of eukaryotic cells is commonly viewed as reflecting the structural organization of the protein-synthesis machinery (288–291). The functional significance of this compartmentalization remains to be deciphered. One can argue that this type of cellular organization would provide increased local concentrations of the macromolecules and substrates implicated in this biological process, thus increasing its efficiency. However, this assumption remains highly speculative. Knowledge of the cellular tar-

E. coli	376-I R E G G R T V G A G V V A K V L G-393
T. thermophilus	388-I R E G G R T V G A G V V T K I L E-405
S. cerivisiae mito	420-I R E G G R T V G T G L I T R I I E-437
E. gracilis chloro	391-I R E G G R T V G A G V V L S I I Q-408
M. vannielii	408-I R D M G M T V A A G M A I Q V T A K N K-428
S. cerevisiae cyto	424-V R D M R Q T V A V G V I K S V D K T E K A A K V T K A A Q K A A K K-458
M. racemosus	424-V R D M R Q T V A V G V I K A V E K V D K A G K V T K A A A K A S K K-458
D. melanogaster F₁	426-V R D M R Q T V A V G V I K A V N F K D A S G G K V T K A A E K A T K G K K-463
A. salina	425-V R D M R Q T V A V G V I K S V N F K D P T A G K V T K A A E K A G K K-461
Human	426-V R D M R Q T V A V G V I K A V D K K A A G A G K V T K S A Q K A Q K A K-462

FIG. 10. Aminoacid sequences of the carboxy terminus of elongation factors EF-Tu and EF-1α from various origins. Primary sequences are derived from the nucleotide sequences of the genes encoding for the elongation factors EF-Tu from *Escherichia coli* (276), *Thermus thermophilus* (277), *Saccharomyces cerevisiae* mitochondria (278), *Euglena gracilis* chloroplast (279), or *Methanococcus vannielii* (280) and for the elongation factors EF-1α from the cytoplasm of *Saccharomyces cerevisiae* (281), *Mucor racemosus* (282), *Drosophila melanogaster* (283), *Artemia salina* (284), or human MOLT-4 lymphoid cells (285).

get(s) involved in the attachment of these macromolecules to the cytoskeletal framework would be of great interest for a clearer understanding of the functional significance of this kind of association.

It must be stressed that the association of initiation factors, on the one hand, and that of elongation factors and aminoacyl-tRNA synthetases, on the other, could be related to distinct physical mechanisms. Indeed, it is generally accepted that most, if not all, initiation factors interact with mRNA or 40-S ribosomal subunit prior to the initiation of translation (273, 292) and remain bound during the mRNA-scanning process, but there is no obvious requirement for a direct interaction between ribosomes or mRNA and aminoacyl-tRNA synthetases. Elongation factors must associate only transiently to ribosomes at each step of the elongation process. Genetic studies indicate that yeast initiation factor eIF-2 is involved in the process of ribosomal scanning of mRNA in search of a translational start site (293, 294). Its eIF-2β subunit contains a "zinc-finger" motif (293) similar to that found in a variety of specific DNA-binding proteins (295). This nucleic acid-binding motif, which is conserved in the corresponding human eIF-2 subunit, might mediate eIF-2 association within the initiation complex through interaction with initiator tRNA, ribosomal RNA, or mRNA. In addition, three polylysine repeats are present at the amino-terminal moiety of yeast eIF-2β. Their actual function is unknown, but they could also be potential sites for binding to nucleic acids.

The mode of association of eukaryotic elongation factors and aminoacyl-tRNA synthetases to or near mRNA engaged in translation represents an

even more puzzling question. Some have postulated that eukaryotic aminoacyl-tRNA synthetases are bound to the ribosomes, thus allowing a concentration of aminoacyl-tRNAs in the vicinity of their site of utilization.
However, aminoacyl-tRNA is not by itself a substrate for protein synthesis,
but must be complexed with EF-1 : GTP. It follows that binding of all 20
aminoacyl-tRNA synthetases to ribosomes would imply the binding of at
least 20 molecules of EF-1 per ribosome, one for each aminoacyl-tRNA. This
is precluded by topological constraints. Moreover, the ribosome concentration in eukaryotic cells is estimated to be 1–2 μM (296), while the concentration of each aminoacyl-tRNA synthetase is one order of magnitude lower
(about 0.2 μM) (214). This discrepancy excludes a stable, stoichiometric
association between aminoacyl-tRNA synthetases and ribosomes.

A possible association of eukaryotic aminoacyl-tRNA synthetases to the
plasma or endoplasmic reticulum membranes has also been suggested (235),
because of the hydrophobic properties displayed by the aminoacyl-tRNA
synthetases from the multienzyme complex. However, as stated in the preceding section, the aminoacyl-tRNA synthetases that do not associate into
complexes (10 of those from eukaryotes and all 20 from yeast) are not hydrophobic proteins. The association of aminoacyl-tRNA synthetases with membranes cannot be dismissed, but if it exists, it is probably mediated by
electrostatic interactions, since the presence of a polyanion-binding domain
is a common denominator of all of these eukaryotic enzymes. However,
membrane-bound polyribosomes do not correspond to all of the mRNA
found in mammalian cells. If aminoacyl-tRNA synthetases are clustered near
the sites of protein synthesis, they must also be associated in the vicinity of
the other class of "active" mRNA: those bound to other components of the
cytoplasmic framework. The requirement for a unique target, due to the
absence of isoenzymes, implies that this target would be distributed in
membranes, as well as in the filamentous networks. No structural component fulfilling these conditions has yet been identified.

If the polyanion-binding property displayed by eukaryotic aminoacyl-
tRNA synthetases as well as by other translational components corresponds
to the ability to associate *in vivo* with polycationic carriers, then the mRNA
itself is a good candidate for a unique binding site. However, this model has
several limitations. First, a stable association between aminoacyl-tRNA synthetases and the 5'-non-coding region or the coding region of mRNA must
be excluded. This would constitute steric hindrance for a free scanning by
the pre-initiation complex or the translating ribosome. Second, such a
putative association to the mRNA would not be a strict prerequisite for
translation; otherwise, truncated methionyl- and lysyl-tRNA synthetases
lacking their amino-terminal polycationic domains would not sustain the
growth of yeast cells. This finding confirms and extends *in vivo* the observa-

tion made *in vitro* that this binding domain is dispensable for catalysis, and suggests that a more discrete biological function could be attributed to these polycationic chain extensions. Overexpression of a truncated enzyme could compensate for the detrimental effects resulting from a decreased local concentration of these enzymes at the site(s) of protein synthesis. More accurate experimental approaches, such as site-directed mutagenesis of the corresponding lysine codons, followed by re-integration of these derivatives in place of the wild-type alleles, should be useful to clarify this point.

Altogether, these observations support the earlier proposal (289, 291) that aminoacyl-tRNA synthetases and elongation factors are kept in the vicinity of the mRNA through dynamic electrostatic interactions, thus creating a nebula of proteins and substrates required for protein synthesis around polyribosomes. In addition, it can be tentatively proposed that tRNA is also implicated in this dynamic equilibrium. Indeed, the polycationic domains of aminoacyl-tRNA synthetases may also act as a magnet for tRNA and thus favor retention of deacylated tRNAs within the diffuse area surrounding mRNAs. One of the drawbacks of this model is that it does not explain why and how mRNAs are anchored to cellular components.

A consequence of this model is that any post-translational modification leading to a decrease in the global positive net charge of the polycationic domains of these enzymes should result in a decrease in the efficiency of protein synthesis. Thus, some patterns of translation regulation could be a consequence of some impairments in cellular compartmentalization. The observation that aminoacyl-tRNA synthetases as well as elongation factors are subjected to phosphorylation events could be related to such mechanisms. For instance, it was shown that *in vitro* phosphorylation of EF-1 (297) or some components of the multienzyme complex of aminoacyl-tRNA synthetases (229) results in a decreased affinity for polyanionic carriers, as compared to the unmodified proteins. In the case of EF-2, a similar behavior was observed following *in vitro* ADP-ribosylation of the purified protein (286).

Little is known about the functional significance of these post-translational modification events. A role of phosphorylation in the regulation of aminoacyl-tRNA synthetase activities from the multienzyme complex was proposed (298) and later dismissed (299). *In vivo* phosphorylation of several aminoacyl-tRNA synthetases from the multienzyme complex in rabbit reticulocytes has been reported (217). Some class I aminoacyl-tRNA synthetases also undergo phosphorylation modification *in vivo*: threonyl-tRNA synthetase (300) and histidyl-tRNA synthetase (301) from CHO cells and threonyl-tRNA synthetase from rabbit reticulocytes (302). Phosphorylation has little effect, if any, on the aminoacylation reaction (229, 302).

It must be stressed that all of the "*in vivo*" measurements of phosphorylation were conducted on cells displaying some particular features. The CHO cell lines used in the above-mentioned studies (*300, 301*) overproduce at least 20-fold the corresponding aminoacyl-tRNA synthetases. No data concerning the phosphorylation state of the cognate enzymes from wild-type, exponentially growing CHO cells have been reported. In studies dealing with aminoacyl-tRNA synthetases from rabbit reticulocytes (*217, 302*), it must be noted that this cell type is very atypical, displaying a poor cytoarchitecture. In addition, phosphorylation experiments with isolated reticulocytes cannot be conducted under conditions closely related to an *in vivo* system.

No quantitative data concerning the *in vivo* phosphorylation level of these enzymes were reported in the above studies. To gain more insight into the physiological significance of post-translational modification of aminoacyl-tRNA synthetases by phosphorylation, it would be of prime interest to determine the extent to which phosphorylation occurs under the condition of either activated or repressed protein synthesis. This extent could be rather low in exponential growth, as no phosphorylated polypeptide was detected following immunoprecipitation of the multienzyme complex from CHO cells metabolically labeled with ^{32}P (*114*). In the absence of accurate data concerning the phosphorylation state of eukaryotic aminoacyl-tRNA synthetases, it can be speculated that introducing a negative charge in the binding domain of these enzymes might induce their release from the nebula surrounding mRNA. This kind of post-translational modification thus could play an important role in the regulation of protein synthesis.

V. Conclusions and Perspectives

Our knowledge of the structure/function relationships among aminoacyl-tRNA synthetases has extensively improved in the past few years. However, most studies have been conducted *in vitro*, with highly purified enzymes. In light of the recent progress in the field of protein synthesis in eukaryotic cells, further studies should focus more on cellular aspects of protein synthesis. The finding that a dispensable domain carrying a basic net charge is a common feature of most, if not all, aminoacyl-tRNA synthetases argues in favor of a specific physiological function for this defined structural feature. Some aspects of protein synthesis regulation should also be related to the spatial organization of cellular proteins.

To conclude, it must be emphasized that research in the field of aminoacyl-tRNA synthetases offers promising prospects. In addition to their essential role in the specific acylation of tRNA, several aspects of cellular biology of the cell seem to be relevant to these enzymes or some derivatives. (1) In prokaryotes, alanyl- and threonyl-tRNA synthetases are involved in autogenous regulation of their expression through binding to DNA and

RNA, respectively (165, 166). (2) Some of these enzymes, from prokaryotes or eukaryotes, are able to synthesize Ap_4A, a compound whose physiological significance is presently unknown, but is thought to act as a pleiotropic alarmone (303). (3) Mitochondrial leucyl- or tyrosyl-tRNA synthetases from lower eukaryotes are implicated in intron splicing (81, 103). (4) Lysyl-tRNA synthetase from E. coli is involved in ColE1 plasmid replication (46, 47).

Aminoacyl-tRNA synthetases or derivatives thereof have also been shown to participate in other cellular functions. In yeast, the GCN2 gene product, the carboxy-terminal region of which is homologous to histidyl-tRNA synthetase, is endowed with a regulatory function related to aminoacid availability within the cell (132). In addition, yeast mutants defective in translational accuracy have been isolated. One of these, the omnipotent suppressor SUP1 (304), also identified as the allosuppressor SAL4 (305), displays an amino-terminal aminoacid sequence that shares some homology with methionyl-and tyrosyl-tRNA synthetases. In E. coli, an open reading frame corresponding to a protein encoded by the gX gene, whose function is unknown (306), is homologous to the carboxy-terminal two-thirds of lysyl-tRNA synthetase (47). The actual function of these aminoacyl-tRNA synthetase-related proteins remains to be deciphered.

ACKNOWLEDGMENTS

This work was supported in part by grants UPR 2401 from the Centre National de la Recherche Scientifique and 415-89 from the Association pour la Recherche sur le Cancer. I am grateful to F. Fasiolo, J. Gangloff, M. Härtlein, and J. P. Waller for communicating their results before publication, to J. P. Waller for suggestions, to J. R. Garel for critical reading of the manuscript, and to J. Mauger for help in the preparation of the manuscript.

REFERENCES

1. A. H. Mehler and K. Chakraburtty, Adv. Enzymol. 35, 443 (1971).
2. L. L. Kisselev and O. O. Favorova, Adv. Enzymol. 40, 141 (1974).
3. D. Söll and P. Schimmel, in "The Enzymes" (P. D. Boyer, ed.), 3rd Ed., Vol. 10, p. 489. Academic Press, New York, 1974.
4. P. R. Schimmel and D. Söll, ARB 48, 601 (1979).
5. P. R. Schimmel, Adv. Enzymol. 49, 187 (1979).
6. L. L. Kisselev, This Series 32, 237 (1985).
7. A. R. Fersht, Bchem 26, 8031 (1987).
8. P. Schimmel, ARB 56, 125 (1987).
9. C. Zelwer, J. L. Risler and S. Brunie, JMB 155, 63 (1982).
10. S. Brunie, P. Mellot, C. Zelwer, J. L. Risler, S. Blanquet and G. Fayat, J. Mol. Graphics 5, 18 (1987).
11. T. N. Bhat, D. M. Blow, P. Brick and J. Nyborg, JMB 158, 699 (1982).
12. P. Brick, T. N. Bhat and D. M. Blow, JMB 208, 83 (1989).
13. R. W. Chambers, This Series 11, 489 (1971).
14. E. J. Murgola, ARGen 19, 57 (1985).
15. L. H. Schulman and J. Abelson, Science 240, 1591 (1988).

16. P. Schimmel, *Bchem* **28**, 2747 (1989).
17. J. Normanly and J. Abelson, *ARB* **58**, 1029 (1989).
18. J. Lapointe, L. Duplain and M. Proulx, *J. Bact.* **165**, 88 (1986).
19. N. C. Martin, M. Rabinowitz and H. Fukuhara, *Bchem* **16**, 4672 (1977).
20. A. Schön, C. G. Kannangara, S. Gough and D. Söll, *Nature* **331**, 187 (1988).
21. R. Uy and F. Wold, *Science* **198**, 890 (1977).
22. W. Leinfelder, E. Zehelein, M. A. Mandrand-Berthelot and A. Böck, *Nature* **331**, 723 (1988).
23. W. Leinfelder, T. C. Stadtman and A. Böck, *JBC* **264**, 9720 (1989).
24. B. J. Lee, P. J. Worland, J. N. Davis, T. C. Stadtman and D. L. Hatfield, *JBC* **264**, 9724 (1989).
25. C. J. Bruton and L. A. M. Cox, *EJB* **100**, 301 (1979).
26. F. Berthelot and M. Yaniv, *EJB* **16**, 123 (1970).
27. M. Härtlein, R. Frank and D. Madern, *NARes* **15**, 9081 (1987).
28. J. D. Heck and G. W. Hatfield, *JBC* **263**, 868 (1988).
29. T. J. Borgford, N. J. Brand, T. E. Gray and A. R. Fersht, *Bchem* **26**, 2480 (1987).
30. D. J. Arndt and P. Berg, *JBC* **245**, 665 (1970).
31. T. Webster, H. Tsai, M. Kula, G. A. Mackie and P. Schimmel, *Science* **226**, 1315 (1984).
32. H. Hayashi, J. R. Knowles, J. R. Katze, J. Lapointe and D. Söll, *JBC* **245**, 1401 (1970).
33. M. Härtlein and D. Madern, *NARes* **15**, 10199 (1987).
34. I. N. Hirshfield and H. P. J. Bloemers, *JBC* **244**, 2911 (1969).
35. G. Eriani, G. Dirheimer and J. Gangloff, *NARes* **14**, 5725 (1989).
36. W. R. Folk, *Bchem* **10**, 1728 (1971).
37. P. Hoben, N. Royal, A. Cheung, F. Yamao, K. Biemann and D. Söll, *JBC* **257**, 11644 (1982).
38. G. E. Willick and C. M. Kay, *Bchem* **15**, 4347 (1976).
39. R. Breton, H. Sanfaçon, I. Papayannopoulos, K. Biemann and J. Lapointe, *JBC* **261**, 10610 (1986).
40. S. Laberge, Y. Gagnon, L. M. Bordeleau and J. Lapointe, *J. Bact.* **171**, 3926 (1989).
41. G. L. E. Koch and C. J. Bruton, *FEBS Lett.* **40**, 180 (1974).
42. D. G. Barker, J. P. Ebel, R. Jakes and C. J. Bruton, *EJB* **127**, 449 (1982).
43. F. Dardel, G. Fayat and S. Blanquet, *J. Bact.* **160**, 1115 (1984).
44. B. Akesson and L. Lundvik, *EJB* **83**, 29 (1978).
45. L. Rymo, L. Lundvik and U. Lagerkvist, *JBC* **247**, 3888 (1972).
46. K. Kawakami, Y. H. Jönsson, G. R. Björk, H. Ikeda and Y. Nakamura, *PNAS* **85**, 5620 (1988).
47. A. Gampel and A. Tzagoloff, *PNAS* **86**, 6023 (1989).
48. M. L. Lee and K. H. Muench, *JBC* **244**, 223 (1969).
49. H. Hennecke, A. Böck, J. Thomale and G. Nass, *J. Bact.* **131**, 943 (1977).
50. J. F. Mayaux, G. Fayat, M. Fromant, M. Springer, M. Grunberg-Manago and S. Blanquet, *PNAS* **80**, 6152 (1983).
51. T. Samuelsson and L. Lundvik, *JBC* **253**, 7033 (1978).
52. J. Anselme and M. Härtlein, *Gene* **84**, 481 (1989).
53. J. R. Katze and W. Konigsberg, *JBC* **245**, 923 (1970).
54. M. Härtlein, D. Madern and R. Leberman, *NARes* **15**, 1005 (1987).
55. F. Kalousek and W. H. Konigsberg, *Bchem* **13**, 999 (1974).
56. R. Freedman, B. Gibson, D. Donovan, K. Biemann, S. Eisenbeis, J. Parker and P. Schimmel, *JBC* **260**, 10063 (1985).
57. S. Chousterman and F. Chapeville, *EJB* **35**, 51 (1973).
58. D. G. Barker, C. J. Bruton and G. Winter, *FEBS Lett.* **150**, 419 (1982).

59. G. Winter, G. L. E. Koch, B. S. Hartley and D. G. Barker, *EJB* **132**, 383 (1983).
60. M. D. Jones, D. M. Lowe, T. Borgford and A. R. Fersht, *Bchem* **25**, 1887 (1986).
61. D. R. Joseph and K. H. Muench, *JBC* **246**, 7610 (1971).
62. C. V. Hall, M. van Cleemput, K. H. Muench and C. Yanofsky, *JBC* **257**, 6132 (1982).
63. D. A. Barstow, A. F. Sharman, T. Atkinson and N. P. Minton, *Gene* **46**, 37 (1986).
64. K. C. Chow and J. T. F. Wong, *Gene* **73**, 537 (1988).
65. S. D. Putney, R. T. Sauer and P. R. Schimmel, *JBC* **256**, 198 (1981).
66. S. D. Putney, N. J. Royal, H. Neuman de Vegvar, W. C. Herlihy, K. Biemann and P. Schimmel, *Science* **213**, 1497 (1981).
67. D. L. Ostrem and P. Berg, *PNAS* **67**, 1967 (1970).
68. T. A. Webster, B. W. Gibson, T. Keng, K. Biemann and P. Schimmel, *JBC* **258**, 10637 (1983).
69. G. Fayat, S. Blanquet, P. Dessen, G. Batelier and J. P. Waller, *Biochimie* **56**, 35 (1974).
70. G. Fayat, J. F. Mayaux, C. Sacerdot, M. Fromant, M. Springer, M. Grunberg-Manago and S. Blanquet, *JMB* **171**, 239 (1983).
71. Y. Mechulam, G. Fayat and S. Blanquet, *J. Bact.* **163**, 787 (1985).
72. B. Chatton, P. Walter, J. P. Ebel, F. Lacroute and F. Fasiolo, *JBC* **263**, 52 (1988).
73. X. Jordana, B. Chatton, M. Paz-Weisshaar, J. M. Buhler, F. Cramer, J. P. Ebel and F. Fasiolo, *JBC* **262**, 7189 (1987).
74. O. S. Bhanot, Z. Kucan, S. Aoyagi, F. C. Lee and R. W. Chambers, *in* "Methods in Enzymology" (L. Grossman and K. Moldave, eds.), Vol. 29, p. 547. Academic Press, New York, 1974.
75. U. Englisch, S. Englisch, P. Markmeyer, J. Schischkoff, H. Sternbach, H. Kratzin and F. Cramer, *Biol. Chem. Hoppe-Seyler* **368**, 971 (1987).
76. C. S. Lin, R. Irwin and J. G. Chirikjian, *NARes* **6**, 3651 (1979).
77. R. Benarous, C. M. Chow and U. L. RajBhandary, *Genetics* **119**, 805 (1988).
78. C. M. Chow and U. L. RajBhandary, *MCBiol* **9**, 4645 (1989).
79. S. Kunugi, Y. Uehara-Kunugi, F. von der Haar, J. Schischkoff, W. Freist, U. Englisch and F. Cramer, *EJB* **158**, 43 (1986).
80. M. Labouesse, C. J. Herbert, G. Dujardin and P. P. Slonimski, *EMBO J.* **6**, 713 (1987).
81. C. J. Herbert, M. Labouesse, G. Dujardin and P. P. Slonimski, *EMBO J.* **7**, 473 (1988).
82. A. Tzagoloff, A. Akai, M. Kurkulos and B. Repetto, *JBC* **263**, 850 (1988).
83. C. M. Chow, R. L. Metzenberg and U. L. RajBhandary, *MCBiol* **9**, 4631 (1989).
84. J. Gangloff, A. Schutz and G. Dirheimer, *EJB* **65**, 177 (1976).
85. S. W. Ludmerer and P. Schimmel, *JBC* **262**, 10801 (1987).
86. F. Fasiolo, B. W. Gibson, P. Walter, B. Chatton, K. Biemann and Y. Boulanger, *JBC* **260**, 15571 (1985).
87. P. Walter, J. Gangloff, J. Bonnet, Y. Boulanger, J. P. Ebel and F. Fasiolo, *PNAS* **80**, 2437 (1983).
88. E. Schwob, A. Sanni, F. Fasiolo and R. P. Martin, *EJB* **178**, 235 (1988).
89. A. Tzagoloff, A. Vambutas and A. Akai, *EJB* **179**, 365 (1989).
90. B. Lorber, D. Kern, A. Dietrich, J. Gangloff, J. P. Ebel and R. Giegé, *BBRC* **117**, 259 (1983).
91. M. Sellami, F. Fasiolo, G. Dirheimer, J. P. Ebel and J. Gangloff, *NARes* **14**, 1657 (1986).
92. G. A. Reid, *NARes* **16**, 1212 (1988).
93. M. Mirande and J. P. Waller, *JBC* **263**, 18443 (1988).
94. W. Freist, H. Sternbach, F. von der Haar and F. Cramer, *EJB* **84**, 499 (1978).
95. L. K. Pape and A. Tzagoloff, *NARes* **13**, 6171 (1985).
96. L. K. Pape, T. J. Koerner and A. Tzagoloff, *JBC* **260**, 15362 (1985).
97. H. Heider, E. Gottschalk and F. Cramer, *EJB* **20**, 144 (1971).

98. I. Weygand-Durasevic, D. Johnson-Burke and D. Söll, *NARes* **15**, 1887 (1987).
99. C. C. Chen and E. W. Somberg, *BBA* **613**, 514 (1980).
100. G. Natsoulis, F. Hilger and G. R. Fink, *Cell* **46**, 235 (1986).
101. H. G. Faulhammer and F. Cramer, *EJB* **75**, 561 (1977).
102. A. L. Majumder, R. A. Akins, J. G. Wilkinson, R. L. Kelley, A. J. Snook and A. M. Lambowitz, *MCBiol* **9**, 2089 (1989).
103. R. A. Akins and A. M. Lambowitz, *Cell* **50**, 331 (1987).
104. A. Hossain and N. R. Kallenbach, *FEBS Lett.* **45**, 202 (1974).
105. A. M. Myers and A. Tzagoloff, *JBC* **260**, 15371 (1985).
106. D. Kern, R. Giegé and J. P. Ebel, *Bchem* **20**, 122 (1981).
107. F. Fasiolo, N. Befort, Y. Boulanger and J. P. Ebel, *BBA* **217**, 305 (1970).
108. A. Sanni, M. Mirande, J. P. Ebel, Y. Boulanger, J. P. Waller and F. Fasiolo, *JBC* **263**, 15407 (1988).
109. M. Diatewa and A. J. C. Stahl, *BBRC* **94**, 189 (1980).
110. T. J. Koerner, A. M. Myers, S. Lee and A. Tzagoloff, *JBC* **262**, 3690 (1987).
111. F. Pan, H. H. Lee, S. H. Pai, T. C. Yu, J. Y. Guoo and G. M. Duh, *BBA* **452**, 271 (1976).
112. Y. A. Motorin, A. D. Wolfson, A. F. Orlovsky and K. L. Gladilin, *FEBS Lett.* **220**, 363 (1987).
113. G. Bec, P. Kerjan, X. D. Zha and J. P. Waller, *JBC* **264**, 21131 (1989).
114. M. Mirande, D. Le Corre and J. P. Waller, *EJB* **147**, 281 (1985).
115. M. Lazard, M. Mirande and J. P. Waller, *Bchem* **24**, 5099 (1985).
116. B. Cirakoglu and J. P. Waller, *EJB* **151**, 101 (1985).
117. M. Mirande, B. Cirakoglu and J. P. Waller, *JBC* **257**, 11056 (1982).
118. P. Thömmes, R. Fett, B. Schray, N. Kunze and R. Knippers, *NARes* **16**, 5391 (1988).
119. M. Mirande and J. P. Waller, *JBC* **264**, 842 (1989).
120. J. D. Dignam, D. G. Rhodes and M. P. Deutscher, *Bchem* **19**, 4978 (1980).
121. M. A. Le Meur, P. Gerlinger, J. Clavert and J. P. Ebel, *Biochimie* **54**, 1391 (1972).
122. S. M. Kane, C. Vugrincic, D. S. Finbloom and D. W. E. Smith, *Bchem* **17**, 1509 (1978).
123. F. W. L. Tsui and L. Siminovitch, *NARes* **15**, 3349 (1987).
124. J. M. Lazar and J. M. Clark, *BBRC* **77**, 1384 (1977).
125. C. Gros, G. Lemaire, R. van Rapenbusch and B. Labouesse, *JBC* **247**, 2931 (1972).
126. K. Nishio and M. Kawakami, *J. Biochem.* **96**, 1867 (1984).
127. S. S. Dignam and J. D. Dignam, *JBC* **259**, 4043 (1984).
128. J. P. Pailliez and J. P. Waller, *JBC* **259**, 15491 (1984).
129. R. V. Emmerich and I. N. Hirshfield, *J. Bact.* **169**, 5311 (1987).
130. R. A. Van Bogelen, V. Vaughn and F. C. Neidhardt, *J. Bact.* **153**, 1066 (1983).
131. Y. Akahori, H. Handa, K. Imai, M. Abe, K. Kameyama, M. Hibiya, H. Yasui, K. Okamura, M. Naito, H. Matsuoka and Y. Kurosawa, *NARes* **16**, 9497 (1988).
132. R. C. Wek, B. M. Jackson and A. G Hinnebusch, *PNAS* **86**, 4579 (1989).
133. A. G. Hinnebusch, *Microbiol. Rev.* **52**, 248 (1988).
134. B. Cirakoglu, M. Mirande and J. P. Waller, *FEBS Lett.* **183**, 185 (1985).
135. G. Bec and J. P. Waller, *JBC* **264**, 21138 (1989).
136. T. McDonald, L. Breite, K. L. W. Pangburn, S. Hom, J. Manser and G. M. Nagel, *Bchem* **19**, 1402 (1980).
137. A. Ducruix, N. Hounwanou, J. Reinbolt, Y. Boulanger and S. Blanquet, *BBA* **741**, 244 (1983).
138. F. Fasiolo, Y. Boulanger and J. P. Ebel, *EJB* **53**, 487 (1975).
139. M. J. Toth and P. Schimmel, *JBC* **261**, 6643 (1986).
140. M. Jasin, L. Regan and P. Schimmel, *Nature* **306**, 441 (1983).
141. D. Cassio and J. P. Waller, *EJB* **20**, 283 (1971).

142. P. Mellot, Y. Mechulam, D. Le Corre, S. Blanquet and G. Fayat, *JMB* **208**, 429 (1989).
143. D. H. Jones, A. J. McMillan and A. R. Fersht, *Bchem* **24**, 5852 (1985).
144. A. R. Fersht, *Bchem* **14**, 5 (1975).
145. W. H. Ward and A. R. Fersht, *Bchem* **27**, 1041 (1988).
146. C. Monteilhet and D. M. Blow, *JMB* **122**, 407 (1978).
147. P. Dessen, G. Zaccaï and S. Blanquet, *JMB* **159**, 651 (1982).
148. P. Carter, H. Bedouelle and G. Winter, *PNAS* **83**, 1189 (1986).
149. P. Dessen, S. Blanquet, G. Zaccaï and B. Jacrot, *JMB* **126**, 293 (1978).
150. B. Cirakoglu and J. P. Waller, *EJB* **149**, 353 (1985).
151. B. Lorber, H. Mejdoub, J. Reinbolt, Y. Boulanger and R. Giegé, *EJB* **174**, 155 (1988).
152. G. Lemaire, C. Gros, S. Epely, M. Kaminski and B. Labouesse, *EJB* **51**, 237 (1975).
153. O. Kellermann, A. Brevet, H. Tonetti and J. P. Waller, *EJB* **88**, 205 (1978).
154. M. Mirande, O. Kellermann and J. P. Waller, *JBC* **257**, 11049 (1982).
155. F. A. Siddiqui and D. C. H. Yang, *BBA* **828**, 177 (1985).
156. G. Vellekamp, R. K. Sihag and M. P. Deutscher, *JBC* **260**, 9843 (1985).
157. J. F. Mayaux and S. Blanquet, *Bchem* **20**, 4647 (1981).
158. P. Plateau, J. F. Mayaux and S. Blanquet, *Bchem* **20**, 4644 (1981).
159. P. Plateau and S. Blanquet, *Bchem* **21**, 5273 (1982).
160. S. Blanquet, P. Plateau and A. Brevet, *MCBchem* **52**, 3 (1983).
161. A. Brevet, P. Plateau, B. Cirakoglu, J. P. Pailliez and S. Blanquet, *JBC* **257**, 14613 (1982).
162. S. Z. Wahab and D. C. H. Yang, *JBC* **260**, 5286 (1985).
163. R. M. Starzyk, T. A. Webster and P. Schimmel, *Science* **237**, 1614 (1987).
164. D. M. Blow, T. N. Bhat, A. Metcalfe, J. L. Risler, S. Brunie and C. Zelwer, *JMB* **171**, 571 (1983).
165. S. D. Putney and P. Schimmel, *Nature* **291**, 632 (1981).
166. M. Springer, M. Graffe, J. Dondon and M. Grunberg-Manago, *EMBO J.* **8**, 2417 (1989).
167. C. Hountondji, P. Dessen and S. Blanquet, *Biochimie* **68**, 1071 (1986).
168. G. M. Nagel, M. S. Johnson, J. Rynd, E. Petrella and B. H. Weber, *ABB* **262**, 409 (1988).
169. C. Hountondji, S. Blanquet and F. Lederer, *Bchem* **24**, 1175 (1985).
170. C. Hountondji, F. Lederer, P. Dessen and S. Blanquet, *Bchem* **25**, 16 (1986).
171. P. Brick and D. M. Blow, *JMB* **194**, 287 (1987).
172. A. R. Fersht, J. Knill-Jones, H. Bedouelle and G. Winter, *Bchem* **27**, 1581 (1988).
173. H. Edwards and P. Schimmel, *Cell* **51**, 643 (1987).
174. M. Mirande, Y. Gache, D. Le Corre and J. P. Waller, *EMBO J.* **1**, 733 (1982).
175. M. Mirande, J. P. Pailliez, J. Schwencke and J. P. Waller, *BBA* **747**, 71 (1983).
176. L. Regan, J. D. Dignam and P. Schimmel, *JBC* **261**, 5241 (1986).
177. S. F. Beresten, T. A. Zargarova, O. O. Favorova, B. I. Rubikaite, A. G. Ryazanov and L. L. Kisselev, *EJB* **184**, 575 (1989).
178. F. H. C. Crick, *JMB* **38**, 367 (1968).
179. L. E. Orgel, *JMB* **38**, 381 (1968).
180. R. Wetzel, *Origins Life* **9**, 39 (1978).
181. A. T. Alzhanova, A. N. Fedorov, L. P. Ovchinnikov and A. S. Spirin, *FEBS Lett.* **120**, 225 (1980).
182. A. T. Alzhanova, A. N. Fedorov and L. P. Ovchinnikov, *FEBS Lett.* **144**, 149 (1982).
183. A. N. Fedorov and L. P. Ovchinnikov, *EJB* **169**, 185 (1987).
184. G. Zaccaï, P. Morin, B. Jacrot, D. Moras, J. C. Thierry and R. Giegé, *JMB* **129**, 483 (1979).
185. M. Kanehisa, P. Klein, P. Greif and C. Delisi, *NARes* **12**, 417 (1984).
186. M. O. Dayhoff, W. C. Barker and L. T. Hunt, *in* "Methods in Enzymology" (C. H. W. Hirs and S. N. Timasheff, eds.), Vol. 91, p. 524. Academic Press, New York, 1983.

187. J. Garnier, D. J. Osguthorpe and B. Robson, *JMB* **120**, 97 (1978).
188. P. Y. Chou and G. D. Fasman, *Adv. Enzymol.* **47**, 45 (1978).
189. P. Dunnil, *Biophys. J.* **8**, 865 (1968).
190. A. Dietrich, R. Giegé, M. B. Comarmond, J. C. Thierry and D. Moras, *JMB* **138**, 129 (1980).
191. A. Podjarny, B. Rees, J. C. Thierry, J. Cavarelli, J. C. Jésior, M. Roth, A. Lewitt-Bentley, R. Kahn, B. Lorber, J. P. Ebel, R. Giegé and D. Moras, *J. Biomol. Struct. Dyn.* **5**, 187 (1987).
192. M. Ruff, J. Cavarelli, V. Mikol, B. Lorber, A. Mitschler, R. Giegé, J. C. Thierry and D. Moras, *JMB* **201**, 235 (1988).
193. S. W. Ludmerer and P. Schimmel, *JBC* **262**, 10807 (1987).
194. P. Walter, I. Weygand-Durasevic, A. Sanni, J. P. Ebel and F. Fasiolo, *JBC* **264**, 17126 (1989).
195. P. Ritter, M. D. Enger and A. Hampel, *in* "Onco-Developmental Gene Expression" (W. Fishman and S. Sell, eds.), p. 47. Academic Press, New York, 1976.
196. P. Hele and L. Hebert, *BBA* **479**, 311 (1977).
197. M. A. Ussery, W. K. Tanaka and B. Hardesty, *EJB* **72**, 491 (1977).
198. R. M. Denney, *ABB* **183**, 156 (1977).
199. C. M. Arbeeny, K. L. Briden and W. S. Stirewalt, *BBA* **564**, 191 (1979).
200. P. O. Ritter, M. D. Enger and A. E. Hampel, *BBA* **562**, 377 (1979).
201. W. K. Roberts and M. L. Olsen, *BBA* **454**, 480 (1976).
202. E. J. Walker, G. B. Treacy and P. D. Jeffrey, *Bchem* **22**, 1934 (1983).
203. M. Charezinski and T. Borkowski, *ABB* **207**, 241 (1981).
204. R. D. Walter and E. Ossikovski, *Mol. Biochem. Parasitol.* **14**, 23 (1985).
205. R. Perego and U. Del Monte, *Cell Biol. Int. Rep.* **10**, 477 (1986).
206. S. J. Shafer, S. Olexa and R. Hillman, *Insect Biochem.* **6**, 405 (1976).
207. B. Cirakoglu and J. P. Waller, *BBA* **829**, 173 (1985).
208. M. T. Norcum, *JBC* **264**, 15043 (1989).
209. C. V. Dang and D. C. H. Yang, *Int. J. Biochem.* **14**, 539 (1982).
210. C. V. Dang, D. L. Johnson and D. C. H. Yang, *FEBS Lett.* **142**, 1 (1982).
211. C. Vennegoor and H. Bloemendal, *EJB* **26**, 462 (1972).
212. D. L. Johnson and D. C. H. Yang, *PNAS* **78**, 4059 (1981).
213. C. V. Dang, B. Ferguson, D. Johnson Burke, V. Garcia and D. C. H. Yang, *BBA* **829**, 319 (1985).
214. O. Kellermann, H. Tonetti, A. Brevet, M. Mirande, J. P. Pailliez and J. P. Waller, *JBC* **257**, 11041 (1982).
215. D. E. Godar, D. E. Godar, V. Garcia, A. Jacobo, U. Aebi and D. C. H. Yang, *Bchem* **27**, 6921 (1988).
216. K. Som and B. Hardesty, *ABB* **166**, 507 (1975).
217. A. M. Pendergast, R. Venema and J. A. Traugh, *JBC* **262**, 5939 (1987).
218. O. Kellermann, A. Brevet, H. Tonetti and J. P. Waller, *EJB* **99**, 541 (1979).
219. O. Kellermann, C. Viel and J. P. Waller, *EJB* **88**, 197 (1978).
220. P. Sivaram, G. Vellekamp and M. P. Deutscher, *JBC* **263**, 18891 (1988).
221. A. K. Bandyopadhyay and M. P. Deutscher, *JMB* **60**, 113 (1971).
222. M. P. Deutscher and R. C. Ni, *JBC* **257**, 6003 (1982).
223. A. Brevet, C. Geffrotin and O. Kellermann, *EJB* **124**, 483 (1982).
224. D. L. Johnson, C. V. Dang and D. C. H. Yang, *JBC* **255**, 4362 (1980).
225. P. F. Agris, D. K. Woolverton and D. Setzer, *PNAS* **73**, 3857 (1976).
226. P. F. Agris, D. Setzer and C. W. Gehrke, *NARes* **4**, 3803 (1977).

227. C. L. Harris, K. Marin and D. Stewart, *BBRC* **79**, 657 (1977).
228. O. Henriksen and M. Smulson, *BBRC* **49**, 1047 (1972).
229. A. M. Pendergast and J. A. Traugh, *JBC* **260**, 11769 (1985).
230. D. E. Godar and D. C. H. Yang, *Bchem* **27**, 2181 (1988).
231. Y. A. Motorin, A. D. Wolfson, A. F. Orlovsky and K. L. Gladilin, *FEBS Lett.* **238**, 262 (1988).
232. A. Brevet, O. Kellermann, H. Tonetti and J. P. Waller, *EJB* **99**, 551 (1979).
233. R. K. Sihag and M. P. Deutscher, *JBC* **258**, 11846 (1983).
234. C. V. Dang and D. C. H. Yang, *JBC* **254**, 5350 (1979).
235. M. P. Deutscher, *J. Cell Biol.* **99**, 373 (1984).
236. C. V. Dang, R. L. Glinski, P. C. Gainey and R. H. Hilderman, *Bchem* **21**, 1959 (1982).
237. G. J. Vellekamp, C. L. Coyle and F. J. Kull, *JBC* **258**, 8195 (1983).
238. H. Berbec and A. Paszkowska, *MCBchem* **86**, 125 (1989).
239. K. J. Kontis and S. M. Arfin, *MCBiol* **9**, 1832 (1989).
240. A. Jacobo-Molina, R. Peterson and D. C. H. Yang, *JBC* **264**, 16608 (1989).
241. G. Vellekamp and M. P. Deutscher, *JBC* **262**, 9927 (1987).
242. A. K. Bandyopadhyay and M. P. Deutscher, *JMB* **74**, 257 (1973).
243. H. J. K. Saxholm and H. C. Pitot, *BBA* **562**, 386 (1979).
244. C. V. Dang, T. P. Mawhinney and R. H. Hilderman, *Bchem* **21**, 4891 (1982).
245. M. Mirande, B. Cirakoglu and J. P. Waller, *EJB* **131**, 163 (1983).
246. A Gulik and G. Orsini, *Mol. Biol. Rep.* **10**, 23 (1984).
247. M. Lazard, M. Mirande and J. P. Waller, *JBC* **262**, 3982 (1987).
248. M. Jacobs-Lorena and H. M. Fried, in "Translational Regulation of Gene Expression" (J. Ilan, ed.), p. 63. Plenum, New York, 1987.
249. A. G. Ryazanov, *FEBS Lett.* **178**, 6 (1984).
250. H. Jakubowski, *J. Theor. Biol.* **133**, 363 (1988).
251. C. V. Dang, D. C. H. Yang and T. D. Pollard, *J. Cell Biol.* **96**, 1138 (1983).
252. M. Mirande, D. Le Corre, D. Louvard, H. Reggio, J. P. Pailliez and J. P. Waller, *Exp. Cell Res.* **156**, 91 (1985).
253. W. K. Tanaka, K. Som and B. A. Hardesty, *ABB* **172**, 252 (1976).
254. R. Lenk, L. Ransom, Y. Kaufmann and S. Penman, *Cell* **10**, 67 (1977).
255. M. Schliwa, J. van Blerkom and K. R. Porter, *PNAS* **78**, 4329 (1981).
256. M. Cervera, G. Dreyfuss and S. Penman, *Cell* **23**, 113 (1981).
257. R. Lenk and S. Penman, *Cell* **16**, 289 (1979).
258. W. J. Van Venrooij, P. T. G. Sillekens, C. A. G. van Eekelen and R. J. Reinders, *Exp. Cell Res.* **135**, 79 (1981).
259. A. M. Bonneau, A. Darveau and N. Sonenberg, *J. Cell Biol.* **100**, 1209 (1985).
260. R. Lemieux and G. Beaud, *EJB* **129**, 273 (1982).
261. D. A. Ornelles, E. G. Fey and S. Penman, *MCBiol* **6**, 1650 (1986).
262. R. C. Bird and B. H. Sells, *BBA* **868**, 215 (1986).
263. P. R. Walker and J. F. Whitfield, *JBC* **260**, 765 (1985).
264. M. Terasaki, L. B. Chen and K. Fujiwara, *J. Cell Biol.* **103**, 1557 (1986).
265. J. B. Lawrence and R. H. Singer, *Cell* **45**, 407 (1986).
266. R. H. Singer, G. L. Langevin and J. B. Lawrence, *J. Cell Biol.* **108**, 2343 (1989).
267. J. B. Lawrence, R. H. Singer, C. A. Villnave, J. L. Stein and G. S. Stein, *PNAS* **85**, 463 (1988).
268. W. R. Jeffery, *Dev. Biol.* **103**, 482 (1984).
269. W. B. Isaacs and A. B. Fulton, *PNAS* **84**, 6174 (1987).
270. I. Blikstad and E. Lazarides, *PNAS* **80**, 2637 (1983).

271. A. Zumbé, C. Stähli and H. Trachsel, *PNAS* **79**, 2927 (1982).

272. J. H. Heuijerjans, F. R. Pieper, F. C. S. Ramaekers, L. J. M. Timmermans, H. Kuijpers, H. Bloemendal and W. J. Van Venrooij, *Exp. Cell Res.* **181**, 317 (1989).

273. J. G. Howe and J. W. B. Hershey, *Cell* **37**, 85 (1984).

274. J. Hradec and Z. Dusek, *BJ* **172**, 1 (1978).

275. S. P. Domogatsky, T. N. Vlasik, T. A. Seryakova, L. P. Ovchinnikov and A. S. Spirin, *FEBS Lett.* **96**, 207 (1978).

276. T. Yokota, H. Sugisaki, M. Takanami and Y. Kasiro, *Gene* **12**, 25 (1980).

277. L. Seidler, M. Peter, F. Meissner and M. Sprinzl, *NARes* **15**, 9263 (1987).

278. S. Nagata, Y. Tsunetsugu-Yokota, A. Naito and Y. Kaziro, *PNAS* **80**, 6192 (1983).

279. P. E. Montandon and E. Stutz, *NARes* **11**, 5877 (1983).

280. K. Lechner and A. Böck, *MGG* **208**, 523 (1987).

281. S. Nagata, K. Nagashima, Y. Tsunetsugu-Yokota, K. Fujimura, M. Miyazaki and Y. Kaziro, *EMBO J.* **3**, 1825 (1984).

282. J. E. Linz, L. M. Lira and P. S Sypherd, *JBC* **261**, 15022 (1986).

283. B. Hovemann, S. Richter, U. Walldorf and C. Cziepluch, *NARes* **16**, 3175 (1988).

284. F. J. Van Hemert, R. Amons, W. J. M. Pluijms, H. Van Ormondt and W. Möller, *EMBO J.* **3**, 1109 (1984).

285. J. H. G. M. Brands, J. A. Maassen, F. J. Van Hemert, R. Amons and W. Möller, *EJB* **155**, 167 (1986).

286. A. S. Sitikov, E. K. Davydova, T. A. Bezlepkina, L. P. Ovchinnikov and A. S. Spirin, *FEBS Lett.* **176**, 406 (1984).

287. K. Kohno, T. Uchida, H. Ohkubo, S. Nakanishi, T. Nakanishi, T. Fukui, E. Ohtsuka, M. Ikehara and Y. Okada, *PNAS* **83**, 4978 (1986).

288. P. Nielsen, S. Goelz and H. Trachsel, *Cell Biol. Int. Rep.* **7**, 245 (1983).

289. A. S. Spirin and M. A. Ajtkhozhin, *TIBS* **10**, 162 (1985).

290. E. G. Fey, D. A. Ornelles and S. Penman, *J. Cell Sci., Suppl.* **5**, 99 (1986).

291. A. G. Ryazanov, L. P. Ovchinnikov and A. S. Spirin, *Biosystems* **20**, 275 (1987).

292. N. Sonenberg, *This Series* **35**, 173 (1988).

293. T. F. Donahue, A. M. Cigan, E. K. Pabich and B. C. Valavicius, *Cell* **54**, 621 (1988).

294. A. M. Cigan, E. K. Pabich, L. Feng and T. F. Donahue, *PNAS* **86**, 2784 (1989).

295. K. Struhl, *TIBS* **14**, 137 (1989).

296. D. W. E. Smith, *Science* **190**, 529 (1975).

297. E. K. Davydova, A. S. Sitikov and L. P. Ovchinnikov, *FEBS Lett.* **176**, 401 (1984).

298. Z. Damuni, F. B. Caudwell and P. Cohen, *EJB* **129**, 57 (1982).

299. D. L. Schelling and P. Cohen, *Biochem. Soc. Trans.* **10**, 387 (1987).

300. S. C. Gerken and S. Arfin, *JBC* **259**, 11160 (1984).

301. S. C. Gerken, I. L. Andrulis and S. M. Arfin, *BBA* **869**, 215 (1986).

302. C. V. Dang and J. A. Traugh, *JBC* **264**, 5861 (1989).

303. A. Varshavsky, *Cell* **34**, 711 (1983).

304. P. Breining and W. Piepersberg, *NARes* **14**, 5187 (1986).

305. M. Crouzet, F. Izgu, C. M. Grant and M. F. Tuite, *Curr. Genet.* **14**, 537 (1988).

306. S. Cole, *EJB* **122**, 479 (1982).

Nucleosome Positioning: Occurrence, Mechanisms, and Functional Consequences

ROBERT T. SIMPSON

Laboratory of Cellular and Developmental Biology National Institute of Diabetes and Digestive and Kidney Diseases National Institutes of Health Bethesda, Maryland 20892

Development of the structural paradigm for the repetitive, nucleosomal subunit organization of chromatin in the 1970s led immediately to questions as to the possible role of this structure in replication and transcription. The first level of chromatin structure has been described as beads on a string, each bead containing 166 base-pairs (bp)[1] of DNA wrapped around an octamer of the four smaller histones and secured in place by a molecule of H1, the lysine-rich histone. These beads are connected in tandem by "linker"

[1] Abbreviations used: bp, base-pairs; MPE-Fe, methidium-propyl ethylenediaminetetraacetic acid/Fe^{2+} complex; MMTV, murine mammary tumor virus; GR, glucocorticoid receptor; GRE, glucocorticoid response element.

DNA, which varies in length from nearly zero in yeast and some neuronal cells to 80 bp in echinoderm sperm. In tissues of most species, the linker is about 20–40 bp (1).

The assumption has always been that DNA sequences in linker DNA would be more accessible to proteins than those same sequences if sequestered in the core particle of the nucleosome. For one protein, micrococcal nuclease, this assumption was established long ago. This enzyme cuts chromatin DNA in linker regions preferentially. If this differential accessibility of linker and core particle DNA applies to a *trans*-acting regulatory factor, the exact location of a nucleosome relative to the DNA sequence might be of critical importance in regulation of the activity of that DNA element.

This is the essence of the interest in and concern about what has come to be called nucleosome positioning (1). A positioned nucleosome is located in a precise site relative to DNA sequence in all cells of a given population. In this situation, any particular DNA sequence in the region of the positioned nucleosome would always lie in the same relationship to histones—in the linker or in the core particle, in the central or the peripheral region of the core particle, etc. The diametrically opposite situation would have nucleosomes located randomly; the location of any specific sequence in a population of cells would reflect the statistical probabilities that derive from the fraction of DNA in core particle, chromatosome, and linker regions. Further, the location (relative to the histone octamer) of the sequence would vary for different cells, even in the same experimental population.

In this review, I summarize briefly the salient features of chromatin structure involved in positioning, review examples of non-random location of nucleosomes, examine mechanisms that have been proposed for positioning and experimental tests of several of these, and discuss some recent efforts to ascertain whether positioning could and/or does have any effect on the function of DNA in chromatin. There are many studies of positioning or lack thereof that I have not included due to limitations of space and a desire to emphasize the mechanisms and the possible functional significance of positioning.

I. Chromatin

Maturation of the structural paradigm for chromatin was indicated by publication of the long-anticipated monograph *Chromatin* by van Holde (1). This book provides the background in the physical and compositional studies of chromatin, which are important in understanding the structural contexts of nucleosome positioning. Since the topic under consideration here relates mainly to the intimate interactions of histones and DNA, only the primary levels of chromatin organization are relevant to our discussion.

The core particle is the primary structural element of chromatin. It has a disk shape, 5.5 nm long and 12 nm in diameter. A central core of two each of the four smaller histones (H2A, H2B, H3, and H4) is wrapped by 1.75 turns of DNA, 146 bp in length, in a shallow helical path. The structure of the core particle has been determined by X-ray crystallography at 7 Å resolution (2), and higher-resolution studies using DNA fragments of defined sequence should be available soon (3). An additional 20 bp of DNA is thought to complete two full turns of the nucleic acid around the octamer and to be bound by a single molecule of H1, forming the chromatosome (4). Bending of DNA into a rather tight helix has been thought relevant in positioning nucleosomes, as is discussed in more detail in Section V,A.

It is important to note that both the crystal studies and solution studies of core particles indicate different domains of DNA structure within the core particle. The path of DNA around the histone octamer is not isotropic in X-ray studies of core particle crystals. There are relatively sharp bends at about 15 and 40 bp on either side of the pseudodyad of the particle (2) (Fig. 1A). Unusual features of DNA core particle structure have also been suggested by a site hypersensitive to dimethyl sulfate modification about 10 bp on either side of the pseudodyad (5); sites at ± 1.5 helical turns from the dyad are more reactive than other segments of core particle DNA to attack by singlet oxygen (6). Recent observations suggest that photo-induced thymine dimer formation is favored at sites where DNA in the vicinity of adjacent thymines is bent toward the major groove. There is preferential formation of such dimers at sites located two and four helical turns on each side of the pseudodyad of the nucleosome in nuclei *in vivo*, further reinforcing the idea that the helical path of DNA around the histone octamer is anisotropic (7). Studies of attack by hydroxyl radicals on an *in vitro* core particle assembled on a cloned DNA segment indicate an altered helical periodicity for the central three turns, from -1.5 to $+1.5$ (8).

Physicochemical studies show that the peripheral 20 or so bp of DNA at each end of the core particle segment differ in their interactions with the octameric histone core from the central DNA (Fig. 1B). Thermal denaturation of core particles is biphasic; about 35% of the hyperchromicity appears as a reversible transition roughly 20°C below the major, irreversible melting of the core particle DNA (9–11). Circular dichroism, sedimentation, and nuclear magnetic resonance experiments indicate that a similar amount of core particle DNA is altered in conformation in a fashion consistent with dissociation from tight binding to histones at a temperature somewhat below optical melting (9–11). The DNA that behaves in this fashion—dynamically capable

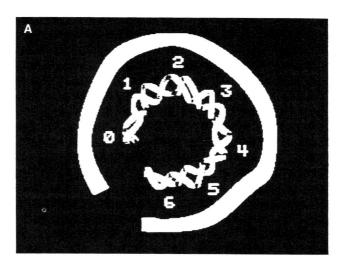

A

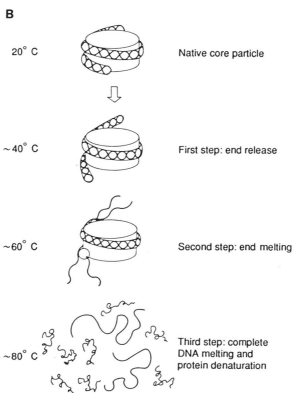

B

20° C — Native core particle

~40° C — First step: end release

~60° C — Second step: end melting

~80° C — Third step: complete DNA melting and protein denaturation

of existing in a tightly bound state, on the one hand, or a more accessible, linker-like state, on the other—is the 20 bp at each end of the core particle (*11*). When H1 histone is present in the chromatosome, this dynamic DNA is fixed in the tightly bound conformation (*4*).

The major conclusion from this is an extension of what we have come to understand about DNA structure in the past decade or so. Far from being the completely regular, rigid, cylindrical, double-helical molecule we used to envision, it is apparent that DNA has many variations in its structure, including bending, variations in width of major and minor grooves, and opposite handedness of the helix (for reviews, see *12* and *13*). In chromatin, added to this diversity, DNA can exist in several states, more than the initial simple distinction of linker versus core particle conformations. One can envision a potential spectrum of accessibilities of DNA ranging from the open linker, through the dynamic DNA at the ends of the core particle, to the tightly bound central region of the nucleosome. The possible role of the "punctuation marks" (the ends of the chromatosome, the ends of the core particle segment, and the two pairs of bends) in this spectrum remains to be defined. Since the major interest in nucleosome positioning is its possible role in chromatin function, the anisotropy of DNA and variations in its interactions with histones along the chromatin strand should be kept in mind as we proceed to examine positioning and its effects.

II. Detecting Nucleosome Positioning

Enzymatic and chemical reagents cut chromatin DNA in distinct patterns, depending on its location in a core particle or between core particles. To detect positioning, one must be able to locate the cutting site. The methods used to accomplish this *in vitro* and *in vivo* are functionally similar. For most experiments, what is required is a "molecular ruler." The origin of the ruler is defined by a restriction endonuclease cutting site. Lengths of fragments from this site are determined by chromatographic separation of DNA fragments.

FIG. 1. Domains of DNA in the core particle. (A) Anisotropic path of DNA in the core particle. The path of half of the DNA, as determined in the crystallographic study by Richmond *et al.* (*2*), is shown. Position 0 is the pseudodyad, or center, of the 146 bp of DNA which wind around the histone octamer. Other positions shown are the number of helical repeats of DNA away from the center. The terminal repeat was not resolved well in the study referred to and is not shown. Note the discontinuities in a smooth path occurring at positions 1.5 and 4, emphasized by the white band drawn to approximate the bending of the DNA. (Reprinted by permission from *Chromatin*, p. 258. Copyright © 1989 by Springer-Verlag.) (B) The 20 or so bp of DNA at each end of the core particle differ in properties from central DNA. Schematized drawings of core particles are shown at various temperatures, as indicated. For discussions in this review, the second state, "end release," is of particular significance. (Reprinted by permission from *Chromatin*, p. 249. Copyright © 1989 by Springer-Verlag.)

Finally, the analysis requires some means of detecting only those fragments that abut the restriction site. For *in vitro* experiments, this is usually provided by a direct end-label; for *in vivo* experiments, either indirect end-labeling (*14, 15*) or a synthetic oligonucleotide and primer extension may be used (*16*). Together, these allow one to determine the cutting sites on a specific segment of DNA. The reagents used to incise the phosphodiester backbone of DNA have particular cutting-site patterns in chromatin. In almost all experiments, since the reagents have (variable) sequence selectivity on DNA alone, comparison of cutting patterns for chromatin and uncomplexed DNA, as a control, is essential.

Micrococcal nuclease, the most commonly used reagent in positioning investigations, cuts chromatin DNA preferentially in linker regions, between nucleosome core particles. Positioned nucleosomes in a micrococcal nuclease experiment are signaled by chromatin cutting sites at least 140 bp apart. The chromatin sites may or may not be strongly cut in the naked DNA (control) samples, but there should be sites strongly cut in naked DNA that are protected in chromatin for one to assign operationally the presence of a nucleosome. The complex of methidium-propyl EDTA with Fe^{2+} (MPE-Fe) (*17*) has been used recently as a substitute for micrococcal nuclease; it has the virtue of less sequence selectivity in cutting sites compared to the bacterial enzyme. For both reagents, the problem of sequence preference in naked DNA has complicated the assignment of nucleosome positions, but has not precluded definition of the organization of chromatin around specific genes.

Another class of reagents, used primarily in the high-resolution localization of nucleosomes, attacks DNA within or outside nucleosomes, but detects the rotational position of the nucleic acid on the surface of the histone octamer within the core particle. For example, DNase I cuts core particle DNA at intervals of about 10 bp in the nucleosome (*18*). The exact periodicity of cutting is less than that for free DNA and may vary along the length of the core particle; this is not of concern for our discussions and we will use a simple integral 10 for helix periodicity. We assume that cutting at 10-bp intervals reflects the periodic availability of some aspect of the DNA when lying on a surface, since the same phenomenon was found for DNA adsorbed to inorganic crystalline surfaces (*19*). The crystal structure of this enzyme and a DNA fragment confirmed these speculations; the enzyme bends DNA away from itself and attacks through the minor groove of the double helix (*20*). This explains both the preference for cutting core particle DNA, which is already bent into a tight helix, and the periodicity of cutting by this nuclease. Similar experimental results are obtained by cutting DNA with hydroxyl radicals, usually generated by a Fenton reaction with ascorbic acid, hydrogen peroxide, and either Fe^{2+} or Cu^+ (*21*). The radical, a smaller reagent than the enzyme, does not lead to as striking a difference in cutting between accessible and nonaccessible sites, but has the advantage of nearly lacking any sequence specificity in its attack on protein-free DNA.

Since DNase I cuts the DNA at the points where the minor groove is directly opposite the contact point with the histone octamer core of the nucleosome, it is very effective in determining the rotational orientation of DNA relative to the octamer. In most cases, it lacks the ability to determine accurately the translational orientation of DNA on the octamer surface. Thus, a hypothetical piece of DNA in four positions on a histone core, each differing by 10 bp from its neighbor, might be interpreted as a positioned nucleosome with somewhat muddy end-cutting sites. In one case, a cutting site frequency has been observed that is similar to that observed for canonical core particles (which should have a totally random DNA sequence and therefore totally random naked DNA cutting sites), with low cutting frequency at sites 30, 60, 80, and 110 nucleotides from the 5' end of the DNA (22, 23), suggesting that the inferred translational location was correct. To confuse even this example, the opposite strand of the nucleosome DNA did not exhibit the canonical cutting site frequency pattern (23).

In general, precise translational localization of a nucleosome by DNase I or chemical reagent attack remains a problem. A general caveat for all of the methods described above when applied to reconstituted systems in vitro should be noted: in a mixed population of chromatin and naked DNA, the more rapid digestion or cutting of the protein-free DNA will remove its contributions to the digestion pattern early in a time- or enzyme-concentration series. This will not lead to false information about the location of a protein footprint, but it can lead to mistaken estimates about the homogeneity of the material under study.

A seemingly appropriate solution to the problem of high-resolution translational location of positioned nucleosomes (micrococcal nuclease serves quite adequately for low-resolution translational localization) would be extension of the exonuclease methods developed by Wu (24) for location of the binding sites of regulatory proteins to DNA. The bound proteins block exonuclease digestion and thereby locate their site of interaction with DNA. Unfortunately, formation of a nucleosome does not totally block the progress of exonuclease III. It has long been known that the enzyme can digest through core particles, pausing at 10-bp intervals (25, 26). Some studies that compare carefully the first pause for exonuclease III in a chromatin sample with pauses in a slightly digested naked DNA sample (this enzyme, like all others, has bothersome sequence specificity) can lead to interpretable data; others, with inadequate DNA controls coupled with underdigested chromatin samples, are more suspect in their conclusions.

A method primarily used for highly repetitive samples (satellite DNA or *in vitro* tandemly repeated sequences) is based on having a particular restriction endonuclease site within the repeated DNA segment. Core particles are prepared with micrococcal nuclease (and usually exonuclease III and S1 nuclease trimming); DNA is isolated and cut with the restriction enzyme. On electrophoresis, positioned nucleosomes will yield two distinct fragments, corresponding in length to the distances from the restriction enzyme site to the ends of the positioned core particle. There is a potential problem with this approach, discussed in studies of repeated sequences. The sequence preference of micrococcal nuclease can yield internal cleavages within the core particle at $(A+T)$-rich regions spaced about 10 bp apart, leading to a biased population (27). These might contain a distinct set of subnucleosomal fragments after secondary cleavage with a restriction endonuclease.

A final method for attempting to determine the positions of nucleosomes uses restriction enzyme accessibility for DNA in chromatin. The assumption in these experiments is that a DNA restriction endonuclease recognition site in a nucleosome will not be cut, while the same site in a linker or nucleosome-free region will be cleaved. No systematic test of this hypothesis in a model, defined system has been made, and no comparison of the possible recognition of 4-bp cutters versus 6-bp cutters has been offered. An important but yet unanswered question is the possible recognition of a restriction endonuclease site (especially for a four-bp cutter) when it is in the proper rotational position on the nucleosome core particle to present its appropriate features to an enzyme attacking it from the solution phase. Nevertheless, the general impression gained from investigations that have used this method to ask not exactly where a nucleosome is located, but is there a nucleosome including the sequence of interest, is that the accessibility of restriction enzyme sites does provide information about the presence or absence of a core particle (or other proteins bound at the site, either specifically or nonspecifically). It is probable that the inability of a restriction endonuclease to cut chromatin DNA at a particular site results from that site being localized in a nucleosome core particle. Interpretation of the observation that a restriction endonuclease cuts chromatin DNA at a particular site, implying that the site is in linker or non-nucleosomal DNA, seems less likely to be a firm conclusion.

III. First Investigations of Positioning

At the time of development of the concept that chromatin is organized as repetitive, histone-bound subunits that alternate with more accessible DNA, the potential importance of this organization for regulation of the function of DNA in the nucleus rapidly became apparent. Two early studies on the simian virus 40 (SV40) minichromosome suggested that nucleosome locations are random (28, 29); the high fraction of this genome that is transcribable and the possibility of heterogeneity in the functional state of the virus temper the significance we can now attach to these studies in considering eukaryotic genomic organization. Another early experiment used two approaches to ask about positioning on the whole chromatin of both rat liver and *Drosophila* embryos (25). Trimer nucleosome DNA that was denatured, reannealed, and digested with S1 nuclease yielded a smear of fragment sizes, not the specific 200-, 400-, and 600-bp bands expected for homogeneously positioned nucleosomes. Similarly, digestion of core-particle DNA with exonuclease III followed by annealing did not yield solely the single-stranded, 70-nt fragments expected if all of the genome was positioned. As noted by the authors, a multiplicity of cell types in the *Drosophila* embryos might contribute to the results, but this would be less likely in the mammalian liver tissue. The conclusion was that the bulk of nucleosomes in chromatin is not positioned in the same location in all cells.

An *ab initio* argument leading to the same conclusion has been made (30), namely, since all cells in an organism contain the same DNA sequences and since the nucleosome spacing, or repeat length, can vary for different tissues in an organism, it is impossible for precise positioning to occur for all chromatin. There is no evidence to contradict this thought. However, the possibility of positioning of a fraction of nucleosomes and the likely functional effects of such a structure remain attractive and are certainly not precluded by these studies of bulk chromatin.

IV. *In Vitro* Studies of Positioning

Chao *et al.* first suggested that a specific location might exist for histone binding on a unique DNA segment (31). They associated core histones with a 140-bp and a 200-bp segment of *Escherichia coli* DNA containing the *lac* operator and analyzed the complexes by DNase I and exonuclease III digestion. Given that the first DNA piece is about the core-particle length, it did not seem surprising that a core particle was formed; maximization of histone DNA contacts would seem to force this result (but see discussion of the Ramsay *et al.* experiment below). Results were not as definitive with the longer fragment; the authors interpreted the data to indicate the presence of four locations for the core particle. Complicating the interpretation of these pioneering experiments was the fact that a sequence selectivity of the nuclease was not recognized at that time, and hence naked DNA controls were not reported. Nevertheless, these experiments were the first indication that some feature of DNA structure, probably determined by sequence, could lead to a preferred location for histone binding to the nucleic acid.

Several years later, the same conclusion was reached in experiments utilizing a 250-bp cloned fragment of sea urchin DNA that included a gene for 5-S ribosomal RNA (23). These experiments were done at base-level resolution on uniquely end-labeled DNA fragments, and clearly showed at least a 120-bp segment of the core particle complex, centered at the start site of transcription of the RNA, wherein cutting occurred at 10-bp intervals (Fig. 2). Many sites highly susceptible to DNase I in naked DNA were not cut in the complex with histones. Peripheral regions of the DNA were cut nearly identically in both the free nucleic acid and the complex with histones. The clear conclusion was that a positioned nucleosome formed with only DNA and histones; the rotational position of the DNA on the surface of the histone octamer was precise to a single base-pair. Interestingly, for one of the DNA strands, the relative susceptibilities of the various sites along the core particle segment agreed with those previously defined for native, isolated, random sequence core particles (22); but for the other strand, cutting site frequencies differed strikingly from the expected pattern. The resolution of this paradox, in terms of sequence preference of nuclease cutting or alterations to the current model of nucleosome structure, or other yet unknown features of the experiment, has not yet been achieved.

Reconstitution *in vitro* of 5-S rRNA gene-containing DNA with histones has been carried out for other organisms also, with results that are difficult to interpret, given the relative constancy of the 5-S RNA sequence in various species, although sequences 5′ to the gene diverge widely. Association of histones with the *Xenopus borealis* somatic gene led to a position similar to that described above for the sea urchin gene, with the pseudodyad of the core particle being at +1 of the gene DNA (32). In contrast, a study using the *Xenopus laevis* somatic gene suggested that a nucleosome was positioned at +20 to +200 (33). In the latter case, a longer DNA fragment was utilized, raising the possibility that close-packing of nucleosomes, known to occur in reconstitutions of histones with long DNA, might contribute to the results. All of the 5-S *in vitro* positioned nucleosomes contain flanking DNA in addition to part of the gene sequence; perhaps features of the non-genic part of the core particle DNA lead to the location of the nucleosome. Experiments that used DNA containing the 5′-flanking sequences of the *X. borealis* gene linked to the gene from *X. laevis*, on the one hand, and the 3′-flanking sequences of the *X. laevis* gene linked to the *X. borealis* gene, on the other, using similar-sized DNA fragments, would be informative.

A similar effort used a 145-bp length of bacterial DNA and associated this with chicken core histones *in vitro* (34). Again, a specific location of histone binding to DNA was found, although somewhat surprisingly, the core particle was formed with only about 130 bp of the DNA fragment; 17 bp at one end of the DNA segment did not interact with the histone octamer. Taken

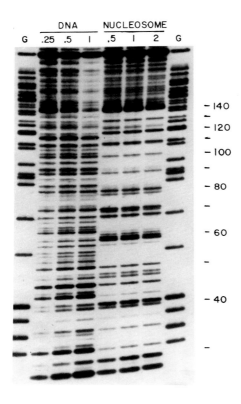

FIG. 2. *In vitro* positioning of a nucleosome on a DNA fragment containing the 5-S rRNA gene of the sea urchin *Lytechinus variegatus*. A uniquely end-labeled fragment of sea urchin DNA was associated with chicken erythrocyte core histones and the complex, as well as control, naked DNA, was digested with DNase I. Fragments were separated by gel electrophoresis, and the location of cutting sites was determined by autoradiography. Lanes labeled "G" are chemically cleaved DNA cut at guanine residues. Digestions were performed at three nuclease concentrations, as indicated, for both naked DNA and the complex with histones. Fragment lengths are indicated at the side of the autoradiogram. Note the similarity of cutting patterns for DNA and the complex at the peripheral regions of the gel and the marked alterations in the region of the positioned core particle. In this region, sites cut in naked DNA are often blocked in the nucleosome. Conversely, some cutting sites in the nucleosome are only poorly cut in the control DNA. The periodicity of cutting sites in the nucleosome is about equal to the helical repeat of DNA (see text for a discussion of the mechanism of DNase-I cutting of nucleosomal DNA). (Reprinted by permission from *PNAS* **80**, 51. Copyright © 1983 by the National Academy of Sciences.)

together, these results strongly imply that structure (probably bending; Section V,A) of a DNA segment can lead to formation of a precisely located nucleosome *in vitro*. Structural features of DNA can provide a more powerful positioning signal than the energy derived from maximizing the electrostatic protein–DNA contacts that can occur in binding of a 145-bp length of DNA to a histone octamer.

While not capable of the resolution of the end-label experiments described above, electron-microscope investigations of positioning on more complex DNA fragments have yielded some interesting information. The replication and transcription termination region of SV40 contains a morphologically curved DNA segment. Association of histones with a piece of DNA containing this domain led to a two- to five-fold preferential formation of a nucleosome on the curved DNA compared to neighboring sequences (35). This region was one of several areas where positioned nucleosomes were described earlier in a biochemical study (36). An even more striking preference for nucleosome formation (five- to seven-fold) was found for a highly curved 223-bp fragment of *Crithidia fasciculata* DNA; this DNA, even uncomplexed, is nearly circular when observed in the electron microscope (35).

V. Mechanisms of Positioning Nucleosomes

A. How Does DNA Structure Determine Position?

Figure 3 illustrates schematically the mechanisms of positioning nucleosomes we will consider. Limited mutagenesis studies of two of the examples of *in vitro* positioned nucleosomes mentioned above (37, 38) did not lead to any definitive location of positioning signals; both studies concluded that the most likely location for such signals is in the 20- to 30-bp region on either side of the pseudodyad of the particle. For the 5-S gene DNA, it seems likely that the signals reside within the gene, given the divergence of 5'-flanking sequences, the conservation of gene sequences, and the similar location of a nucleosome for *Lytechinus variegatus* and *X. borealis* somatic genes (23, 32). In theory, positioning signals could take the form of specific sequence or structural motifs recognized by a part of the histone octamer, much as *trans*-acting regulatory proteins bind to specific DNA sequences. However, it now seems more likely that some periodic structural feature of the DNA, such as bending, facilitates the formation of a positioned nucleosome. In this scenario, there is probably redundancy in the positioning "signal," making it less likely that small alterations in only one portion of the sequence would disturb the location of a nucleosome.

What periodic features of DNA could create bending? Early on, an analy-

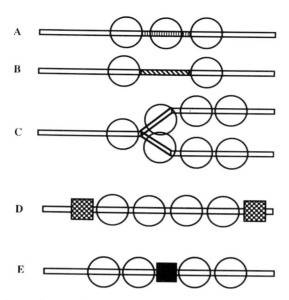

FIG. 3. Possible mechanisms for positioning nucleosomes. DNA is schematized as a double line, with regions that bend easily shown with straight cross-lining and regions that resist bending shown with diagonal cross-lining; nucleosomes are shown as open circles, and non-histone proteins that bind to specific DNA sequences are shown as checkerboard or solid squares. Possible mechanisms are as follows. (A) A segment of DNA that is curved or easily bent can locate a nucleosome due to favorable energetics of winding around the histone octamer. (B) A segment of DNA that resist bending can preclude nucleosome formation and locate adjacent nucleosomes on ambivalent DNA. (C) Nucleosomes could form next to a replication origin with positioning determined by proximity to the origin and the repeat length in the cell under investigation. (D) Non-histones binding to DNA could block formation of a nucleosome and lead to positioning by sandwiching nucleosomes between two such regions. (E) A similar block to nucleosome formation could lead to positioning by forming a single boundary and stochastic location of nucleosomes or, perhaps, by direct interaction with nucleosomal components. Note that situation (A) or (B) could create the boundary equivalent of a non-histone protein bound to DNA in situations (D) and (E).

sis of the limited numbers of eukaryotic DNA sequences then available indicated periodic repeats of the form $A_2N_3T_2N_3$ (39); this suggested that base-pair tilting could generate bending of such structures and thereby help to determine the preferred location of a nucleosome. Preferential micrococcal-nuclease cutting-sites spaced at about 200-bp intervals in the non-transcribed regions of the *Drosophila* heat-shock locus 67B are present in both chromatin and naked DNA (40). The possibility that they reflect periodic variations in DNA structure that may also result in organized chromatin structure is apparent. If this is so, the variations in DNA structure would occur in linker DNA and would therefore have to function by exclusion of histone binding, not by facilitating nucleosome formation.

In an experimental approach to this problem, several hundred core-particle segments of DNA derived from a micrococcal nuclease digest of H1-stripped chromatin were cloned (41, 42). Sequencing nearly 200 independent clones suggested that alternating (A+T)- and (G+C)-rich regions tended to occur with a period of about 10 bp. The rotational orientation of DNA on the histone octamer was such that (A+T)-regions faced inward toward the octamer at sites where the minor groove of DNA was compressed. Conversely, (G+C)-regions faced inward where the major groove was compressed. Similar orientations were determined in other studies for bending of DNA induced by the cAMP-binding regulatory protein of $E.$ $coli$ (43).

A recent related study examined the reconstitution of nucleosomes on two cloned fragments of DNA derived from chicken mononucleosomes (44). One fragment contained a repeated consensus sequence of $C_{4-5}ATAAGG$; the other fragment had alternating A_{3-4} and T_{4-5} runs at about 10-bp intervals; both were 182 bp long. By gel electrophoresis, the former DNA appeared straight and the latter, bent, migrating as if it were about 250 bp long. Rotationally related positions were found for the reconstituted nucleosomes, again suggesting that bending and sequence-related anisotropy can determine the rotational location of histone binding to DNA. The bent DNA associated with histones more readily than the straight molecule under stringent reassociation conditions; once formed, nucleosomes containing either DNA were about as stable.

One can reasonably conclude that the bending and orientation of DNA in these nucleosomes are functions of sequence-determined anisotropy in DNA structure, rather than the particular proteins to which it binds. A concern about extension of the results of the sequencing of core particle DNA derives from the fact that the studies were performed on H1-stripped chromatin. If sliding of nucleosomes occurred during the removal of H1 or the excision of core particles by micrococcal nuclease, the preferred organizations detected by the cloning/sequencing study might indeed reflect the optimal interactions of histone octamers and DNA in isolation, but might not reflect the actual in $vivo$ interactions of these proteins and DNA. Some credence is given to this argument by the observations that the sequence pattern for dinucleosomes (in a study designed to examine linker length and sequence variability, and in one which did not use H1-stripped chromatin) was not that predicted from the previously reported studies of core particles (45).

A recent and important study addresses the role of bending in nucleosome positioning, providing, for the first time, a systematic examination of the length of the signal and the thermodynamics of histone/DNA interactions. Competitive reconstitution experiments *in vitro* were used to examine the energetics of histone octamer binding to several naturally occurring DNA sequences (the sea urchin 5-S sequence, *Xenopus* somatic and minor variant oocyte 5-S genes, and mononucleosomal DNA) and to a set of 157- to 190-bp DNA fragments containing one to six copies of a 20-bp DNA sequence consisting of $W_3N_2S_3N_2^2$ tandemly repeated (*46*). This sequence was designed, in part, from the sequence data from core particles (*41, 42*). Relative to a DNA fragment that contained five copies of the 20-bp repeated sequence, free energies of reconstitution were 300, 1000, 1250, and 1700 kcal/mol for similar overall length fragments containing four, three, two, and one, respectively, copies of the 20-bp element. Natural DNA sequences had free energies of reconstitution, again relative to the same standard, of 1200 (sea urchin 5 S), 1350 (*Xenopus* somatic 5 S), 1600 (*Xenopus* minor oocyte 5 S), and 2800 (total mononucleosomal DNA) kcal/mol. Thus, about 40 bp of the alternating A+T and G+C motif provides the same energetic thrust to formation of a positioned nucleosome as that determined for the most energetically favored of the native DNA sequences examined in this study, the sea urchin 5-S gene segment. While overall, the free-energy difference per bend is relatively small (about 100 cal/mol per bend), the result of repeated bends is quite dramatic; the DNA fragment with 100 bp of the repeated A+T and G+C motif is incorporated into nucleosomes about 100 times more readily than native, random nucleosome DNA.

These bent-DNA positioning signals provide one opportunity to design chromatin for investigation of the role of chromatin structure and function both *in vitro* and *in vivo*. For example, synthetic curved DNA fragments have been used to position nucleosomes in reconstituted chromatin *in vitro*; the results of these studies relating to the initiation of transcription are discussed below (*47*). More extensive reviews of bending of DNA are available (*12, 13, 48*).

Conversely, DNA sequences that lead to structures that do not easily conform to the tightly wound path around the histone octamer may preclude the formation of a nucleosome and thereby form a boundary that might determine the positioning of nucleosomes on adjacent DNA segments. Some controversy has existed over the possible formation of Z-DNA *in vivo* and its ability or inability to form nucleosomes. A recent study has suggested that a particular repeated DNA sequence can determine the positions of neighboring nucleosomes *in vitro* by exclusion of histone binding from the Z-forming DNA segment (*49*). A similar role has been suggested for poly(dA)·poly(dT) sequences (*50*). Long (approximately 80-bp) segments of this isostich are not readily incorporated into nucleosomes, although, at least *in vivo*, shorter

---

[2] W = A or T; N = A or T or G or C; S = G or C (see p. ix). [Eds.]

(approximately 20-bp) segments can bind to histone octamers (51). The particular interest in this sequence and its possible effects on chromatin structure derive from the occurrence of regions of such sequence upstream from several yeast genes and the observation that duplication of a 20-bp element leads to constitutive expression of the gene it flanks (52). The thought is that nucleosome exclusion might ensure promoter availability. The possibility remains that non-histone proteins that interact with such sequences could also lead to promoter accessibility.

B. Other Mechanisms That Might Lead to Positioned Nucleosomes

In any discussion of positioning, one must clarify the possible mechanisms that establish positioned nucleosomes, on the one hand, and functional properties of chromatin (e.g., transcription) that might disrupt positioned nucleosomes and lead to a different positioned array or random location of nucleosomes on the DNA, on the other. For example, I discuss later (Sections VI,C and VI,E) a region 5' to the acid-phosphatase gene of yeast that seems to have positioned nucleosomes when the gene is repressed, indicating that some mechanism can organize chromatin structure; however, this region is not in positioned nucleosomes when the gene is active. Basically, we must not forget the diversity of activities in which chromatin participates and the hierarchies likely to exist in organization of the chromatin structure. (See Fig. 3 for a schematic illustration of the positioning mechanisms discussed below.)

A potential, but as yet undemonstrated, mechanism for positioning nucleosomes is proximity to a replication origin. While the disposition of histones during replication of eukaryotic DNA is still a matter of contention (see 53 for leading references), it is possible that once a nucleosome length of new DNA has been synthesized, it associates with a histone octamer, thereby generating an array of positioned nucleosomes. The locations of nucleosomes might thus be determined by their proximity to an origin of replication.

More thought has been given to the possible role of non-histone proteins bound to specific recognition sequences on DNA as the creators of some degree of regular chromatin organization. Increasingly, specific proteins that bind to cognate sites on DNA are being recognized and purified (see 54 and 55 for a review and leading references). It is assumed that binding of a non-histone to DNA precludes inclusion of that DNA in a nucleosome, and, in fact, there is good evidence that this is the case. Thus, a non-histone protein could create a boundary. When boundaries are not too far apart (in the range of 2000 bp or so), random formation of nucleosomes will lead to an apparent positioned array of particles due to an exclusion formalism formulated for nucleosome distributions (30). The apparent positioning accuracy is highest adjacent to the boundary and decays at longer distances from the non-histone binding site. Note that a segment of DNA that excludes nucleosome formation per se (as discussed above) can form a boundary exactly analogous to a non-histone protein binding site. More surprising is the result that a single boundary can create a limited degree of non-random location of nucleosomes; the length of the linker DNA has a marked role in the distance over which the effect is propagated. It should be noted that some *in vivo* positioned nucleosomes seem to far exceed the degree of localization predicted by the statistical arguments; in other cases, the distributions closely approximate the predicted boundary argument.

While several examples of positioning and thoughts about specific mechanisms are discussed below (Section VI,A), three types of positioning by the binding of non-histone proteins to unique DNA sequences are briefly described here to illustrate the diversity of possible mechanisms that have been proposed in the literature. A positioning protein was suggested a number of years ago (56). Protein d1, which bound to (A+T)-rich segments of DNA at least 7 bp long, coupled with a periodicity of three such segments about 70 bp apart in the α-satellite DNA of African green monkey cells, led to the suggestion that the protein might template the nucleosome DNA into a proper helix that could then associate with an octamer of histones in a specific location (56). There have been no rigorous tests of this hypothesis and the discussions of (A+T)-tracts and bending of DNA described above make the hypothetical role of this protein seem less likely to be critical to nucleosome positioning.

Another protein has been postulated to be the basis for positioning of nucleosomes in the GAL1/10 intergenic control region (57). Here, a protein, initially called factor Y, binds specifically to a short DNA sequence upstream from the two divergently transcribed genes. Positioning of nucleosomes over the upstream region requires the presence of the protein and its cognate DNA binding site. In this case, the distribution and extent of positioning fit well with the statistical boundary model (30). The protein was later purified, named GRF2, and shown to bind to sequences upstream from many genes, an rRNA gene enhancer, at centromeres and telomeres (57a).

Two yeast proteins, α2 and MCM1, which bind to a 31-bp operator as homodimers and act in concert to repress the expression of a-cell mating type-specific genes in α-mating-type cells (see 54 and 59 for a review of the regulation of yeast mating-type gene expression), appear to organize chromatin (58). In this case, discussed in more detail below (Section VI,E), there may be interactions between the non-histone proteins and nucleosomes, leading to a precise location of the nucleosomes immediately flanking the regulatory protein binding site. Certain alterations of the sequence of H4 lead to disruption of the positioning; a more detailed analysis of the regions of both the histones and the regulatory proteins that are necessary for positioning should be very informative.

Although I do not consider higher-order chromatin structure in this review, chromatin folding has been brought up as a possible mechanism in the positioning of nucleosomes in studies of yeast minichromosomes (60). A compact tetranucleosome was formed over a 570-bp segment of DNA only in one chromosomal context (60). Since sequence determination and flanking (potential boundary) elements seemed unlikely to determine positioning, the postulate was made that folding of the small circular episomal chromatin into a constrained structure might determine the location of nucleosomes, in the absence of other features with a higher ranking in the priority scale of positioning signals. The possible role of such a mechanism in the larger genome remains unknown, although most workers in the chromatin field feel quite sure that higher-order structure is relevant to transcriptional regulation.

Clearly, many mechanisms for positioning nucleosomes exist. What remains to be discussed is how frequently nucleosome positioning actually occurs and, more importantly, whether it has any significance for the functional properties of DNA in the eukaryotic nucleus.

VI. Nucleosome Positioning *in Vivo*

A. Nucleosome Positioning on Repetitive (Satellite) Sequences

Many eukaryotic genomes contain highly repetitive satellite sequences that are identical or nearly so. The case of the α-satellite of African green monkey cells illustrates the difficulties in positioning investigations. Like many satellite sequences, which have a repeating DNA motif nearly the length of a single nucleosome (or multiple thereof), this satellite consists of a 172-bp repeated sequence. Equivalence between the DNA repeat length and the length of a nucleosome certainly makes such sequences prime candidates for having a regular array of positioned nucleosomes, possibly making a paracrystalline structure. In 1977, Musich *et al.* showed that micrococcal nuclease cuts this satellite chromatin into 172-bp fragments, and suggested that this resulted from phasing of nucleosomes in the α-satellite chromatin (61). Studies with *Hin*dIII suggested that the linker of the repeated array of chromatin would include this restriction site at position 30 in the repeat. With the evolving realization in the late 1970s that most nucleases have striking sequence selectivities, it was shown by Fittler and Zachau that protein-free α-satellite DNA is also cut into 172-bp fragments by micrococcal nuclease; the suggestion was made that the "phasing" was artifactual (62). Extending their studies, Musich *et al.* more accurately defined the presumptive location of positioned nucleosomes in satellite chromatin; the new data supported a common organization for the nucleosomes, but placed the linker region near base 126 in the repeated sequence (63). Zachau's group studied micrococcal nuclease cutting of naked satellite DNA in more detail with the finding that about one-half of the initial cuts occurred at positions 123 and 132 (64); these would be indistinguishable from the Musich linker location at the resolution of the earlier study. The most recent word in this saga was from the Horz group, who used restriction endonuclease digestion of DNA from trimmed core particles. The conclusion of this study was that eight possible positions could be occupied by nucleosomes on the satellite repeat (65). The major one of these, comprising 35% of the chromatin, was exactly that proposed in the second study by Musich et al. cited above (63).

A caveat to this type of study must be acknowledged. Any sliding or rearrangement of histone binding to DNA during preparation of the core particles will confuse the data and the interpretation. This would be a particular problem where rotational positioning is preserved in the core particle population, as it generally was in this study, but variations in translational positioning are found. One can envision a smoothly bent, tandemly repeated DNA that may (or may not) form a set of phased, positioned nucleosomes in vivo that, due to partial digestions within the particles, rearranges to yield a set of variably located nucleosomes when analyzed as a population of micrococcal nuclease digested core particles. The solution to the arrangement of this satellite chromatin is still not available. It seems clear that the organization of nucleosomes isolated in vitro is variable; the question is how accurately this finding reflects the actual in vivo arrangement of chromatin.

Concern with this possibility is reinforced by other investigations of satellite chromatin structure that have used the core particle isolation and restriction method for analysis. A rat satellite appears to have two major and 16 minor locations for nucleosomes (66, 67). A murine satellite has been described as having 16 nucleosome locations that occur with about equal frequency (68). It should be apparent from discussions previously presented that 16 locations would be expected for a rotationally oriented, but translationally random, segment of DNA; the chromatosome contains 16 turns of DNA, and the linker sequences of repetitious DNA are likely quantized also. The significance of these experiments on satellite DNA, which were interpreted to indicate multiple positions for nucleosomes, is difficult to judge.

Experiments in vitro with a tandemly repeated set of DNA sequences that resemble the satellite DNA discussed above in overall organization may be relevant to this problem. After precise in vitro positioning was demonstrated for sea urchin DNA which contains a gene for 5-S rRNA (23), we constructed a set of DNA fragments designed to serve as substrates for the construction of highly regular chromatin as models for the investigation of higher-order structure (69). All contained the core particle segment of the parental sequence; the total repeat length varied from 172 to 207 bp and the number of repeats ranged up to 55. When associated with histones, these formed regular structures, suggesting the location of a nucleosome at the same position occupied in the monomeric fragment, as judged by the number of particles, micrococcal nuclease susceptibility of the reconstituted chromatin, and the relative susceptibilities of specific endonuclease sites along the tandemly repeated DNA sequence. Similar results were obtained with both linear and closed circular DNA molecules and for several repeat lengths and repeat numbers. Admittedly, none of the methods employed allows base-pair-level resolution of the position of all of the nucleosomes in the reconstituted material.

This same material reconstituted by others and examined using the core particle preparation/restriction enzyme cutting analysis was interpreted to have about half the core particles in a particular location, with a number of altered positions for the remaining half of the nucleosomes (70). Again, these altered positions were generally spaced at about 10-bp intervals. It is hard to reconcile the clarity of the data indicating a truly unique position for the nucleosome formed with the monomeric DNA with the apparent variability in positions on the tandemly repeated sequences. One should note, however, that sequences outside the core particle were altered in construction of the repeated sequences, and no DNase-I mapping experiment examining the fidelity of positioning on monomers of the repeated DNA fragments has been reported. Thus, the formal possibility remains that, if variable positioning does occur in the tandemly repeated chromatin, this might result from the sequence alterations made in constructing the model DNA. Additionally, no DNase-I mapping experiments on the tandemly repeated construct reconstitutions have been reported.

The disparity in the results for the two methods of analysis of a natural, *in vivo*, repeated sequence and an engineered, *in vitro*, repeated sequence suggests that some fundamental difference in methodology may be at the root of the conflicting results. When considering the results derived from core particle isolation followed by analysis of restriction endonuclease fragment lengths, results suggesting a potential artifact due to the sequence preference of the bacterial enzyme and cleavage within the core particle (see Section II) must be considered (27).

B. Nucleosome Positioning on Ribosomal RNA Gene Sequences

Many ribosomal RNA genes are arranged in a fashion somewhat similar to that of the satellite DNAs referred to above, particularly the genes for 5 S and tRNAs. Eight of the tRNA genes of *Xenopus laevis* occur in a 3.2-kbp cluster repeated about 100 times in the genome. In mature erythrocytes, where these genes are inactive, positioned nucleosomes are located along the repeated DNA in a regular fashion, with the exception of one 250-bp, nuclease-sensitive interruption (72). In contrast, no positioning was detected in two tissues where these genes are actively transcribed, although nucleosomes were present, as shown by a canonical micrococcal nuclease ladder.

There have been many studies of positioning on 5-S rRNA genes *in vivo*. Generally, the conclusion has been that positioning occurred (at least on inactive genes). Most investigators have concluded that several locations (but with one predominant position) exist for the nucleosome. A recent study on the 930-bp, highly amplified fragment containing the 5-S gene of *Euplotes eurystomus* clearly shows the presence of four nucleosomes between nuclease-sensitive telomeric regions (73) (Fig. 4). This paper also includes an excellent summary of previous work on the 5-S genes of *Drosophila*, *Xenopus*, and *Tetrahymena*.

In both *Tetrahymena* and *Dictyostelium*, the large rRNA genes are found as palindromes on amplified minichromosomes. In both species, there is very good evidence for a regular chromatin structure with positioned nucleosomes on the non-transcribed regions of the repeats. In *D. discoideum*, there are irregularly spaced, but accurately located, nucleosomes over the 10 kbp of DNA at the termini of the minichromosome (74). The central, non-transcribed 1400 bp of the ribosomal minichromosome of *T. thermophila* has seven nucleosomes, while *T. pyriformis*, which has a 1000-bp, non-transcribed region, has five nucleosomes (75). In each case, the central nucleosome is located with its center at the dyad axis of the palindromic sequence. The mechanism for establishment of the positioning is not known. The fact that both positioned arrays are sandwiched between nucleosome-

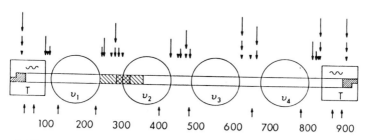

FIG. 4. Chromatin structure of the 5-S rRNA gene of *E. eurystomus*. DNA is represented as the open rectangle and nucleosomes, by circles, called ν_{1-4}. Rightward striping indicates the telomeres; leftward striping, the coding region; and cross-hatching, the intragenic promoter. The squares are presumed to be telomeric complexes with non-histone proteins. Cutting sites for chromatin are above and for naked DNA, below the figure. Short arrows are at micrococcal nuclease sites; long arrows, at DNase-I sites; and arrowheads, at MPE-Fe sites. Note the protection of nearly all protein-free DNA cutting sites in the macronuclear chromatin and the concentration of cutting sites in chromatin for all three probing reagents. (Reprinted by permission from *NARes* **17**, 4705. Copyright © 1989 by IRL Press.)

free regions at the 5' ends of the rRNA genes suggests a double-boundary situation, but the presence of a true dyad symmetry for the central nucleosome also makes thoughts of DNA structure specificity arise.

C. Positioned Nucleosomes on (or around) Structural Genes

There are now several examples of non-random organization of nucleosomes in the vicinity of unique, protein coding genes in organisms varying in complexity from yeast to mammals. One of the first described was the organization of the acid phosphatase gene, PHO5, of Saccharomyces cerevisiae (76). The 5'-flanking region and the gene itself are packaged as a set of relatively positioned nucleosomes when the gene is repressed. The pattern of nuclease cutting is suggestive of that expected on the basis of the boundary stochastic mechanism (30), with the boundary occurring in the 5'-flanking region of the gene. When the gene is active, there is no evidence of positioning of nucleosomes over either the 5'-flanking region or the coding sequences, although nucleosomes are present on at least a portion of the DNA. Interestingly, positioned nucleosomes can be seen in the region just 3' from the coding sequence, irrespective of the state of activity of the PHO5 gene. A candidate for a positioning boundary signal is a long (about 60 bp), internucleosomal region centered about 360 bp upstream from the 5' end of PHO5 mRNA; this region is susceptible to DNase I and micrococcal nuclease and is hypersensitive to DNase I when the gene is derepressed (77).

Later studies at somewhat higher resolution defined the presence of two sets of three positioned nucleosomes flanking the nuclease-sensitive region at −370 in the PHO5 locus (78). Induction of transcription of the gene leads to a major transition in the structure of the region, with an approximately 600-bp region becoming much more accessible to digestion by both micrococcal nuclease and several restriction endonucleases (79). The earlier study had also shown increased susceptibility of one restriction endonuclease site in the 5'-flanking region of the PHO5 gene under derepressed conditions (76).

The chromatin structure of a nearly 9-kbp region of the yeast genome surrounding the locus of heat-shock protein (HSP82) has been determined by DNase-I digestion and indirect end-labeling (80) (Fig. 5). Four DNase-I-hypersensitive regions (each containing internal resistant sites, suggesting protein binding) are present at −4500, −1820, −175, and +3350. Positioned nucleosomes are present adjacent to each of these, except for the −175 region. This is the site of the heat-shock consensus regulatory sequence, the binding site for the protein involved in the regulation of these genes. Upstream from this locus are DNase-I cut-sites that approximate roughly the nucleosomal periodicity. Downstream, in the gene itself, cutting patterns of chromatin and naked DNA are similar, including a region near the 3' end with a striking 85-bp periodicity of cutting sites. Like the acid phosphatase gene, regularly placed, positioned nucleosomes occur just distal to the end

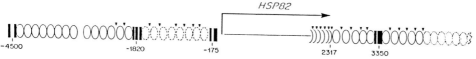

FIG. 5. Chromatin structure of the *S. cerevisiae HSP82* locus. The approximately 9-kb region around the transcription unit (shown by the arrow) was mapped by DNase-I cutting and indirect end-labeling. Filled blocks indicate hypersensitive regions; the open areas within these are sites of low nuclease cleavage, presumably arising from binding of protein factors. Ovals are nucleosomes: continuous ovals are nucleosomes, dotted ovals are likely nucleosomes that do not yield marked DNase-I protection, and dashed ovals are presumed, but as yet undefined, nucleosomes. Triangles indicate major DNase-I cutting sites. The arcs near the 3′ end of the transcription unit signify a unique pattern of nuclease cutting in both chromatin and naked DNA at 85-bp intervals. (Adapted by permission from *JMB* **193**, 73. Copyright © 1987 by Academic Press.)

of the coding region. The flanking regions farthest from the gene have a highly organized, positioned nucleosome structure. The overall chromatin structure of the region is similar, with or without heat shock. This is not too surprising since, while heat shock increases transcription of the gene about 30-fold, there is a significant basal level of expression of *HSP82*. The authors note that the DNase-sensitive regions are about nucleosome size (180 bp on average) and suggest that this might mean that, in other situations, they might contain a nucleosome without disturbing the arrangement of the flanking nucleosomes. Alternatively, they point out, they might arise by displacement of a nucleosome by a *trans*-acting factor. Other nuclease-sensitive regions are also about the size of nucleosomes; more recent studies similarly suggest disruption of a positioned nucleosome during formation of a regulatory complex (see Section VI,A).

The *Drosophila hsp70* locus has two divergently transcribed copies of the gene for this heat-shock protein. Two different cell lines contain differing lengths of the non-transcribed intergenic spacer. As diagrammed in Fig. 6, six positioned nucleosomes appear to be present on the spacer; the lengths of four of them appear similar in the two cell lines, while the discrepancy in spacer length is accommodated by two nucleosomes of shorter length in the short spacer line (*81*). A nuclease-sensitive region, again about 175 bp in length, is present just upstream from the 5′ end of each gene. In the cell line with the shorter spacer, an additional nuclease-hypersensitive site appears on heat shock. The constancy of number and location of nucleosomes between the hypersensitive regions suggests that features other than boundary conditions determine the chromatin organization of the two spacer regions of different length. Interestingly, there is a positioned nucleosome between the 3′ end of each of these sensitive regions and the translation start site, although the bulk of the transcribed region, while having nucleosomes, appears to be randomly organized.

ROBERT T. SIMPSON

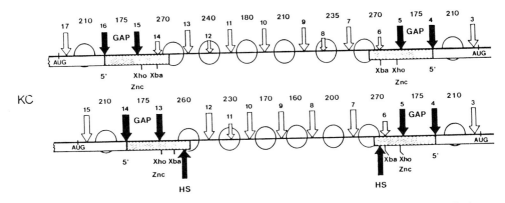

FIG. 6. Chromatin structure of the intergenic spacer between the divergently transcribed *Drosophila hsp70* genes in two cell lines, OR5 and KC, as indicated. The spacer DNA is shown as a single line and the 5′ ends of the genes are shown by the open boxes. The cross-hatched boxes indicate the 5′-flanking "GAP" region, which is hypersensitive to nucleases. Nucleosomes are indicated by circles; their positions are defined by micrococcal nuclease cutting sites, shown by the arrows above each gene depiction. Spacing between these sites is shown by the numbers (in base-pairs) above the arrows. Filled arrows indicate strong cutting sites; those below the gene for the KC cell line are new sites, which appear after heat shock (HS). (Reprinted by permission from *JMB* **172**, 385. Copyright © 1984 by Academic Press.)

The *Drosophila hsp26* locus also has a positioned nucleosome, located at about −140 to −300 relative to the transcription start site (*82*). Flanking this nucleosome are two consensus heat-shock elements, the binding site for the heat-shock regulatory factor. Interestingly, the location of this nucleosome could bring into proximity the two binding sites, essentially creating a static loop [looping has been postulated and in some cases shown to be important in the binding of regulatory proteins to sites well removed from one another in both prokaryotic and eukaryotic gene regulation (*83, 84, 84a*)], which might facilitate interactions between bound heat-shock regulatory proteins and activation of transcription.

The chromatin organization of another set of *Drosophila* genes has been investigated by Worcel *et al.* (*85, 86*). The 5.0-kbp histone gene repeat of *D. melanogaster* contains divergently transcribed genes for H2A and H2B, similarly organized genes for H3 and H4, and a solitary H1 gene. Short, non-transcribed regions separate two of these three gene sets, while a longer, non-transcribed region is present between the 3′ end of the H3 gene and the

5′ end of the H1 gene. As expected, nuclease-hypersensitive regions are present 5′ from each of the genes. On each of the non-transcribed regions, there are positioned nucleosomes. The gene regions, in contrast, are organized as nucleosomes, but the location of the histone/DNA complexes appears to be random.

In chromatin of the mouse β-major globin locus, MPE-Fe[1] cleavage indicates precisely positioned nucleosomes over an extensive region, -3000 to $+1500$ from the cap site in mouse L cells, where the gene is not transcribed (87). Murine erythroleukemia cells, in which expression of the gene can be induced by hexamethylene bisacetamide, have the same positioning, except for a protected region from -200 to $+500$, flanked by reagent-hypersensitive sites. This gap with flanking hyperreactivity is present whether or not globin transcription is induced, suggesting that the transcribable state (as opposed to the transcribed state) determines the organization of the gene chromatin. Two states thus exist, one for a non-transcribable gene and one for a transcribable or transcribed gene. The surprise in this investigation was the apparent retention of positioned nucleosomes on the 3′ half of the gene when it is transcribed. The extensive region with positioned nucleosomes flanking the gene certainly resembles the findings for the other long region of chromatin studied, that of the *S. cerevisiae HSP82* locus (80).

This conclusion has been developing for chromatin structure of unique genes: a positioned arrangement of nucleosomes on non-transcribed, flanking regions or inactive genes; 5′-flanking, nucleosome-free, hypersensitive regions when genes are transcribed or transcribable; and random location of nucleosomes on transcribed coding sequences. In an evolutionary context, it is not surprising that mechanisms have evolved to allow the packaging of larger genomes by histones and, at the same time, ensure access to *cis*-acting DNA elements by *trans*-acting factors.

D. Positioned Nucleosomes near Centromeres and Telomeres

Centromeres and telomeres, two structurally distinctive, functional elements of chromosomes, have unusual chromatin structures in yeast and hypotrichous ciliates, respectively. The centromeres of chromosomes 3 and 11 of *S. cerevisiae* have an approximately 230-bp region that is highly resistant to nuclease cutting, possibly due to the binding of specific proteins necessary for centromere function in chromosome segregation (88, 89). Flanking this are regions of highly organized chromatin with at least a dozen precisely located nucleosomes in a strikingly regular array. Bloom *et al.* performed one of the first experiments approaching the mechanism of positioning of nucleosomes in pursuit of these observations. A major advantage in the study of chromatin structure in yeast is the ability to define the structure of episomal, plasmid minichromosomes and then to vary the DNA sequence of the plasmid and determine what, if any, alterations in chromatin structure accompany the variation. Bloom *et al.* could thus insert the flanking sequences into a plasmid and, after transfer back into yeast, examine the chromatin structure of the region. In fact, the positioned nucleosomes were still present, in the absence of the centromere, suggesting that specific DNA/histone interactions are likely to be the cause of the positioned array of nucleosomes that flank the yeast centromere (88, 89). This seminal study has been extended by a number of investigations of positioning mechanisms and their functional effects in yeast plasmids, as is discussed in Section VI,E.

The ends of the chromosome, the telomeres, are most expeditiously studied in hypotrichous ciliates, organisms that have fragmented their germ-line DNA into gene-sized pieces, discarded 90% of it in the vegetative or somatic macronucleus, and amplified the remainder. The net effect of this unusual approach to nuclear organization is the creation of nuclei that contain nearly 10^7 telomeres (versus 92 in a human cell). Telomeric chromatin in *Oxytricha* has a region of about 100 bp resistant to both nuclease and MPE-Fe, including most of the telomere per se (the telomeric DNA in *Oxytricha* consists of a C_4A_4 repeat). Neighboring this is a well-organized segment of chromatin containing several positioned nucleosomes (90). The fact that the total population appears to have a common chromatin organization suggests a large degree of regularity in the structure of this functionally distinct region of the chromosome in this (and presumedly other eukaryotic) organism(s). The organization of chromatin for two individual genes is similar to that defined for total chromatin, supporting these conclusions. In contrast, the telomeres of the 5-S rRNA gene in *E. eurystomus* are nuclease-sensitive, although they also abut positioned nucleosomes (73). Similarly, the approximately 300-bp $CCCCAA_n$ telomeric repeat of the ribosomal RNA genes of *T. thermophila* is sensitive to micrococcal nuclease, although it, too, is flanked by three precisely positioned nucleosomes adjacent to another nuclease-sensitive region of the palindromic, amplified genes (91).

E. Nucleosome Positioning in Yeast Minichromosomes

One of the most malleable systems for investigation of nucleosome positioning and its functional effects has evolved from the observation that certain circularized yeast DNA fragments transform yeast with a far greater efficiency than those previously studied (92), which transform by homologous recombination. The high-frequency transforming plasmids contain an origin of replication, or autonomously replicating sequence (ARS) that permits existence as high-copy-number episomal plasmids (see 93 and 94 for a review). These plasmids exist as chromatin (95), a finding confirmed by studies of the chromatin organization of these elements (96). The first-described plasmid is a 1453-bp, circular DNA which we have called TRP1ARS1 [it contains the *TRP1* gene for *N*-phosphoribosylanthranilate isomerase (EC 5.3.1.24) and the neighboring ARS1] and others have dubbed it YARp1 (97). The plasmid is highly amplified in yeast, present at about 100 copies per cell; this has facilitated chromatin structure studies and has allowed the development of methods for isolation of the minichromosome to biochemical homogeneity (98).

The structure of the plasmid chromatin is shown in Fig. 7 (96). There are four distinct regions: nuclease-hypersensitive areas of about 180 bp each, located at the 5'-flanking region of the *TRP1* gene and at the ARS1 region; four unstable nucleosomes located on the *TRP1* gene itself; and three precisely positioned, stable nucleosomes on the remaining part of the circular DNA, a region we called UNF (unknown function). The validity of the mapping method was shown by isolation of the minichromosome, and it was shown by electron microscopy that it contains seven morphologically typical nucleosomes (98), although an alternative structure has been proposed by others (97). In fact, in a number of molecules, the nucleosomes appear to be grouped in sets of three and four, separated by long stretches of nucleosome-free DNA (Fig. 7). Interest in these small episomal elements was piqued by the fact that they seem to contain, in a manipulatable form, many of the elements of the whole eukaryotic genome. Although it lacks a centromere and telomeres, the TRP1ARS1 plasmid does have hypersensitive regions in the 5'-flanking region of a transcribed gene and at an origin of replication, unstable nucleosomes on the active gene, and stable, positioned nucleosomes on a non-transcribed region of the genome. It thus contains most of the elements of chromatin present in any eukaryotic cell.

The mechanism for positioning of the three stable nucleosomes on the UNF region of the minichromosome was addressed by inserting three different lengths of DNA between stable nucleosomes I and II, as diagrammed in Fig. 8 (99). The three obvious mechanisms that could lead to positioning (i.e., proximity to the replication origin, sequence preference of histone/DNA interaction, and sandwiching between hypersensitive regions) would lead to quite different results for chromatin structure if a short (half-nucleosome, 75-bp) segment of DNA was added to the minichromosome. The result of this experiment (Fig. 8) showed that the three positioned nucleosomes occupy the same positions in the expanded episomal DNA, demonstrating that the basic mechanism for positioning on the UNF of the TRP1ARS1 plasmid is probably related to sequence/structure-determined histone/DNA interactions. A 155-bp insertion at the same site led to formation of an additional nucleosome, as anticipated. Surprisingly, a 300-bp insert (a tandem replication of the 155-bp insert) led to formation of a single additional nucleosome with long spacers (90 and 55 bp) on either side of the new core particle. Even though two additional nucleosomes could be formed, only one was. The inserted DNA was derived from the sea urchin 5-S rRNA gene discussed previously (23). The *in vitro* and *in vivo* nucleosomes were formed at identical positions. The fact that a sea urchin DNA sequence forms a nucleosome at the same location when as-

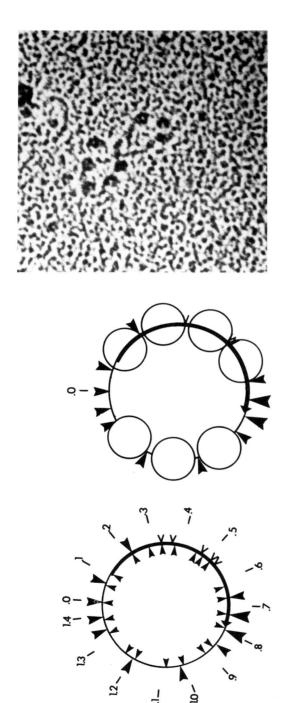

Fig. 7. Chromatin structure of the TRP1ARS1 plasmid in *S. cerevisiae*. (Left) Cutting sites for micrococcal nuclease were determined by indirect end-labeling; sites for protein-free DNA are shown inside the circle, and those for chromatin, outside the circle. The heavy arrow indicates the position of the *TRP1* gene. Larger arrowheads indicate hypersensitive sites. Open, V-shaped arrows indicate cutting sites which are prominent in early digests, but are relegated to a more DNA-like pattern later in the analysis of the minichromosome. (Center) Inferred chromatin structure of the minichromosome. Based on data shown to the left, nucleosomes, shown as large, open circles, were inferred to be present as four, unstable nucleosomes on the *TRP1* gene region and three, stable nucleosomes on the UNF region. Separating these two domains are regions at the 5′ end of the *TRP1* gene and ARS1 which are presumably nucleosome-free and nuclease-hypersensitive. (Right) An electron micrograph of an isolated TRP1ARS1 minichromosome showing seven nucleosomes, located in a group of three and a group of four, as predicted by the nuclease mapping data. We would like to believe that the large, dense object near the group of four nucleosomes might be a molecule of RNA polymerase; it is not wrapped by DNA, as are the nucleosomes. (Adapted by permission from *JMB* **177**, 715. Copyright © 1984 by Academic Press, and from *Methods in Enzymology*, Vol. 170, p. 26. Copyright © 1989 by Academic Press.)

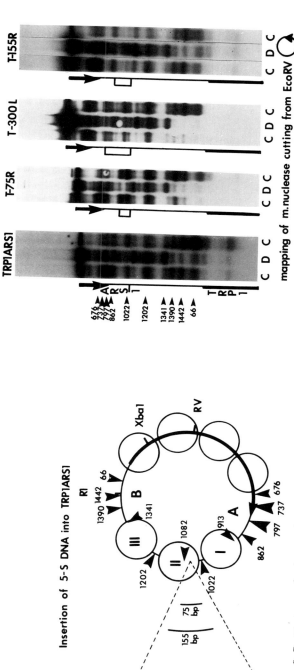

FIG. 8. Positioning mechanisms on the TRP1ARS1 UNF region. (Left) The chromatin structure of the minichromosome is shown. Arrowheads outside the circle are chromatin cutting sites for micrococcal nuclease. Three of the cutting sites for protein-free DNA are shown as arrowheads inside the circle. Numbers are positions (in map units) from the EcoRI (RI) site. The TRP1 gene is shown as a heavy arrow between hypersensitive regions B and A. The three positioned nucleosomes on UNF are designated by Roman numerals. A unique BamHI site was created at 1067 m.u., roughly between nucleosomes I and II. Into this were inserted DNA fragments derived from the sea urchin 5-S rRNA gene (23), discussed in the legend to Fig. 2, of lengths 75, 155, and 300 bp, as indicated. The plasmids were reintroduced into yeast for assembly into chromatin, in vivo, and their structures were determined by indirect end-label mapping from the EcoRV (RV) site counterclockwise. (Right) Nucleosome positions on the parental (TRP1ARS1) and three insertion plasmids. Lanes labeled "C" are protein-free DNA controls, while lanes labeled "D" are minichromosome samples. The bracket indicates the location and length of the inserted DNA. The arrowhead to the left marks the 3' end of the TRP1 gene; cutting sites in this region define hypersensitive region A. There are two regions of high nuclease susceptibility of the inserted DNA in the T-75R construct, the presence of an additional nucleosome, closely apposed to nucleosome II, in the T-155R construct, and the presence of one additional nucleosome flanked by long linkers in the T-300L plasmid. (Reprinted by permission from Nature, vol. 315, p. 250. Copyright © 1985 by Macmillan Journals Ltd.)

171

sembled *in vitro* with chicken histones as it does when assembled into chromatin in a minichromosome *in vivo* with yeast histones strongly suggests the importance of DNA structure in the formation of organized chromatin, at least for this gene.

A pair of boundaries has the ability to force the location of nucleosomes between them, using the yeast plasmid system (*100*). In a construction that has about 560 bp between hypersensitive regions 5' from the *TRP1* and *URA3* genes, four positioned nucleosomes are formed on the intervening DNA, which is a portion of the interrupted and presumedly inactive *TRP1* gene. The four nucleosomes are at different locations than those found in the parent plasmid. These observations clearly show the hierarchical nature of nucleosome positioning; in this case, the boundaries were stronger than whatever led to the location of the nucleosomes on the gene alone.

Studies of the *PHO5* gene in yeast have indicated the presence of positioned nucleosomes over the 5'-flanking and coding sequences when the gene is repressed and suggests that a boundary, due to a nuclease-sensitive region in the 5'-flanking sequences, might be causal (*76–79*). The mechanism of positioning on this gene was directly addressed by cloning portions of the gene and its flanking sequences into the TRP1ARS1 plasmid and examining chromatin structure after assembly *in vivo* in yeast (*101*). Under repressed conditions, the organization of the 5'-flanking region was identical to that determined for the genomic copy of *PHO5*. Deletion of a 278-bp fragment containing the 60-bp, nucleosome-free, nuclease-sensitive region led to nucleosome locations becoming dependent on orientation or location in the plasmid, strongly suggesting that protein binding to this region organizes chromatin structure. Studies of fusion genes showed that the 278-bp fragment contains sufficient information to control transcriptional regulation of the *PHO5* gene. The two identical upstream activator sequences shown by deletion analysis to regulate *PHO5* transcription are located in the 278-bp fragment, and one of these is in the 60-bp, nuclease-sensitive region; one of the sequences is sufficient for regulation.

The *GAL1* and *GAL10* genes of *S. cerevisiae* are divergently transcribed under the control of a set of proteins that interact with their intergenic control region (see *102* for a review). In a series of yeast plasmids containing the control region and alterations of its sequence, nucleosomes were positioned on the promoter region when the genes were repressed. Mutational analysis showed that the critical sequences to generate the positioned array overlapped UAS_G, binding sites for the transcriptional activator GAL4 protein. The organization of chromatin structure was dependent on another protein, factor Y. Alterations of flanking sequences were without effect on nucleosome positioning, suggesting that factor Y (GRF2), probably by an exclusion/boundary mechanism, created the organized chromatin structure (*57a, 103*).

A recent study provides probably the most clear-cut example of extensive positioning (58); again, this is a study of a yeast minichromosome. About 350 bp of DNA containing the *E. coli lac* operator, some bacterial plasmid sequences, and 120 bp of DNA from the 5′-flanking region of the yeast *STE6* gene (see 59 for a review of regulation in α- and a-mating-type yeast cells) was inserted into the hypersensitive region 5′ from the *TRP1* gene. The yeast DNA included the operator for α2. This is a protein produced in α-mating-type cells that binds as a dimer in conjunction with a dimer of another protein, MCM1, to repress transcription of a-mating-type-specific genes, such as *STE6* (*104*). The chromatin structure of the inserted DNA in a-cells, where α2 is not present, was totally random; nearly identical nuclease digestion patterns were obtained for free DNA and chromatin (Fig. 9)

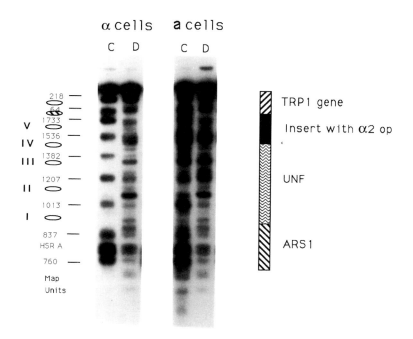

FIG. 9. Chromatin structure around the α2 operator in a yeast plasmid. The plasmid is the TRP1ARS1 DNA with a 354-bp insert in the *Eco*RI site; the insert contains the *E. coli lac* operator and upstream sequences from the yeast *STE6* gene, including the α2 operator (op). Lanes C are minichromosome digests, and lanes D, naked DNA controls. Plasmids were isolated from both α- and a-mating-type cells, as indicated. The positions of nucleosomes I–V are indicated to the left. Note the close similarity of digestion patterns for samples D and C when the plasmid is in a-cells. In contrast, there are extensive differences in digestion patterns in the minichromosome from α-cells, indicating the extensive presence of positioned nucleosomes. (Adapted by permission from *MCBiol*, vol. 10, p. 2055. Copyright © 1990 by the American Society for Microbiology.)

although other studies showed that the minichromosome was packaged into nucleosomes. In contrast, in α-cells, the entire minichromosome, except for the ARS1-hypersensitive region, is organized as precisely positioned nucleosomes. α2/MCM1 binding appears to be responsible for this organization and may nucleate the process, since two new nucleosomes are formed immediately flanking the α2 operator (Fig. 9). Topological studies of the plasmids are consistent with (although not diagnostic of) there being one more nucleosome on the minichromosome in α- versus a-cells. Other studies discussed below (Section VII,B) have shown that α2 binding can move nucleosomes to be adjacent to the α2 operator, reinforcing the conclusion that there is a direct effect of binding of the repressor proteins on the organization of chromatin. A possible direct interaction between histones and the repressor complex is supported by preliminary observations that two of the H4 amino-terminal deletion mutants ($\Delta 4$–19 and $\Delta 4$–23) from Grunstein's laboratory (105) do not form positioned nucleosomes flanking the α2 operator in α-cells (S. Y. Roth, unpublished). Dissection of the interactions that lead to positioning of nucleosomes directly adjacent to the binding site of a non-histone repressor complex should prove highly informative in understanding mechanisms that lead to organized chromatin structures.

F. Positioned Nucleosomes on Mammalian Episomal Chromatin

Chromatin structure of the glucocorticoid-responsive murine mammary tumor virus (MMTV) promoter in the long-terminal-repeat sequences has been investigated by Hager et al. Activation of transcription from this promoter is brought about by binding of the steroid hormone receptor (GR) to DNA sequences called the glucocorticoid response element (GRE). In the genome, hormonal induction of transcription is accompanied by the appearance of a DNase-I-hypersensitive site around the GREs, suggesting a change in chromatin structure (106, 107).

To facilitate study of its structure, the MMTV long terminal repeat was cloned into an episomal vector based on bovine papilloma virus that replicates stably at a high copy number in murine cells in tissue culture (108). Cutting by micrococcal nuclease and MPE-Fe was observed at sites −1019, −826, −651, −444, −250, −60, and +136 relative to the start site of transcription, strongly suggesting the presence of six positioned nucleosomes on the promoter region when the gene is inactive (109). When hormone is added, inducing transcription, the only alteration in cutting is in the region between −60 and −250, which becomes hypersensitive to cleavage by the chemical reagent. This region contains the GREs. The obvious conclusion is that GR binding either requires or induces the disruption or dissociation of a positioned nucleosome that contains the GRE sequences. This alteration in chromatin structure is presumed to allow the binding of NF-1 and TFIID to sites inaccessible for their binding in the uninduced state of the promoter (*110*) (*vide infra*, Section VII,B).

VII. Positioning and Chromatin Function

A. Could Nucleosome Positioning Affect Chromatin Function?

The evolution of ideas about chromatin structure for the past three decades has been from initial ideas that histones would cover the DNA, limiting access to regulatory macromolecules and thereby repressing transcription of most of the genome, to current ideas that largely accept the thought that histones have evolved to package DNA in as transparent a fashion as possible. There are, however, some model systems that have dealt with the constraints, or lack thereof, imposed on functional aspects of DNA by its association with histones.

Initiation and elongation by RNA polymerase are important features of gene regulation that might be influenced by the packaging of DNA with histones, in general, and nucleosome positioning, in particular. Nucleosome formation on short pieces of DNA *in vitro* blocks initiation by prokaryotic RNA polymerase and eukaryotic RNA polymerase II. In contrast, both enzymes appear to be able to transcribe through nucleosome DNA, although there is still disagreement as to the fate of the histones, whether dissociated or not (*111–113*). Consistent with the failure to initiate on nucleosome DNA, when a plasmid containing the adenovirus-2 major-late-promoter is assembled into chromatin prior to transcription in a HeLa cell extract, transcription is markedly inhibited compared to that for free DNA (*114*). Incubation of the DNA in the cell extract prior to chromatin assembly facilitated transcription, suggesting that some factor bound to DNA and prevented formation of a repressive chromatin structure. In a more defined system, association of TFIID, the TATA-binding transcription factor, to the adenovirus major late promoter before chromatin assembly allows transcription; if the order of addition of histones and factor is reversed, transcription is precluded (*115*). The efficiency of even a phage polymerase in transcription of nucleosome-bound DNA is markedly affected by the location of the promoter relative to the core particle, using the artificial bent-DNA positioning signals described earlier (*47*). Together, these studies suggest that nucleosome formation provides a barrier to the initiation of transcription, but does not preclude elongation by RNA polymerase. In contrast, RNA polymerase III appears to neither initiate on nor transcribe through a long array of nucleosome-bound DNA (*116*).

Binding of other proteins is necessary for repression or activation of transcription; nucleosome positioning could affect gene activity through effects on interactions of these *trans*-acting factors with DNA. Although in an artificial system, early experiments suggested that the *E. coli lac* repressor could bind to its operator when that DNA was associated with histones in an *in vitro* assembled complex (*117*). Similarly, data on the interactions of TFIIIA with a 5-S rRNA gene in a positioned nucleosome have been interpreted as indicating the formation of a ternary complex, although most of the TFIIIA footprint that is obvious is on the portion of the intragenic control region external to the positioned nucleosome; the nucleosome is located with position 1 of the gene at the pseudodyad, and the TFIIIA binding site is located at positions 45–100, making it almost exactly half in and half out of the core particle (*32*).

The precise organization of the glucocorticoid-responsive promoter in the long terminal repeat of MMTV determined by Richard-Foy and Hager has been described above (*109*). Perlman and Wrange asked (1) whether the positioned nucleosome at about −60 to −250 could be formed in an *in vitro* system and (2) what alterations in structure would occur if the GR could bind to the reconstituted nucleosome (*118*). Histone transfer led to formation of a precisely positioned nucleosome at −76 to "−219" on a 199-bp fragment containing the promoter and vector sequences [−58 to −198 from MMTV and "−199" to "−256" from pGEM (Promega, Madison, WI)]. In contrast to the striking footprints of GR on histone-free DNA, there were only minor alterations in the digestion pattern of the histone-complexed DNA when GR was added. These did occur at the sites where footprinting occurs in the binary complex and, for one region, were abolished when a mutant DNA known to be deficient in interaction with GR was studied, suggesting that the authors' conclusion that a ternary complex was formed is probably correct. The authors note that the rotational position of the DNA on the histone octamer is such that one of the two postulated major binding sites for GR would be exposed on the surface of the core particle. The paradox of apparent disruption of the nucleosome by GR *in vivo* and the lack of alterations in the DNase map of the *in vitro* nucleosome remain to be resolved. Certainly, an *in vivo* map of the region to compare with the *in vitro* footprints on naked DNA, on the one hand, and the nucleosome, on the other, would be informative.

B. Does Nucleosome Positioning Affect Chromatin Function?

Perhaps the first question to raise here is, does the *presence* of nucleosomes have any effect on chromatin function? Most would agree, based on both presumption and the data detailed above, that it does. Early work, which reduced histone gene dosage in *Drosophila*, showed the activation of transcription of genes that are normally repressed due to position effects (*119*). Position-effect variegation is thought to arise from the location of a gene in a heterochromatic, repressive chromatin environment. Definitive evidence that chromatin structure can affect genetic activity comes from recent studies (105). Deletions of amino acids 4–19 or 4–23 of H4 in yeast led to derepression of transcription of the normally silent mating type loci at HML and HMR. The simplest explanation of these alterations in histone structure affecting gene regulation is that they have altered chromatin structure about the regulated genes. These studies were extended by deleting the genomic copies of the yeast histone H4 gene and maintaining cells with an H4 gene under galactose control on a plasmid. Cells functioned normally when grown in galactose, but when the gene was repressed by growing cells in glucose, several normally repressed genes were actively transcribed, including PHO5 (120). The obvious conclusion is that removal of H4 disrupts nucleosome structure, leading to the activation of transcription of genes normally repressed by some feature of chromatin structure. Study of the chromatin structure of specific gene regions in yeast having about half the normal amount of H2A + H2B dimer showed variations in the degree of disruption of chromatin structure for particular genes. These disruptions, presumably less than that arising from a total lack of H4 in the experiments just mentioned, did not lead to increases in steady-state mRNA concentrations for four genes examined (120a). At variance with these observations, isolation of suppressors of solo δ insertions (which inhibit transcription of the HIS4 and LYS2 genes adjacent to the insertion) in yeast identified them as mutants of H2A and H2B (121). Study of increasing and decreasing histone levels led to the conclusion that alterations of histone dimer stoichiometry affect transcription, presumably by effects on chromatin structure.

There are, as yet, very few experiments that directly address the query about the role of positioning (as opposed to presence) of nucleosomes in chromatin function. In one case, it seems quite likely that a positioned nucleosome does affect chromatin function; this is the MMTV glucocorticoid-responsive promoter. Disruption of a nucleosome by GR binding to the GREs in the promoter allows binding of NF-1 and TFIID to their recognition sites (110); this cascade presumably continues to lead to transcription of the controlled gene. Here, the role of the nucleosome might be to block binding of the two transcription factors, since their concentration is the same in hormone-treated and control cells. The mechanism of disruption and whether actual histone octamer dissociation from the region occurs remain to be established. A recent study of the precisely positioned in vitro nucleosome formed on the MMTV promoter region showed that the GR could bind, but NF-1 could not bind. When GR was bound to the nucleosome, there was some increase in accessibility of the NF-1 binding site end of the nucleosomal DNA to exonuclease III, but binding of NF-1 was still not facilitated (121a). To whatever extent the in vivo and in vitro systems resemble one another, it is difficult to envision the GR alone leading to the structural changes seen in vivo.

Several cis-acting elements are found near the edge of a positioned nucleosome *in vivo*; one such is the ARS1 core domain, an 11-bp sequence absolutely required for high-frequency transformation and the high copy number of ARS plasmids in yeast (see 93 and 94 for a review of the ARS organization). A recent experiment asked whether a location external to the nucleosome is necessary for the ARS to interact with putative *trans*-acting protein factors to function as an efficient replication origin (122). To address this, we made deletions of 10–80 bp adjacent to the ARS core domain, extending into the positioned nucleosome. If the remaining DNA sequence positioned the nucleosome in the same location as in the parent plasmid, the ARS would be located closer and closer to the center of the nucleosome with increasing deletion length. Mapping experiments show that this is indeed the case (Fig. 10). Copy number of the plasmids was assessed as an indication of the efficiency of ARS function (Fig. 10). Deletions up to 50 bp were without effect on copy number; it remained at about 20–40. Larger deletions dropped the copy number to about 1. Inserting the α2 operator 50 bp from the edge of the nucleosome in the low-copy-number −60 deletion reorganized the chromatin structure of the minichromosome, moved the nucleosome to flank the operator, exposed the ARS, and restored the high-copy-number phenotype. This suggests that moving the 11-bp ARS core domain to within about 30–40 bp of the pseudodyad of the core particle severely limits its abilities to interact with putative regulatory proteins. This is of interest in terms of the known differences of the central 80 bp of core particle DNA from the peripheral regions in the crystal structure of the nucleosome and the observations that the peripheral 20 or so bp at each end of the core particle DNA can, under mild stress, assume properties more like those of linker DNA (see Section I).

While the position of the possible nucleosome is not defined, correlative results have been obtained concerning SV40 replication origin function (123). It is known that *cis*-acting transcriptional elements stimulate viral replication. Placing the genomic NF-1 transcriptional activator adjacent to the viral replication origin facilitated replication of a model episome *in vivo*. When the plasmid DNA was assembled with histones, replication in a cell-free system *in vitro* was inhibited. Addition of NF-1 prior to assembly of chromatin *in vitro* reversed the inhibition of replication in the cell-free system, whereas NF-1 had no stimulatory effect on replication of naked DNA. The results are most simply interpreted as indicating disruption of a repressive chromatin structure by binding of the transcriptional regulatory factor.

It is somewhat unusual that transcriptional activation is thought to be coming close to being understood in some eukaryotic systems (see 54, 55 and 84 for a review), while transcriptional repression, probably fully as important, has been slower to progress to definitive mechanisms (see 124, in

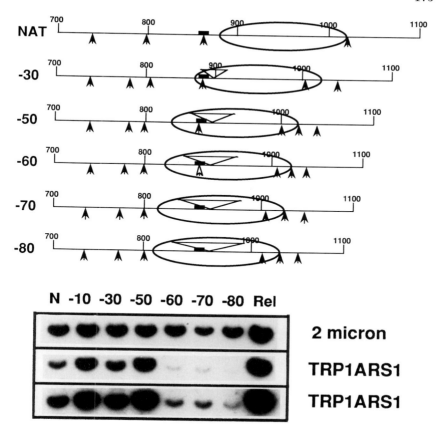

Fig. 10. Effect of location of the ARS sequence in a nucleosome on its function. (Above) Schematic diagram of the locations of nucleosomes (the open ellipses) on TRP1ARS1 DNA in the ARS region. For native (NAT) and the deletions (−30, etc.), the arrowheads indicate micrococcal nuclease cutting sites. Those to the left of the nucleosome are in hypersensitive region A. The black box indicates the location of the 11-bp ARS core sequence. The inverted triangles signify the location and length of the deletions. Note that the deletions move the ARS core sequence farther into the positioned nucleosome with increasing length. (Below) Analysis of ARS function was done by Southern blotting with an oligonucleotide specific for the TRP1ARS1 plasmid DNA (lower two panels) with hybridization to an oligonucleotide specific for 2-μm (another yeast plasmid in these cells) DNA as a control (top panel). The two lower panels are 10-fold differences in exposure time. Note that deletions up to 50 bp have little effect on ARS function as judged by copy number of the plasmid. Deletions of 60 bp and greater markedly reduce function. The estimated copy number in these cells is about 1, the minimum needed for survival, since the plasmid complements a mutation in the yeast genome. The lane labeled "Rel" contains a complete mutation of a sequence closely related to the ARS core sequence located 70 bp from it; it is without effect on copy number. (Reprinted by permission from *Nature*, vol. 343, p. 388. Copyright © 1990 by Macmillan Journals Ltd.)

addition to the above, for a review). In the regulation of a-cell-specific genes in α-mating-type cells, repression by α2 has been postulated to arise from its shielding an activating region of MCM1 (59). We have speculated about how the organization of chromatin might create a novel means for repressing transcription of a gene. The average distance from the ATG of the five a-cell-specific genes whose transcription is repressed by α2/MCM1 to the operator is about 180 bp (125). For the three genes whose sequence is known, the distance from the operator to the most likely TATA box is about 90–100 bp. Formation of a nucleosome flanking the α2 operator would place the TATA box very near the center of the nucleosome, precisely where the ARS core domain functions only poorly. Thus, repression could occur by organization of positioned nucleosomes that place one or more of the key elements in the transcriptional process in an inaccessible chromatin location. This is somewhat analogous to the postulated role for the nucleosome in the MMTV promoter suggested by Hager *et al.* (109, 110). Similarly, the TATA box and upstream activator sequences for *PHO5* were mapped in or near the center of nucleosomes (78, 79). Disruption of the organized chromatin structure flanking the *PHO5* gene would allow access to these *cis*-acting sequences by *trans*-acting factors.

VII. Concluding Thoughts

Most workers in this field would probably agree that there is no experimental evidence for, and sound theoretical arguments against, positioning of nucleosomes for most of any eukaryotic genome. However, strong evidence is accumulating for positioning of some nucleosomes. Almost any mechanism that has been postulated for positioning has found experimental support in some system. It seems clear that there will be hierarchies in the strength of positioning signals and mechanisms that may lead to variability in the location of nucleosomes in different cell types. As studies of the functional consequences of positioning develop, the experiments are uniformly leading to a conclusion that the specific location of a DNA sequence within or outside a nucleosome does have important influence on its function.

Particularly important in evaluating the significance and mechanisms of positioned nucleosomes are studies of so-called minichromosomes—plasmid chromatin that can be manipulated so as to ask questions as opposed to only describing phenomena. There is always a concern that the small size of these chromatin circles may enforce constraints on organization that are diluted out in the milieu of the genome. In yeast, these can be addressed by the abilities to reinsert the modified sequences into the genome by homologous recombination and to examine structure in a more natural environment. Development of similar recombination systems for cells of larger eukaryotes may soon allow such studies to be performed there also.

Studies of what the title to the Prunell and Kornberg article (25) in 1978 called "Relation of Nucleosomes to DNA Sequences" have been through a gradual evolution. Initially, data on bulk chromatin and mixed population viral chromatin suggested basically random location of histone/DNA interactions. With time, technological advances have led to the ability to examine specific gene sequences in chromatin and to vary those sequences (and chromatin structure). Investigations of unique gene chromatin, particularly *cis*-acting elements, have increasingly suggested that positioning occurs. Even later, functional studies have offered evidence that such positioning has major consequences for the activity of chromatin DNA in replication and transcription. My prediction is that the tide is still rising and that even this most basic level of chromatin organization will continue to be recognized as important in the regulation of cellular functions. Extension of this to higher levels of organization of chromatin, interactions with the nuclear matrix, and the three-dimensional organization of the interphase nucleus promise even more exciting times in the understanding of the structure/function relationships of the eukaryotic genome in the coming decade.

ACKNOWLEDGMENT

I thank Jurrien Dean, Mike Kuehl, Randy Morse, Sharon Roth, Chris Szent-Gyorgyi, and Alan Wolffe for critical reading of the manuscript and many members of the LCDB for their interactive criticism and discussion.

REFERENCES

1. K. E. van Holde, "Chromatin." Springer-Verlag, Berlin, 1989.
2. T. Richmond, J. T. Finch, B. Rushton, D. Rhodes and A. Klug, *Nature* 311, 532 (1984).
3. T. J. Richmond, M. A. Searles and R. T. Simpson, *JMB* 199, 161 (1988).
4. R. T. Simpson, *Bchem* 17, 5524 (1978).
5. J. D. McGhee and G. Felsenfeld, *PNAS* 76, 2133 (1979).
6. M. E. Hogan, T. F. Rooney and R. H. Austin, *Nature* 328, 554 (1987).
7. J. R. Pehrson, *PNAS* 86, 9149 (1989).
8. J. J. Hayes, T. D. Tullius and A. P. Wolffe, *PNAS* 87, 7405 (1990).
9. W. O. Weischet, K. Tatchell, K. van Holde and H. Klump, *NARes* 5, 139 (1978).
10. R. T. Simpson and H. Shindo, *NARes* 7, 481 (1979).
11. R. T. Simpson, *JBC* 254, 10123 (1979).
12. E. N. Trifonov, *CRC Crit. Rev. Biochem.* 19, 89 (1985).
13. A. A. Travers, *ARB* 58, 427 (1989).
14. C. Wu, *Nature* 286, 854 (1980).
15. S. A. Nedospasov and G. P. Georgiev, *BBRC* 92, 532 (1980).
16. P. D. Jackson and G. Felsenfeld, *in* "Methods in Enzymology" (S. L. Berger and A. L. Kimmel, eds.), Vol. 152, p. 735. Academic Press, Orlando, Florida, 1987.
17. R. P. Herzberg and P. B. Dervan, *JACS* 104, 313 (1982).
18. M. Noll, *NARes* 1, 1573 (1974).
19. D. Rhodes and A. Klug, *Nature* 286, 573 (1980).
20. D. Suck, A. Lahm and C. Oefner, *Nature* 332, 464 (1988).
21. T. D. Tullius and B. A. Dombroski, *PNAS* 83, 5469 (1986).
22. R. T. Simpson and J. P. Whitlock, Jr., *Cell* 9, 347 (1976).

23. R. T. Simpson and D. W. Stafford, *PNAS* **80**, 51 (1983).
24. C. Wu, *Nature* **317**, 84 (1985).
25. A. Prunell and R. D. Kornberg, *CSHSQB* **42**, 103 (1978).
26. D. Riley and H. Weintraub, *Cell* **13**, 281 (1978).
27. J. D. McGhee and G. Felsenfeld, *Cell* **32**, 1205 (1983).
28. M. Steinmetz, R. E. Streek and H. G. Zachau, *Nature* **258**, 447 (1975).
29. C. Cremisi, P. F. Pignatti and M. Yaniv, *BBRC* **73**, 548 (1976).
30. R. D. Kornberg and L. Stryer, *NARes* **16**, 6677 (1988).
31. M. V. Chao, J. Gralla and H. G. Martinson, *Bchem* **18**, 1068 (1979).
32. D. Rhodes, *EMBO J.* **4**, 3473 (1985).
33. J. M. Gottesfeld, *MCBiol* **7**, 1612 (1987).
34. N. Ramsay, G. Felsenfeld, B. M. Rushton and J. D. McGhee, *EMBO J.* **3**, 2605 (1984).
35. C.-H. Hsieh and J. D. Griffith, *Cell* **52**, 535 (1988).
36. A. Stein, *JBC* **262**, 3872 (1987).
37. P. C. FitzGerald and R. T. Simpson, *JBC* **260**, 15318 (1985).
38. N. Ramsay, *JMB* **189**, 179 (1986).
39. E. N. Trifonov and J. L. Sussman, *PNAS* **77**, 3816 (1980).
40. M. A. Keene and S. C. R. Elgin, *Cell* **27**, 57 (1981).
41. H. R. Drew and A. A. Travers, *JMB* **186**, 773 (1985).
42. S. C. Satchwell, H. R. Drew and A. A. Travers, *JMB* **191**, 659 (1986).
43. M. R. Gartenberg and D. M. Crothers, *Nature* **333**, 824 (1988).
44. S. Pennings, S. Muyldermans, G. Meersseman and L. Wyns, *JMB* **207**, 183 (1989).
45. S. C. Satchwell and A. A. Travers, *EMBO J.* **8**, 229 (1989).
46. T. E. Shrader and D. M. Crothers, *PNAS* **86**, 7418 (1989).
47. A. P. Wolffe and H. R. Drew, *PNAS* **86**, 9817 (1989).
48. A. A. Travers, *TIBS* **12**, 108 (1987).
49. M. M. Garner and G. Felsenfeld, *JMB* **196**, 581 (1987).
50. K. Struhl, *PNAS* **82**, 8419 (1985).
51. G. R. Kunkel and H. G. Martinson, *NARes* **9**, 6869 (1981).
52. D. W. Russell, M. Smith, D. Cox, V. M. Williamson and E. T. Young, *Nature* **304**, 652 (1983).
53. R. A. Laskey, M. P. Fairman and J. J. Blow, *Science* **246**, 609 (1989).
54. K. Struhl, *ARB* **58**, 1051 (1989).
55. P. F. Johnson and S. L. McKnight, *ARB* **58**, 799 (1989).
56. F. Strauss and A. Varshavsky, *Cell* **37**, 889 (1984).
57. M. J. Fedor, N. F. Lue and R. D. Kornberg, *JMB* **204**, 100 (1988).
57a. D. I. Chasman, N. F. Lue, A. R. Buchman, J. W. LaPointe, Y. Lorch and R. D. Kornberg, *Genes Dev.* **4**, 503 (1990).
58. S. Y. Roth, A. Dean and R. T. Simpson, *MCBiol* **10**, 2247 (1990).
59. I. Herskowitz, *Nature* **342**, 749 (1989).
60. F. Thoma and M. Zatchej, *Cell* **55**, 945 (1988).
61. P. R. Musich, J. J. Maio and F. L. Brown, *JMB* **117**, 657 (1977).
62. F. Fittler and H. G. Zachau, *NARes* **7**, 1 (1979).
63. P. R. Musich, F. L. Brown and J. J. Maio, *PNAS* **79**, 118 (1982).
64. W. Horz, F. Fittler and H. G. Zachau, *NARes* **11**, 4275 (1983).
65. X.-Y. Zhang, F. Fittler and W. Horz, *NARes* **11**, 4287 (1983).
66. T. Igo-Kemenes, A. Omori and H. G. Zachau, *NARes* **8**, 5377 (1980).
67. H. Bock, S. Abler, X.-Y. Zhang, H. Fritton and T. Igo-Kemenes, *JMB* **176**, 131 (1984).
68. X.-Y. Zhang and W. Horz, *JMB* **176**, 105 (1984).
69. R. T. Simpson, F. Thoma and J. M. Brubaker, *Cell* **42**, 799 (1985).

70. J. C. Hansen, J. Ausio, V. H. Stanik and K. E. van Holde, *Bchem* **28**, 9129 (1989).
72. P. N. Bryan, H. Hofstetter and M. L. Birnstiel, *Cell* **33**, 843 (1983).
73. A. E. Roberson, A. P. Wolffe, L. J. Hauser and D. E. Olins, *NARes* **17**, 4699 (1989).
74. C. A. Edwards and R. A. Firtel, *JMB* **180**, 73 (1984).
75. T. E. Palen and T. R. Cech, *Cell* **36**, 933 (1984).
76. L. W. Bergman and R. A. Kramer, *JBC* **258**, 7223 (1983).
77. L. W. Bergman, M. C. Stranathan and L. H. Preis, *MCBiol* **6**, 38 (1986).
78. A. Almer and W. Horz, *EMBO J.* **5**, 2681 (1986).
79. A. Almer, H. Rudolph, A. Hinnen and W. Horz, *EMBO J.* **5**, 2689 (1986).
80. C. Szent-Gyorgyi, D. B. Finkelstein and W. T. Garrard, *JMB* **193**, 71 (1987).
81. A. Uvardy and P. Schedl, *JMB* **172**, 385 (1984).
82. S. C. R. Elgin, *JBC* **263**, 19259 (1988).
83. R. Haber and S. Adhya, *PNAS* **85**, 9683 (1988).
84. M. Ptashne, *Nature* **335**, 683 (1988).
84a. N. Mandal, W. Su, R. Haber, S. Adhya and H. Echols, *Genes Dev.* **4**, 410 (1990).
85. B. Samal, A. Worcel, C. Louis and P. Schedl, *Cell* **23**, 401 (1981).
86. A. Worcel, G. Gargiulo, B. Jessee, A. Uvardy, C. Louis and P. Schedl, *NARes* **11**, 421 (1983).
87. R. Benezra, C. R. Cantor and R. Axel, *Cell* **44**, 697 (1986).
88. K. S. Bloom and J. Carbon, *Cell* **29**, 305 (1982).
89. K. S. Bloom, E. Amaya, J. Carbon, L. Clarke, A. Hill and E. Yeh, *J. Cell Biol.* **99**, 1559 (1984).
90. D. E. Gottschling and T. R. Cech, *Cell* **38**, 501 (1984).
91. M. L. Budarf and E. H. Blackburn, *JBC* **261**, 363 (1986).
92. K. Struhl, D. T. Stinchcomb, S. Scherer and R. W. Davis, *PNAS* **76**, 1035 (1979).
93. J. L. Campbell, *TIBS* **13**, 212 (1988).
94. R. M. Umek, M. H. K. Linskens, D. Kowalski and J. A. Huberman, *BBA* **1007**, 1 (1989).
95. V. A. Zakian and J. F. Scott, *MCBiol* **2**, 221 (1982).
96. F. Thoma, L. W. Bergman and R. T. Simpson, *JMB* **177**, 715 (1984).
97. C. M. Long, C. M. Brajkovish and J. F. Scott, *MCBiol* **5**, 3124 (1985).
98. D. S. Pederson, M. Venkatesan, F. Thoma and R. T. Simpson, *PNAS* **83**, 7206 (1986).
99. F. Thoma and R. T. Simpson, *Nature* **315**, 250 (1985).
100. F. Thoma, *JMB* **190**, 177 (1986).
101. L. W. Bergman, *MCBiol* **6**, 2298 (1986).
102. M. J. Fedor and R. D. Kornberg, *MCBiol* **9**, 1721 (1989).
103. M. J. Fedor, N. F. Lue and R. D. Kornberg, *JMB* **204**, 109 (1988).
104. K. L. Wilson and I. Herskowitz, *PNAS* **83**, 2536 (1986).
105. P. S. Kayne, U.-J. Kim, M. Han, J. R. Mullen, F. Yoskizaki and M. Grunstein, *Cell* **55**, 27 (1988).
106. K. S. Zaret and K. R. Yamamoto, *Cell* **38**, 29 (1984).
107. G. L. Hager, H. Richard-Foy, M. Kessel, D. Wheeler, A. C. Lichtler and M. C. Ostrowski, *Recent Prog. Horm. Res.* **40**, 121 (1984).
108. M. C. Ostrowski, H. Richard-Foy, R. G. Wolford, D. S. Berard and G. L. Hager, *MCBiol* **3**, 2045 (1983).
109. H. Richard-Foy and G. L. Hager, *EMBO J.* **6**, 2321 (1987).
110. M. G. Cordingley and G. L. Hager, *NARes* **16**, 609 (1988).
111. J. A. Knezetic and D. S. Luse, *Cell* **45**, 95 (1986).
112. Y. Lorch, J. W. LaPointe and R. D. Kornberg, *Cell* **49**, 203 (1987).
113. R. Losa and D. D. Brown, *Cell* **50**, 801 (1987).
114. T. Matsui, *MCBiol* **7**, 1401 (1987).

115. J. L. Workman and R. G. Roeder, *Cell* **51,** 613 (1987).

116. R. H. Morse, *EMBO J.* **8,** 2343 (1989).

117. M. V. Chao, J. D. Gralla and H. G. Martinson, *Bchem* **19,** 3254 (1980).

118. T. Perlmann and O. Wrange, *EMBO J.* **7,** 3073 (1988).

119. G. D. Moore, D. A. Sinclair and T. A. Grigliatti, *Genetics* **105,** 327 (1983).

120. M. Han, U. Kim, P. Kayne and M. Grunstein, *EMBO J.* **7,** 2221 (1988).

120a. D. Norris, B. Dunn and M. A. Osley, *Science* **242,** 759 (1988).

121. C. D. Clark-Adams, D. Norris, M. A. Osley, J. S. Fassler and F. Winston, *Genes Dev.* **2,** 150 (1988).

121a. B. Pina, U. Bruggemeier and M. Beato, *Cell* **60,** 719 (1990).

122. R. T. Simpson, *Nature* **343,** 387 (1990).

123. L. Cheng and T. J. Kelly, *Cell* **59,** 541 (1989).

124. M. Levine and J. L. Manley, *Cell* **59,** 405 (1989).

125. K. L. Wilson and I. Herskowitz, *MCBiol* **4,** 2420 (1984).

Specific Interaction between RNA Phage Coat Proteins and RNA

GARY W. WITHERELL,
JONATHA M. GOTT
AND OLKE C. UHLENBECK[1]

Department of Chemistry and
Biochemistry
University of Colorado
Boulder, Colorado 80309

The major coat protein from *Escherichia coli* RNA bacteriophages can bind with high specificity to a small region within its RNA genome. The binding site consists of a single hairpin containing the initiation codon of the gene for the phage-encoded subunit of the viral replicase. Coat protein binding is believed to serve two functions in the life cycle of the phage: it acts as a translational repressor of the replicase gene early in infection, and as an initiation site of phage assembly late in infection. This interaction has been extensively studied since the mid-1960s as a prototype of sequence-specific RNA–protein interactions. It is now clear that the phage coat proteins can be considered an example of a class of RNA hairpin binding proteins that are quite common in prokaryotes and eukaryotes. Here, we review the biochemistry of the interaction of phage coat protein with RNA and attempt to provide a molecular understanding of its high specificity.

I. *E. coli* RNA Bacteriophages

The brief summary of phage morphology, classification, and gene expression presented can be supplemented by previous reviews (1, 2) and a symposium volume (3).

The RNA coliphages are small (260 Å in diameter), remarkably simple particles that contain a 3.4- to 4.3-kilobase (kb) single-stranded RNA, a single maturation protein, and 180 coat proteins arranged in icosahedral

---

[1] To whom correspondence may be addressed.

185

Progress in Nucleic Acid Research
and Molecular Biology, Vol. 40

symmetry (4, 5). Four different groups of RNA bacteriophages have been identified, based on serological cross-reactivity (6–9), replicase specificity (10), and physical properties such as RNA and protein size (11), electrophoretic mobility, and pH sensitivity. The most commonly studied representatives are MS2, R17, fr, and f2 (group I), GA (group II), Qβ (group III), and SP (group IV). Distinctions among these groups are not absolute, but the general classification scheme is consistent with the degree of sequence homology among the genomes of MS2 (12–14), GA (15), Qβ (16), SP (17), and fr (18), as well as parts of R17 (19) and JP34 (20).

As summarized in Fig. 1, all four phage groups encode equivalent functions with small differences in genome organization. The maturation protein is encoded at the 5' end of the genome and is required for phage attachment (21). While group I and group II phages have only one form of the major coat protein, group III and group IV phages produce a second form that arises from the failure to terminate at the normal coat protein stop-codon approximately 5% of the time. This read-through coat protein is incorporated into the phage particle and is also involved in attachment of these phages (22–25). All four groups encode a replicase protein that combines with E. coli proteins to form the RNA replicase (26, 27). A separate lysis gene ("L" in Fig. 1) is present in the genomes of groups I and II phages, overlapping the coat and replicase genes in a different reading frame (28–30). In contrast, the lysis activity found in group-III-infected cells is intrinsic to the maturation protein (31, 32).

The infectious cycle of the RNA coliphage has been described in detail (33). Phages attach to the F pili of the E. coli cell by the maturation and read-through proteins, and the RNA enters the cell through the central channel of the pilus (34). Once the coding (plus)-strand RNA genome is inside the cell, gene expression and RNA replication are closely coordinated to produce more than 5000 phages in about a 60-minute infection cycle. Translation of the coat protein gene begins immediately, and large amounts of coat protein are made throughout the infection cycle. Much lower levels of the other phage proteins are needed for productive infection, and their synthesis is temporally regulated. After a short lag, translation of the phage replicase gene begins and continues until approximately 20 minutes post-infection (35, 36). Expression of the lysis and maturation proteins peaks slightly later, in the middle of the infection cycle.

Phage RNA replication involves a complex that includes the phage-encoded replicase, host translational elongation factors EF-Tu and EF-Ts, ribosomal protein S1, and a 12-kDa host factor (37–40). The latter two subunits are necessary for initial synthesis of the minus-strand replication template from the infecting Qβ genome, but are not required for subsequent plus-strand synthesis (41). Since no double-stranded RNA replication inter-

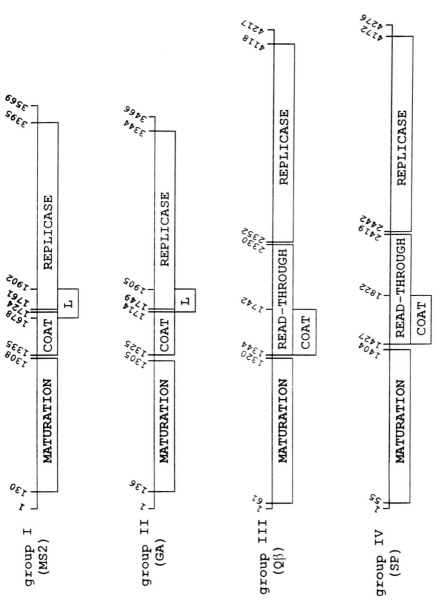

FIG. 1. Genetic maps of representative group I–IV RNA bacteriophage. The coding regions of each phage are indicated by boxes. Numbers mark nucleotide positions within the genome. L, Lysis gene.

mediate occurs, proteins can be synthesized from nascent RNA strands (42). As the concentration of phage components builds up inside the cell, phage assembly begins. The maturation protein must bind specifically to the RNA early in the assembly process in order to generate infectious particles (43). Phage assembly then involves the binding of coat protein to a unique site on the RNA, followed by a cooperative condensation of the remainder of the RNA with coat protein (44–46). Phages are released from the cell after disruption of the cell wall by the phage lysis activity (30).

The level and timing of expression of phage genes and their coordination with RNA replication are a consequence of two general types of mechanisms that affect the access of ribosomes and replicase to their respective binding sites. One mechanism involves the use of alternate RNA conformations. When the RNA first enters the cell, only the ribosome binding site (RBS) of the coat protein gene is available while the replicase, lysis, and maturation protein sites are inaccessible due to competing RNA structures (47, 48). In MS2, a sequence element within the coat protein gene base-pairs with the replicase RBS (12, 49). As a result, continued translation of coat protein is needed to disrupt the occluding structure and allow initiation at the replicase RBS.

The expression of the lysis protein in MS2 also depends on translation of coat protein. In this case, the mechanism follows classical translational coupling, in which the lysis gene RBS is blocked by sequences close to the end of the coat protein gene. Passage of ribosomes through this region destabilizes these RNA structures, allowing terminating ribosomes to reinitiate (50). Finally, translational initiation of the maturation protein gene can only occur on nascent RNA strands early in replication (51). As the nascent strands are further elongated and folded into mature secondary and tertiary structures, translation of the maturation protein gene is repressed.

A second mechanism affecting the efficiency of translational initiation and RNA synthesis involves the specific binding of proteins to RNA. During the initiation of RNA replication, the replicase binds to a number of regions of the RNA, including the RBS of the coat protein gene (52, 53). This clears the RNA of ribosomes that could potentially interfere with replication (54, 55). The specific binding of the maturation protein to a region near the 3' end of the RNA and another within the maturation protein gene (56) could also affect translation during infection, although this has not been demonstrated. Finally, the termination of replicase synthesis about 20 minutes post-infection is caused by the binding of coat protein to the replicase RBS, preventing ribosome access. This last interaction is the major focus of this review.

A number of experiments led to the conclusion that the phage coat protein is a specific translational repressor of the replicase gene. First, phages containing chain-termination mutations in the f2 (57), MS2 (58, 59), and Qβ *(60, 61)* coat protein genes specifically overproduce the replicase gene product. Second, MS2 and R17 coat proteins bind to their respective RNAs, but not to other RNAs *(62–64)*. Third, the addition of MS2 *(65–67)*, f2 *(68, 69)*, or Qβ *(70)* coat protein to an *in vitro* translation system decreases replicase synthesis drastically, while leaving translation of other genes unaffected. Fourth, formation of a stoichiometric complex between R17 *(71)*, Qβ *(72)*, MS2 *(73)*, and fr *(74)* coat proteins with their respective RNAs protects the replicase RBS from nuclease digestion and permits the isolation of an RNA fragment containing the site. Finally, the MS2 replicase RBS, purified on the basis of its protection by ribosomes, binds MS2 coat protein *in vitro (75)*.

Taken together, the observations indicate that each phage coat protein recognizes a short region of its RNA genome containing the replicase RBS. When the intracellular coat protein concentration becomes high enough, the protein binds to this operator, preventing ribosomes from forming an initiation complex. This mechanism therefore conforms to that of classical negative genetic regulation. Since the original definition for the regulatory elements *(76)* did not stipulate the mechanism of regulation, the prefix "translational" for the coat protein repressor and the RNA operator are not strictly necessary and are not used here.

II. Components of the Interaction

A. Coat Proteins

Bacteriophage coat protein for biochemical studies is generally isolated from purified virus. More recently, the MS2 and R17 coat protein genes have been overexpressed from bacterial plasmids *(77, 78)*. In this case, the coat protein assembles into phage-like capsids that can be purified by differential centrifugation and ion-exchange chromatography. Purification of coat protein from either phage or capsid is facilitated by the fact that the protein renatures easily. The particle is first dissociated by harsh denaturing conditions, such as 66% acetic acid *(63)*, 9.4 M urea *(72)*, or phenol *(25)*. After removal of the RNA by precipitation or chromatography, the denatured coat protein is partially renatured in 1 mM acetic acid by dialysis or gel-exclusion chromatography *(73, 79)*. After the addition of 1 mM dithiothreitol, the protein can be stored for months without losing activity. Most coat proteins can be successfully renatured by the transfer from storage buffer directly into a variety of neutral buffers of moderate ionic strength. In many cases, these renatured proteins are fully active in both RNA binding and capsid assembly.

The coliphage coat proteins contain 129–131 amino acids and have a monomer molecular weight of approximately 14,000. MS2 and R17 coat proteins, which are identical, exist as dimers over a broad concentration range (1 nM– 1 μM) in neutral buffers (80, 81). In contrast, Qβ coat protein can also form significant amounts of 11-S aggregates containing five or six monomers associated by disulfide bonds (82).

At concentrations above 1 μM, phage coat proteins aggregate into a variety of particles, including phage-like T = 3 capsids, smaller T = 1 capsids, and larger double shells (83–85). The aggregation is highly cooperative and very sensitive to temperature, ionic strength, and the type of ions present (86). Once formed, the aggregates are very stable under a much wider variety of conditions. Removal of a few carboxy-terminal amino acids of f2 coat protein with carboxypeptidase blocks the formation of aggregates, suggesting that this terminus is located at a protein–protein interface (87). The presence of RNA, DNA, or other polyanions promotes the formation of capsid-like aggregates. (This phenomenon is discussed in more detail in Section V).

Direct sequencing of f2 (88), R17 (3, 89), and Qβ (90) coat proteins has been supplemented in recent years by genomic sequencing, such that the amino-acid sequence of at least one member of each of the four phage groups is now known. A possible alignment (shown in Fig. 2) has 18 positions of sequence identity among all four groups. The coat proteins of groups I and II phage are more similar to each other than to those of groups III and IV, which are also highly homologous. However, many of the changes within and between groups are conservative substitutions, and there is considerable antigenic cross-reactivity among some members of different groups (1).

The structure of MS2 virus has recently been determined to 3.3-Å resolution by X-ray crystallography (93). Although this resolution is insufficient to provide unambiguous localization of all of the aminoacid side-chains, the C_α carbon backbone can clearly be traced. Since the crystals diffract to at least 2.6 Å, a higher resolution structure can be anticipated. As expected for icosahedral viruses, three independent, but similar, coat protein structures are arranged about a pseudo-3-fold axis of symmetry. The two types of dimers in this packing (A/B and C/C) are similar to one another and show an unusually extensive contact surface (Fig. 3). These are presumably closely related to the dimers that exist in solution (80–81) and interact stoichiometrically with the RNA hairpin.

Quite surprisingly, the topology of the MS2 coat protein chain is unlike that seen in the crystal structures of 16 plant and animal viruses of similar icosahedral symmetry (92). Instead of having an eight-stranded antiparallel β-barrel structure, the MS2 protein folds into seven β-strands and two α-helices. Five of the β-strands corresponding to the center of the protein sequence form a twisted β-sheet that faces the interior of the virus (Fig. 3). The remaining two β-strands containing the amino-terminal sequence join

```
MS2/R17    A--SNFTQFVLVDNGGTGDVTVAP-SNFANGVAEWIS
f2         A--SNFTQFVLVDNGGTGDVTVAP-SNFANGVAEWIS
fr         A--SNFEEFVLVNDGGTGDVKVAP-SNFANGVAEWIS
JP34       A---TLRSFVLVDNGGTGDVTVVPVSN-ANGVAEWLS
GA         A---TLRSFVLVDNGGTGNVTVVPVSN-ANGVAEWLS
QB         AKLETVTLGNIGKDGKQTLVLNPRGVNPTNGVASLSQ
SP         AKLNQVTLSKIGKNGDQTLTLTPRGVNPTNGVASLSE


MS2/R17    SNS-RSQAYKVTCSVRQSSAQNRKYTIKVEVPKVATQ
f2         SNS-RSQAYKVTCSVRQSSAQNRKYTIKVEVPKVATQ
fr         SNS-RSQAYKVTCSVRQSSANNRKYTIKVEVPKVATQ
JP34       NNS-RSQAYRVTASYRASGADKRKYTIKLEVPKIVTQ
GA         NNS-RSQAYRVTASYRASGADKRKYAIKLEVPKIVTQ
QB         AGAVPALEKRVTVSVSQPSR-NRK-NYKVQV-KIQNP
SP         AGAVPALEKRVTVSVAQPSR-NRK-NFKVQI-KLQNP


MS2/R17    TVG---GVELPVAAWRSYLNMELTIPIFATNSDCELI
f2         TVG---GVELPVAAWRSYLNLELTIPIFATNSDCELI
fr         VQG---GVELPVAAWRSYMNMELTIPVFATNDDCALI
JP34       VVN---GVELPVSAWKAYASIDLTIPIFAATDDVTVI
GA         VVN---GVELPGSAWKAYASIDLTIPIFAATDDVTVI
QB         TACTANGSCDPSVTRQAYADVTFSFTQYSTDEERAF-
SP         TACTRD-ACDPSVTRSAFADVTLSFTSYSTDEERAL-


MS2/R17    VKA-MQGLLKDGNPIPSAIAANSGIY
f2         VKA-MQGLLKDGNPIPSAIAANSGIY
fr         VKA-LQGTFKTGIAPNTAIAANSGIY
JP34       SKS-LAGLFKVGNPIADAISSQSGFYA
GA         SKS-LAGLFKVGNPIAEAISSQSGFYA
QB         VRTELAALLASPL-LIDAIDQLNPAY
SP         IRTELAALLADPL-IVDAIDNLNPAY
```

Fig. 2. Alignment of coat protein sequences. Optimal sequence alignments are shown for MS2/R17, f2, fr, JP34, GA, Qβ, and SP coat proteins. Positions with five or more sequence identities are shaded.

two α-helices made from the carboxy-terminal sequence to form the outer surface of the virus. Interactions between these two terminal structures contribute substantially to the interaction between the monomers. The high β-strand content is consistent with early solution measurements (91).

The aminoacid side-chains that contact the RNA in the interior of the virus remain to be established. A considerable number of amino acids that face the interior are hydrophilic and therefore have the potential of forming hydrogen bonds. At least six positively charged residues face the interior and

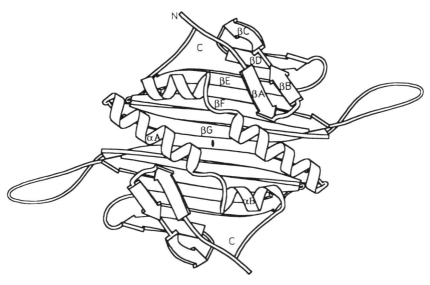

FIG. 3. Ribbon diagram of the coat protein dimer present in the X-ray crystal structure of phage MS2 (93). The short β-sheets (β_A and β_B) at the amino termini and the α-helices (α_A and α_B) at the carboxy termini form the outside surface of the virus. (From L. Liljas, unpublished).

are available for neutralizing phosphoric residues. The electron density map reveals some unassigned density in the neighborhood of Thr-45, Lys-43, and Lys-61 which may represent parts of the RNA chain. Since the internal MS2 RNA molecule is randomly oriented with respect to the protein lattice, the density most likely represents non-specific contacts, shared by many sub-units. In the presence of the translational operator, one may expect exten-sive contacts and possibly some rearrangement of the protein structure.

B. RNA Binding Sites

The section of the RNA genome containing the coat protein binding site can be identified by a nuclease protection experiment. First carried out on R17 (71), the experiment involves forming a complex between coat protein and RNA, cleaving with ribonuclease T_1, filtering the mixture through a nitrocellulose filter, eluting, and sequencing the RNAs bound to the filter. The 59-nucleotide protected fragment of R17 RNA includes the 3′ end of the coat protein gene, the intercistronic region, and the 5′ end of the replicase gene, which can be drawn in a secondary structure containing two hairpins (Fig. 4A). Several subsequent experiments indicated that only the smaller 3′ hairpin interacted with coat protein; the other hairpin was present due to its resistance to RNAse T_1 (75, 94). Similar T_1-protected fragments were also

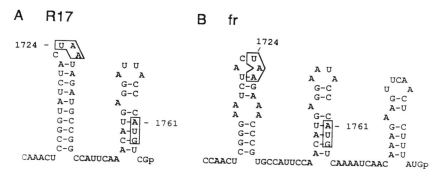

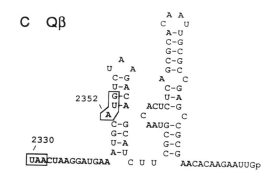

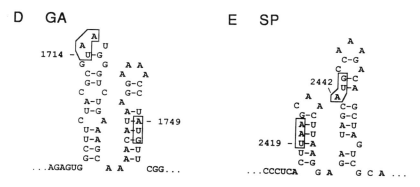

FIG. 4. Localization of the coat protein binding sites. (A–C) Proposed secondary structures of the regions of R17 (71), fr (74), and Qβ (72) RNAs protected from ribonuclease T1 digestion by homologous coat protein. (D and E) Potential secondary structures of the analogous regions of the GA and SP genomes. The coat protein (or read-through protein) termination codons and replicase initiation codons are boxed and numbered as in Fig. 1. The sequence of the protected region in MS2 (73) is virtually identical to that of R17 and is therefore not shown.

isolated for Qβ (72) and fr (74). Each of these contained the initiator region of the phage replicase gene, along with flanking regions of different lengths (Fig. 4B and C). This protection is group-specific, with Qβ coat protein unable to protect MS2 RNA, and vice versa. The equivalent regions of the GA and SP genomes can be folded into similar secondary structures (Fig. 4D and E).

Enzymatic RNA synthesis methods have replaced nuclease protection as a means of obtaining RNA for coat protein binding studies. A 21-nucleotide R17 coat protein binding site was synthesized from smaller fragments using T4 RNA ligase (95). The synthetic RNA bound coat protein with the same affinity as the natural, nuclease-protected, 59-nucleotide RNA. The recent development of *in vitro* transcription of synthetic DNA by T7 RNA polymerase (96) provides a more efficient method for preparing RNA for binding studies. Fragments made by this method corresponding to the coat protein binding sites of R17 (97), fr (98), Qβ (79), and GA (L. Wilhelm, unpublished) are fully active in binding to their corresponding coat proteins.

The exact boundaries of the R17 and Qβ binding sites have been determined by preparing a series of oligomers of incremental lengths and measuring their affinities to coat protein. The data, summarized in Fig. 5, can be interpreted in a relatively straightforward fashion, but give a somewhat different picture for the two coat proteins. In the case of the R17 binding site, an abrupt decrease in K_a is observed when the single-stranded A_{-17} is removed (99), suggesting that this residue contacts the protein. In-

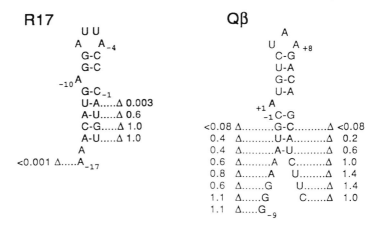

FIG. 5. Boundaries of the R17 and Qβ coat protein binding sites. Oligomers corresponding to the binding sites for R17 and Qβ were truncated from either the 5′ or 3′ end and tested for coat protein binding. The K_a for each deletion tested is given relative to $K_a = 1$ for the full-length oligomer. Subscripts refer to nucleotide position relative to the adenosine (+1) of the replicase initiation codon (boxed in Fig. 4).

terestingly, the K_a is the same whether or not this nucleotide is base-paired (100). When nucleotides are sequentially removed from the 3' terminus of the R17 binding site, a more gradual decrease in K_a is observed (99). It is quite possible that no direct contact between the protein and the RNA occurs in this region of the molecule, and the 3' bases are simply needed to maintain the helical structure of the hairpin. In contrast, all eight base-pairs of the Qβ hairpin are required for optimal binding, and both the corresponding 5' and 3' deletion experiments indicate a steady decrease in K_a as the helix is truncated (79).

Since the nuclease protection experiments identified only a single contiguous region of the phage genome, it is tempting to conclude that no other part of the phage RNA is involved in the binding of coat protein. However, it was possible that, like many ribosomal proteins (101) or tRNA synthetases (102), the coat protein contacts several non-contiguous portions of the genomic RNA. During subsequent nuclease digestion, portions of the RNA may be cut free from the rest and be released from the protein during isolation of the complex on the filter. In order to eliminate this possibility, it is necessary to show that the nuclease-protected fragment can rebind to coat protein with the same affinity as the intact phage RNA. Competition experiments show that intact MS2 RNA binds coat protein just as well as several labeled subfragments isolated by a protection experiment (73). The same conclusion was reached using R17 RNA and a synthetic 21-nucleotide binding site (103). These experiments indicate that the coat protein derives all of its free energy of binding through contacts with the replicase initiator.

Remarkably similar RNA secondary structures can be proposed for the three replicase initiator regions identified by protection experiments and the two additional regions located by RNA sequencing (Fig. 4). In every case, the replicase initiation codon is contained within a small hairpin of 7–10 base-pairs, a loop of three or four residues, and an extrahelical, or "bulged," adenosine residue. In the case of the R17/MS2 hairpin, the indicated secondary structure is supported by temperature-jump relaxation kinetics (94), nuclear magnetic resonance (NMR) studies (104), and absorbance-temperature profiles (74, 105). These data indicate that the hairpins are strongly favored at 37°C, such that the initiator AUG is in a base-paired region. Partial nuclease digestion experiments on the 59-nucleotide fragment of R17 are also consistent with the indicated structure (103). Less extensive data supporting the other secondary structures in Fig. 4 are also available (74).

The RNA structural features present in the phage coat protein binding sites are frequently found in other RNAs. For instance, the most common hairpins in ribosomal RNAs contain loops of four nucleotides (106). Hairpins with three and four residues in the loop are thermodynamically more stable than smaller or larger loops (107). Among the large number of conformations available to the residues in the loop, one can distinguish between those in which the residues cross the major or minor groove of the helical stem (108). The precise conformation of the loop residues will depend on their sequence. Model building suggests considerable potential for base–base and base–backbone interactions, especially in the four-base loops.

The "bulged" adenosine residue is also a common feature in rRNA (109) and is likely to have a profound effect on the structure of the operator. The structures of short DNA helices containing unpaired nucleotides studied by NMR indicate that an extra adenosine (110–112) or guanosine residue (113) is generally stacked into the helix, while unpaired cytidines tend to be extrahelical in solution (114). Where intercalated into the helix, the purines induce a wedge-like conformation, causing a bend in the helix angle of 18°–24° (112, 113). In contrast, X-ray crystallographic studies of DNA helices containing unpaired adenosines show them to be extrahelical (115, 116). This apparent discrepancy is probably due to the low hydration and the spermine used in crystallization as well as the considerable crystal packing forces, which tend to align the oligomers into long DNA strands stacked upon each other (115). It is likely that in solution the extra nucleotides are normally found in both intercalated and extrahelical states, with the fraction in each state affected by sequence context and solution properties. The inclusion of an unpaired nucleotide appears to increase conformational flexibility of the entire helix. Hairpins containing a bulged adenosine, cytidine, or uridine show much greater changes in nuclease sensitivity upon intercalation of ethidium bromide or methidium propyl EDTA-Fe(II) than the perfect duplex and it has been postulated that a bulge facilitates switching between alternative helix conformations (117, 118).

III. Interaction between Coat Protein and RNA

A. Studying the Interaction

Incubation of bacteriophage coat protein with its corresponding genomic RNA results in the formation of two types of RNA–coat protein particles as detected by sucrose density-gradient centrifugation (62–64, 119). Complex I, the coat protein–translational operator complex, is formed at low ratios of coat protein to RNA and migrates close to free RNA on a density gradient. Complex I contains between one and six protein molecules per RNA strand. Complex II is formed at higher ratios of coat protein to RNA and migrates slightly slower than intact phage particles on a density gradient. Complex II closely resembles phage particles by electron microscopy, but is not infectious due to the lack of maturation protein. While complex I only forms with homologous RNAs, complex II can be formed with any RNA (46).

The predominant method for studying the interaction of coat protein and RNA has been the nitrocellulose filter-binding assay. This assay is based on the fact that while free RNA does not bind to filters in neutral buffers, free protein or RNA bound to protein binds tightly. This is true for complex I made with relatively short RNAs. Complex I made with longer (>200-nucleotide) RNAs and Complex II pass through the filter, so their formation cannot be assayed in this manner. A series of experiments was performed to demonstrate that the assay correctly reports the equilibrium between free and bound RNA prior to filtration and that filtration does not disrupt the equilibrium (103). It was shown that all of the input protein bound to the filters, that filter-bound protein was unable to bind RNA, and that multiple washings did not dissociate the complex.

Even at saturating protein concentrations, a certain fraction (10–50%) of the input radiolabeled RNA does not bind to the filters. Although this observation is potentially a consequence of the propensity of RNA hairpins to form a duplex that does not bind protein, analysis of the RNA on sizing columns indicated only monomer hairpins when the RNA is heated and cooled prior to analysis (105). The RNA that passes through the filters can be mixed with fresh protein and will bind to filters in the same proportion as before (103). Since the fraction of RNA that passes through the filters depends on the type and batch of filters used, the phenomenon appears to be a consequence of an unknown reaction at the filter surface that results in dissociation of the complexes (120, 121). In any case, the protein-excess experiment is used to define a "retention efficiency" for the complex that is assumed for all protein-to-RNA ratios.

After normalization using the determined retention efficiency, the data from a protein-excess binding experiment can be fitted to a theoretical bimolecular binding curve as long as the protein concentrations are between 0.1 nM and 1 μM. At lower concentrations the protein dimers dissociate to inactive monomers, and at higher concentrations the phage-like complex II forms, which does not bind to filters. The coat protein concentration required to half-saturate the RNA is equal to the equilibrium dissociation constant (K_d), provided that both the stoichiometry of the complex and the fraction of active protein are known.

Early studies on the R17 coat protein/RNA interaction suggested a stoichiometry of either one (94, 103) or two (73) proteins per RNA. A more complete investigation using gel-filtration chromatography, filter binding, and fluorescence quenching concluded that the preformed dimer of coat protein binds a single R17 translational operator hairpin (81). Under filter-binding conditions, R17 coat protein elutes from an HPLC sizing column at a volume consistent with a dimer, and the RNA-bound coat protein migrates with an apparent molecular weight predicted for a complex of a protein dimer with one RNA. No free protein was detected in mixtures containing two equivalents of protein per RNA, suggesting that all of the protein was capable of binding RNA. RNA-excess assays performed either on nitrocellulose filters or by fluorescence quenching gave the expected stoichiometry of two proteins per RNA. Similar filter-binding assays with the Qβ system gave an apparent stoichiometry of about six proteins per RNA (79). Although there are no sizing column data, it is likely that Qβ resembles R17, with a stoichiometry of two proteins per RNA, and that a fraction of the Qβ protein is inactive in binding RNA. The association constants of four different coat proteins with their respective operators measured at 0°C in a similar buffer are given in Table I. Although the binding conditions are not physiological, it is reassuring that the values are all quite similar, considering the similar functions of these complexes in the cell.

Independent determinations of the association and dissociation rate constants for R17 coat protein binding to a 21-nucleotide hairpin gave $k_{on} = 1.10$ μM^{-1} sec^{-1} and $k_{off} = 0.72$ sec^{-1} (122). The ratio of the rate constants ($k_{on}/k_{off} = 160$ μM^{-1}) agrees quite well with the experimental value of the equilibrium constant ($K_a = 600$ μM^{-1}), as would be expected for a simple binding equilibrium. Since R17 coat protein binds to the 21-mer and intact R17 RNA with similar K_a values, it is likely that the rate constants are also quite similar. The value of k_{on} is considerably less than expected for a diffusion-controlled reaction, presumably reflecting the orientation necessary for correct binding. This contrasts with several DNA binding proteins, in which k_{on} can be much faster than the diffusion-controlled limit as a consequence of a mechanism involving nonspecific binding and sliding to the target site (123). The slow k_{on} and poor non-specific binding suggest that R17 coat protein finds its target as a result of random collision.

Since the nitrocellulose filter-binding assay separates the components of the equilibrium mixture upon filtration and assumes a constant filter-retention efficiency, it was desirable to use an alternate method to determine the affinity. This was done by making use of the fact that the intrinsic fluores-

TABLE I
SOLUTION PROPERTIES OF BACTERIOPHAGE COAT PROTEIN/RNA INTERACTIONS

	R17	fr	GA	Qβ
K_a (μM^{-1})	600	2800	1300	400
ΔG (kcal/mol)	−11.0	−11.9	−11.5	−10.5
ΔH (kcal/mol)	−19.0	−23.0	—	−6.7
ΔS (cal/molK)	−30.0	−40.4	—	+13.7
pH optimum	8.5	8.5	7.0	6.0
Ion-pairs	5	5	3	5
ΔG nonelect. (kcal/mol)	−9.2	−9.3	−8.3	−8.7

cence of R17 coat protein (due to four tyrosines and two tryptophans) is quenched by about 45% upon addition of saturating concentrations of RNA (81). The affinity of the R17 coat protein to a synthetic RNA determined by fluorescence quenching was the same as that measured with the nitrocellulose assay. This result confirms the fact that the filter binding assay accurately reports the RNA–protein equilibrium.

Complexes between the R17 coat protein and certain RNAs can also be detected with a gel-retention assay, since the bound RNA migrates more slowly through the gel than free RNA. Although this method has been used to quantitate DNA–protein interactions (124, 125), it does not appear to report equilibrium constants for the R17 system accurately (126, 127). Complexes with K_a values as high as 600 μM^{-1} are not stable on the gels, and binding affinities determined with tighter binding RNAs do not agree with parallel filter-binding experiments. This lack of a quantitative gel-retention assay may be the result of the propensity of coat protein to aggregate at the high concentrations that occur as the coat protein/RNA complex enters the gel. Another possibility is that the small size of the complex limits stabilizing cage effects within the gel matrix, resulting in dissociation of the complex during electrophoresis (124, 125).

A non-physiological assay for the binding of R17 coat protein to its operator in vivo has been developed (128; J. M. Gott, unpublished). The assay utilizes two compatible plasmids, one expressing coat protein, the other producing β-galactosidase from the replicase initiation site. When present in the same cell, coat protein expression results in a 90% reduction in β-galactosidase levels, indicating that translational repression occurs. When variants of the R17 translational operator are placed upstream from the lacZ gene, repression of β-galactosidase correlates with the in vitro affinity of the operators for coat protein. This assay can be used as a screening system for coat protein mutants that can bind the MS2 hairpin, or to locate mutants that can restore binding to hairpin variants of low affinity.

B. Solution Properties

The solution properties of several bacteriophage coat protein/RNA interactions determined by nitrocellulose filter-binding assays are similar, but not identical (79, 98, 122; L. Wilhelm, unpublished) (Table I). All four systems tested show a fairly broad, bell-shaped pH dependence of K_a. The differing pH optima suggest that the pK_a's of the titratable groups involved in binding are different in each case. Poor binding at the extremes of pH can also be the result of titration of nucleotide functional groups resulting in an altered RNA structure.

The temperature dependence of K_a allowed the calculation of ΔH and ΔS for three different coat protein/RNA interactions. A substantial decrease in affinity with temperature is observed in the R17 and fr systems. The favorable enthalpy of the interactions is offset by an unfavorable entropy. In contrast, Qβ shows a much smaller favorable enthalpy and a favorable entropy. These results suggest that the interactions involved in binding are quite different, although they might also be a reflection of differences in the unbound states of either protein or RNA.

The effect of ions on RNA binding has been extensively tested in the R17 system (122). No detectable difference in affinity is seen among potassium, sodium, lithium, or ammonium cations. Anion effects are relatively large, however, with the K_a's at a given concentration decreasing approximately 50-fold in the order $CH_3CO_2^- > Cl^- > Br^- > NO_3^- > SCN^- > I^-$. These data can be explained by the differing roles that cations and anions may play in the interaction. The cations tested are thought to bind equally well to the hairpin, while anions are thought to bind differentially to the coat protein. The nitrocellulose filter-binding assay is quite sensitive to the divalent cation concentration. The absence of Mg^{2+} causes variable retention efficiency in the plateau region of the binding curve, making an estimate of the K_a difficult, while high concentrations inhibit binding. The same behavior is observed when Mg^{2+} is replaced by Ca^{2+} or Cu^{2+}.

Both electrostatic and nonelectrostatic interactions contribute to complex formation. In all of the coat protein/RNA interactions, the K_a decreases with increasing ionic strength, indicating that salt titrates electrostatic contacts between the protein and the RNA. Record *et al.* have developed a quantitative analysis of the ionic strength dependence of K_a for DNA–protein interactions based on ion displacement (129). Because application of this analysis to RNA–protein interactions requires several untested assumptions, the number of ion-pairs determined is considered to be an upper limit. The R17, fr, and Qβ interactions contain a maximum of five ion-pairs, while the GA interaction contains a maximum of three ion-pairs. It has been estimated that at 1 M salt, each lysine-phosphate type ion-pair contributes about $+0.2$ kcal/mol (130). Using this estimate, the number of ion-pairs, and the ΔG of the interaction at 1 M salt, the nonelectrostatic contribution to the total free energy of the interaction can be calculated (Table I). Thus, although up to five ion-pairs may be formed in each homologous complex, approximately 80% of the binding free energy is the result of non-electrostatic interactions.

IV. Recognition

The anthropomorphic team "recognition" is used to indicate the fact that each phage coat protein binds to its cognate translational operator in preference to the more than 60 other hairpins present in the phage genome (2). A remarkably high specificity is achieved by a combination of tight binding to the operator and quite weak binding to other RNA sequences. Competition experiments reveal that under conditions in which the K_a for the operator is 330 μM^{-1}, binding to non-specific sequences can be estimated to be at least six orders of magnitude weaker (103). An important goal is to understand the structural features in the operator responsible for the high affinity of binding and the reason why non-operator sequences bind so poorly.

A useful approach to understanding how recognition is achieved is to measure the affinity of coat protein to nucleotide sequence variants of the binding site. These biochemical analogs of mutagenesis experiments have been performed for several different coat proteins. The most extensive survey involves more than 100 variants of the R17 translational operator (99, 131, 132). Some of the same oligonucleotides were used for the rather similar fr (98) and GA (L. Wilhelm, unpublished) operators. In addition, a complete analysis of the Qβ operator has been reported (79). The binding properties of most variant RNAs can be divided into two classes. Either the variant bound with an affinity close to that of wild type, suggesting that the sequence change did not alter the interaction with the protein, or the variant bound with a K_a several orders of magnitude lower than wild type, suggesting that the interaction was impaired as a result of the sequence change. This large decrease in affinity for incorrect sequences provides additional evidence for the specificity of the interaction and makes interpretation of the data relatively straightforward.

A. A Consensus Structure

It is possible to summarize the structural features necessary for recognition of these four translational operators using "consensus" sequence-structure diagrams, as shown in the second column of Fig. 6. These diagrams not only indicate the nucleotides important for binding, but also illustrate the amount of experimental data used to arrive at the model. Virtually every oligonucleotide that conforms to the consensus structure binds its respective coat protein, while every oligonucleotide that does not conform to the structure is unable to bind. For each coat protein, several RNAs were prepared in which many of the residues were changed simultaneously (Fig. 6). Consistent with the model, these "weirdmers" bind coat protein normally.

A major conclusion of the experiments with variants is that the secondary structure of the RNA hairpin is an essential component of the recognition process. While the identity of a base-pair is generally not important for binding, mutations that disrupt base-pairs bind poorly. This conclusion is underscored by considering three examples of R17 binding sites that fit the consensus yet bind coat protein poorly (Fig. 7). In one, an equally stable conformation that would not bind coat protein may exist. Alternatively, since all of the base-pairs are A·U pairs, the hairpin may not be sufficiently stable

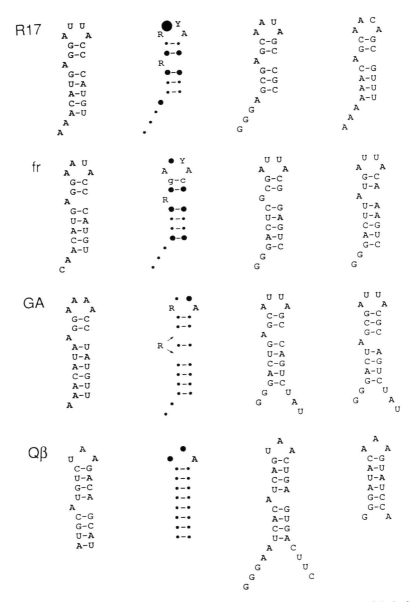

FIG. 6. Consensus diagrams for coat protein binding sites. Binding sites, models for binding sites, and two "weirdmers" (left to right) of the R17, fr, GA, and Qβ coat proteins. Dots represent positions that can be changed without altering the K_a, the size of the dot corresponding to the number of mutations that were tested at that position. When the dot is in a base-pair, both residues must be changed to maintain the integrity of the pair. R and Y represent positions that must be a purine or pyrimidine, respectively. Untested positions are indicated by lower-case letters; extra nucleotides are not permitted in the loop.

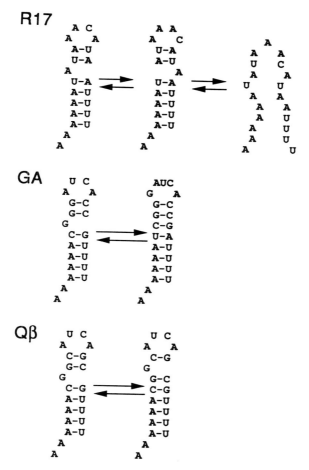

FIG. 7. R17 hairpin variants that bind coat protein poorly. Possible alternative conformations are shown.

to permit tight binding. In the second, a more stable alternate conformation prevents the correct structure from forming and abolishes binding. In the third, the presence of a G·C pair adjacent to the bulged G permits the formation of an alternative conformation that would not be expected to bind protein. If the two conformations can interconvert during the experiment, a lower K_a would be expected.

The availability of a consensus binding site for the phage coat proteins makes it possible to search RNA sequences for additional potential binding sites. While the sites differ from typical recognition sites for DNA binding proteins, due to considerable potential sequence variation in the base-paired residues, it is still possible to analyze the sites in terms of their information content and to develop search programs (133). Based on the consensus models, one would expect the coat protein binding sites to appear in a random sequence from one in every 33,000 nucleotides for R17 to one in every 130,000 nucleotides for Qβ. A search of the 3600-nucleotide MS2 plus and minus strands located an additional potential R17 coat protein binding site near the 5' end of the maturation protein gene (132). Similarly, an additional Qβ coat protein binding site in the plus strand and two in the minus strand of Qβ RNA were found (79). It is not known whether these additional sites have biological relevance.

B. "Bulged" Adenosine

Analysis of mutations of the bulged adenosine residue illustrates the complexities encountered in interpretation of binding data as well as the idiosyncratic binding properties of the different coat proteins. A bulged adenosine appears in all of the phage coat protein binding sites, as well as in the binding sites of several E. coli ribosomal proteins on 5-S (134) and 16-S (135) rRNA. This has led to the hypothesis that this structural motif is important in the recognition of RNA by proteins (134), either by providing nucleotide functional groups in a favorable configuration, or by uniquely affecting the structure or stability of the RNA helix. However, this generalization is not supported by the observation that mutations in and around the bulged adenosine residue affect protein binding very differently in the three systems in which it has been studied.

Data relevant to the bulged adenosine for R17, GA, and Qβ coat proteins are summarized in Fig. 8. In each case, K_a values are normalized to the corresponding wild-type value to aid comparison. For R17 coat protein, it is clear that a bulged purine at position -10 is essential for binding (99). If the bulged adenosine is deleted or if its position is changed, no binding is observed. As shown in Fig. 7, alternative conformations that disrupt the bulge show lower K_a's. Experiments with a number of modified adenosine residues fail to clearly identify any functional group on the purine ring that is responsible for the specificity, while purines with bulky substituents generally reduce binding (97). The interpretation of these experiments is complicated by the fact that changing the structure of the bulged nucleotide is likely to affect the ability of the nucleotide to intercalate and may alter the degree to which the helix is distorted by the intercalation.

Despite a very similar operator structure, the GA coat protein complex shows a different dependence on the bulged adenosine residue (L. Wilhelm, unpublished). While a bulged purine is essential for GA coat protein binding, it can be located at *either* of two positions. This clear contrast with R17

R17 REQUIRES THE BULGE AT -10

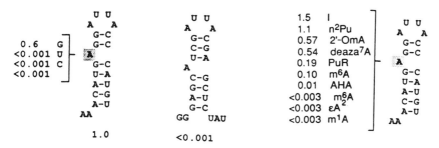

GA IS LESS PARTICULAR

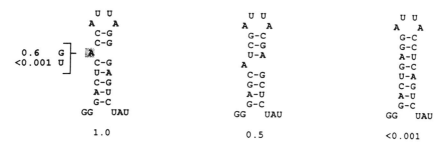

Qβ DOES NOT REQUIRE A BULGED NUCLEOTIDE

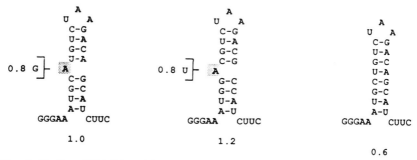

FIG. 8. Binding of R17, GA, and Qβ coat proteins to bulge variants. The K_a for each variant is normalized to that of the wild-type hairpin for each phage coat protein. I, Inosine; n^2Pu, 2-aminopurine ribonucleoside; 2'-OmA, 2'-O-methyladenosine; deaza^{7}A, 7-deazaadenosine; PuR, purine ribonucleoside; m^6A, 6-methyladenosine; AHA, N^6-(6-aminohexyl)adenosine; m_2^6A, 6,6-dimethyladenosine; εA, ε-adenosine; m^1A, 1-methyladenosine.

coat protein is best seen by considering the oligomer with a bulged adenosine one position below the normal one (Fig. 8). GA coat protein can bind
this oligomer, whereas R17 coat protein cannot. This apparent indifference
to the position of the bulged nucleotide is striking, since the structure of the
two RNAs with bulges in different positions would be expected to be very
different.

Data on variants of the Qβ coat protein binding site reveal that although
a bulged adenosine appears in the native site, it is not needed for normal
binding (79). It can be mutated to a pyrimidine or deleted entirely without
altering the K_a. These results underscore the idiosyncratic nature of these
closely related RNA binding proteins and indicate that the bulged adenosine
is not necessarily a general protein recognition motif.

C. A Covalent Bond?

A number of experiments led to the proposal of a transient covalent
complex between Cys-46 of R17 and fr coat proteins and position −5 of their
operators (131). While the evidence is incomplete and contradictory, it is
worthwhile to review it to illustrate the difficulties of using solution experiments to establish a structural fact. The data for R17 (99), fr (98), and GA (L.
Wilhelm, unpublished) coat protein binding to variants at position −5 are
summarized in Fig. 9. R17 and fr coat proteins show a preference for
pyrimidines at this position and have a nearly 100-fold higher affinity to the
unnatural C_{-5} variant than to the wild-type U_{-5} variant. Strikingly, the
rather similar GA coat protein shows little preference for specific nucleotides
at position −5. The C_{-5} variant is the only example of a tighter binding
variant among more than 100 RNA fragments tested in the R17 system.

No tight binding variants were found in the Qβ system. The fact that a
tighter interaction is possible emphasizes the point that the K_a for the RNA–
protein interaction has not evolved to be the highest possible value, but

N	R17	fr	GA	R17 Ala-46
U	1.0	1.0	1.0	1.0
C	52.	72.	1.2	1.5
A	0.01	0.007	0.5	0.13
G	0.07			<0.001

```
        U  N
      A    A
        G-C
        C-G
      A
        G-C
        U-A
        C-G
        A-U
        G-C
      G
    G
```

FIG. 9. Binding to −5 variants. RNA hairpins with U, C, A, or G at position −5 (N, shaded
box) were tested for binding to the R17, fr, and GA phage coat proteins and to the Ala-46 mutant
of R17 coat protein. K_a values are relative to that for the U_{-5} hairpin for each coat protein.

rather to be the optimum value for its regulatory function. If a cytidine appeared at -5 in R17 phage, the replicase gene would be shut off prematurely in the infectious cycle. A careful analysis of R17 coat protein binding to the C_{-5} variant (127) indicates that while the dissociation rate constant is slower, the general properties of the interaction closely resemble those of the U_{-5} hairpin, suggesting that the increased K_a is the result of a local change in the protein–RNA contact.

A possible explanation for the unusually high affinity of the C_{-5} variant comes from work by Schimmel and co-workers on the interaction of *E. coli* tRNA^{Ala} and alanyl-tRNA synthetase (ARS). On the basis of experiments showing that the synthetase catalyzes the exchange of a proton from water to the carbon-5 position of U_8, they proposed that a transient "Michael adduct" forms between a nucleophile on the protein (probably a cysteine) and carbon-6 of U_8 (136) (Fig. 10). Although subsequent protonation at carbon-5 would be expected to be reversible when the enzyme releases the RNA, tritium exchange was explained by the occasional loss of stereospecificity at that step. The first step of this mechanism is the same as that established for thymidylate synthase (137) and related enzymes. In thymidylate synthase, formation of the covalent-nucleotide adduct creates a delocalized negative charge, allowing attack on the methyl group of tetrahydrofolate to make thymidylate. This mechanism is also believed to be used by a number of nucleic acid modifying enzymes, including DNA (Cyt-5-) methyltransferase (138), tRNA (Ura-5-) methyltransferase (139), tRNA Ψ synthetase (140), dUMP hydroxymethylase (141), and dCMP hydroxymethylase (142). The only difference for the proposed adduct of Ala-tRNA synthetase is that no chemical reaction occurs and the Michael addition only assists in binding. The amount that the adduct would contribute to the binding would depend on the equilibria shown in Fig. 10, which, in turn, would depend on the local environment of the uridine when bound to the protein.

The postulate that a Michael adduct forms between R17 coat protein and position -5 of the RNA hairpin has several attractive features. Most importantly, it would provide a simple explanation for the tighter binding of the C_{-5} variant. Cytidine is more reactive to attack at carbon-6 than uridine, so the equilibrium of the first step in Fig. 10 would be shifted to the right,

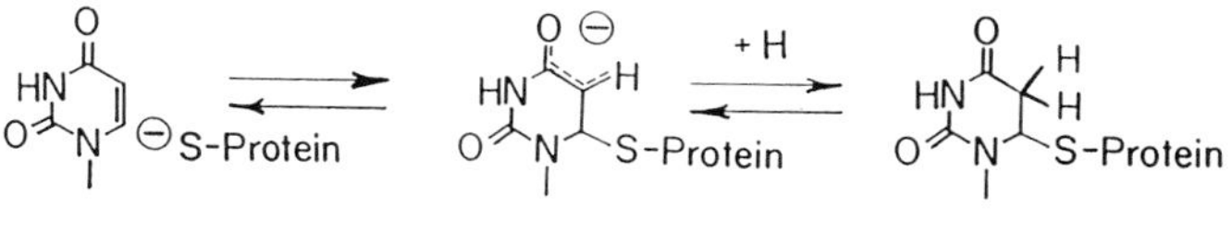

FIG. 10. Michael addition reaction. Nucleophilic attack by a protein sulfhydryl at carbon-6 of the pyrimidine (step 1) yields a covalent intermediate with a delocalized negative charge. A possible subsequent protonation is indicated by the second step.

thereby increasing K_a. In addition, it is known that chemical modification of Cys-46 (but not Cys-101) of MS2 coat protein eliminates RNA binding (*143*), suggesting the sulfur of Cys-46 as a possible nucleophile.

Experiments to provide support for a Michael adduct between R17 coat protein and RNA have either been inconclusive or have indicated that no Michael adduct forms. Complexes formed in D_2O between R17 coat protein and RNA containing either uridine or cytidine at position -5 do not dissociate more slowly than complexes formed in H_2O (*127*). Since a significant isotope effect is expected for the dissociation of a C–D bond, this rules out protonation as the rate-limiting step. However, if binding is rate-limiting or no protonation occurs, the same experimental result would be observed. Unlike ARS, no detectable tritium exchange is observed from a complex made with an RNA specifically labeled with [5-^{3}H]uridine at position -5 (*144*). However, this would also be the expected result if no protonation occurs or if it is entirely stereospecific.

The introduction of an electron-withdrawing group, such as fluorine or bromine, at the carbon-5 of a pyrimidine undergoing a Michael addition reaction greatly favors the equilibrium of the first step (*145*). Indeed, when high concentrations of 5-halogenated pyrimidine nucleosides and nucleotides are incubated with R17 coat protein, the protein is inactivated (*146*). Since similar rates of inactivation of ARS by 5-bromouridine (5BrU) are reported (*147*) and no inactivation of R17 coat protein is observed with the corresponding halogenated deoxynucleotides, it was postulated that inhibition is the result of the nucleotide specifically attaching to the Michael addition site. However, analysis of the inactivated protein does not reveal any attached nucleotide or deribosylated 5BrU as reported for ARS (*148*), and instead shows the formation of an intramolecular disulfide between Cys-46 and Cys-101 (G. Hillebrand, unpublished). This is consistent with the fact that dithiothreitol can reverse 5BrU-inactivation of the coat protein. Although schemes for the formation of the disulfide from a Michael adduct intermediate can be proposed, other explanations for the oxidation of R17 coat protein are equally possible (*149*). Therefore, the 5BrU-inactivation data cannot be used to establish the formation of a Michael adduct. Experiments using RNA containing a unique 5BrU or 5-fluorouracil (5FU) at position -5 have also been inconclusive. While the 5BrU RNA binds tighter than the U_{-5} hairpin, it may be the result of increased hydrophobicity of the bromine, as the 5FU RNA binds with the same K_a as the U_{-5} hairpin (*144*).

The postulated role of Cys-46 as the relevant nucleophile in the potential Michael addition reaction has recently been tested using site-directed mutagenesis of MS2 coat protein. Since Cys-46 can be replaced by a number of other amino acids without greatly affecting the ability of the protein to repress the wild-type operator *in vivo* (*128*), it is clear that the amino acid is not essential for the interaction. Presumably, the bulky modification re-agents used to establish the requirement for Cys-46 (143) either disrupted the structure of the protein or sterically blocked RNA binding. However, *in vitro* experiments with the ala-46 mutant suggest that Cys-46 is important for the specificity of the interaction (J. M. Gott, unpublished). The Ala-46 protein binds the wild-type operator with an affinity similar to that of the wild-type protein. However, the Ala-46 protein does not bind to operator containing C_{-5} any tighter than the wild-type sequence, and shows a re-duced preference for pyrimidines (Fig. 9). In fact, the Ala-46 MS2 coat protein shows a binding specificity for mutations at position -5 that is sim-ilar to GA coat protein, which also has an alanine at position 46. One possible interpretation of these results is that the Michael adduct does form between Cys-46 of MS2 coat protein and the pyrimidine at -5, but the contact only contributes to the affinity of the interaction when the RNA contains a cytidine. While other interpretations remain possible, the data clearly sug-gest that Cys-46 must be in close proximity to the nucleotide at position -5.

D. How Recognition Works

All of the data suggest that the recognition of the operator hairpin by coat protein is achieved in a manner quite similar to that in which a protein is recognized by another protein. The sequence of the RNA defines a precise tertiary structure required for contact with the protein. Given the structural requirements for binding, it is likely that extensive contact occurs between the surfaces of the two macromolecules involving both the nucleotides and the sugar–phosphate backbone of the RNA. Other RNA sequences do not bind because their three-dimensional shape is different, resulting in the loss of correct contacts and the introduction of potential contacts that sterically hinder association.

Both the coat protein and the RNA may alter their conformation upon complex formation. Unlike tRNA^{Gln}, in which a base-pair is disrupted upon synthetase binding (150), the hairpin secondary structure is believed to re-main intact upon protein binding (94). However, changes in the conforma-tion of the single-stranded residues may occur. A more extensive change in the coat protein structure is suggested by an increased propensity for the coat protein to aggregate when RNA is bound (83, 86, 151, 152).

The absence of a clear sequence requirement for the operator residues involved in base-pairs was anticipated by nucleotide sequence comparisons of tRNA isoacceptors and rRNAs. As discussed in Section VI, similar results have been found for a variety of other RNA binding proteins. Nucleotide-specific contacts between protein and RNA are generally made with the single-stranded nucleotides, and a major role of the base-pairs is to maintain the correct spatial orientation of the essential single-stranded nucleotides.

This preference for single-stranded residues by RNA binding proteins is usually explained by the difficulty of recognizing nucleotide functional groups in an A-form RNA helix, due to the depth of the major groove and the difficulty of distinguishing base-pairs in the minor groove (153). However, several tRNA synthetases require specific base-pairs (154–156). In the co-crystal between tRNA^{Gln} and glutamyl-tRNA synthetase this is achieved by a contact in the minor groove (150).

It is important to point out that the essential nucleotides in the coat protein binding site identified by mutation experiments do not necessarily correspond to sites of direct protein contact. Some single-stranded residues may be part of a more complex folding of the hairpin that is altered when the residues are changed. For example, the essential R_{-7} and A_{-4} residues in the R17 site may interact with one another to form a non-Watson–Crick pair instead of binding directly to the protein. Formation of this pair could constrain the backbone of the RNA in such a way as to promote binding. Similarly, the essential bulged purine in the R17 site may only be required to bend the RNA helix in a configuration necessary for binding. Thus, recognition could be primarily the result of the protein contacting the phosphodiester backbone, which is constrained in a particular configuration by the sequence. Indeed, studies using phosphorothioate-substituted RNAs have identified four particular phosphates in the R17 operator as important for protein binding (157).

V. Phage Assembly, Encapsidation, and Cooperative Binding

It is important to distinguish between phage assembly and encapsidation of RNA by phage coat protein. Phage *assembly* produces infectious particles and involves both coat protein and maturation protein. Assembly is a highly specific process, since mixed infections of Qβ and MS2 do not produce particles with mixed coat proteins or non-homologous RNAs (45). Assembly is closely integrated with replication and translation events and therefore is relatively inefficient *in vitro* (43). In contrast, *encapsidation* (the formation of complex II) is an efficient process that occurs when high concentrations of coat protein are mixed with RNA. The presence of RNA results in fewer abnormal particles and stimulates the rate of aggregation of coat protein at lower protein concentrations, and under a wider range of conditions than in its absence (46, 86, 151). Encapsidation can also occur inside cells that overproduce coat protein (J. M. Gott, unpublished). The encapsidation reaction is a co-condensation in which the coat protein dimers polymerize as the RNA compacts (46). RNA cannot enter a preformed protein shell (83, 158). As would be expected from the biological role of these proteins, the encapsidation reaction is highly cooperative, with no discernible intermediates (46).

Although encapsidation has been extensively studied as a model for the assembly process, the reaction is much less specific than assembly for the sequence of the RNA in the reaction. Capsid formation with fr coat protein is nearly as efficient with Qβ RNA, poly(U), or even polyvinyl sulfate as it is with homologous fr RNA (46). Presumably, the common polyanionic character of these polymers is responsible for neutralizing positively charged aminoacid side-chains on the coat protein. Since one would expect the initiation step to be limiting in the reaction, it is not surprising that longer non-specific RNAs are more effective than shorter ones in promoting capsid formation (152).

While non-specific RNA sequences stimulate capsid formation, there is clear evidence that the operator is even more effective. Stoichiometric amounts of a 20-nucleotide binding site stimulate capsid formation at a lower coat protein concentration than an equivalent amount of oligo(A) (152). The resulting "operator capsid" contains 90 copies of the operator bound to the 90 coat protein dimers in the capsid. Experiments with variants of the RNA binding site show that a correlation is observed between the K_a for the RNA–protein interaction and the protein concentrations required for encapsidation. The relative importance of the operator sequence in the encapsidation reaction decreases as the length of the attached non-specific RNA increases. The presence of the R17 operator in a 1.1-kb fragment of β-galactosidase sequence gives it an advantage over an identical RNA without the operator in a competitive encapsidation reaction. On the other hand, the 3.6-kb R17 RNA is no more effective at encapsidation of R17 coat protein than the 4.2-kb Qβ RNA, which lacks the R17 operator. Presumably, as the number of non-specific sites increases, the relatively small advantage of the operator sequence becomes insignificant.

Despite the relative lack of importance of the operator in the encapsidation reaction, it is likely to play an important role in phage assembly. This is a consequence of the fact that while encapsidation assays employ a constant high level of coat protein, the coat protein concentration increases gradually during assembly. Early in infection, when the coat protein concentration is low, protein binds to the high-affinity operator site in preference to the weaker non-specific sites. As coat protein concentrations increase later in infection, assembly continues around the nucleation site at the operator. This provides an explanation for the specificity of assembly. Indeed, when complex I is first formed with ^{3}H-labeled MS2 coat protein, the radioactivity can only be chased into capsids with MS2 coat protein, not Qβ coat protein (159).

Each coat protein monomer in the phage capsid makes extensive contact with surrounding monomers. The icosahedral, $T = 3$ symmetry requires three different surfaces of interaction along the 2-fold, 5-fold, and quasi-3-fold axes of symmetry. The energy derived from these extensive protein–protein contacts accounts for the cooperativity seen in the assembly process. In an attempt to measure the amount of cooperativity of a single protein–protein interaction, an RNA containing two operator sites was constructed (160). Two coat protein dimers can bind such an RNA at protein concentrations too low to permit complex II formation. This system therefore represents a model intermediate in the assembly reaction. It is unknown which protein interfaces interact, but clear cooperativity is observed using a nitrocellulose filter-binding assay. Cooperative free energies as high as −5.1 kcal/mol are observed, depending on the buffer conditions. In general, the cooperativity is greatest under conditions of low pH and high salt, conditions that favor RNA phage (86, 151) and plant viral (161–163) capsid assembly.

VI. Hairpin Binding Proteins

The bacteriophage operators provided early examples of protein binding sites on high-molecular-weight RNA molecules. At the time, it was considered striking that the recognition sequence could be folded into a hairpin. The subsequent definition of RNA binding sites of a substantial number of other proteins made it clear that hairpins often appear in recognition sites. Some of the better-characterized examples of hairpin binding proteins are listed in Table II, and the corresponding RNA secondary structures are depicted in Fig. 11. A wide range of systems is represented, including several other translational operators, a transcriptional regulatory element, several structural protein binding sites, a site of specific nuclease attachment, and a region defining mRNA stability.

For many of these systems, experiments defining the sequence requirements for binding have been performed using either an isolated RNA fragment or a site embedded in a longer RNA. It is clear that, like the coat proteins, the different systems show highly idiosyncratic rules for binding. However, in every case tested, the hairpin secondary structure must be maintained for binding, and the sequence specificity resides primarily in a subset of the single-stranded residues. For example, base-pairs have been replaced by other base-pairs in the ribosomal protein operators (165, 187), the iron-responsive element (IRE) (183b), the binding site of p57 (184), and the target site of α-sarcin (175) without affecting binding by their respective proteins. Transplantation experiments using various IREs also suggest that base-pair changes in the stem do not affect iron regulation *in vivo* (181). In contrast, changes in one or more of the single-stranded residues in the L10 operator (187), α-sarcin hairpin (175), or IRE (180, 182) reduce or eliminate

TABLE II
SELECTED EXAMPLES OF HAIRPIN BINDING PROTEINS[a]

Protein	Organism	Location of hairpin	Function	References
Ribosomal protein L1	E. coli	mRNA leader, L11 operon	Translational repression	164, 165
HIV tat	Human retrovirus	HIV mRNA	Transcriptional activation	166–170
70K protein	Mammals	U1 snRNA	snRNP assembly	171–173
α Sarcin	Fungus	23-S, 25-S and 28-S rRNAs	Ribonuclease	174, 175
Ribosomal protein L4	E. coli	mRNA leder, S10 operon	Transcriptional and translational repression	176–178
IRE binding protein	Mammals	Ferritin mRNA	Translational repression, mRNA stability	179–183b
p57	Mammals	mRNA leader, encephalo-myocarditis virus	Cap-independent translation	184
Ribosomal protein L10	E. coli	mRNA leader, rplJ operon	Translational repression	185–187

[a]HIV tat, Human immunodeficiency virus *trans*-activator; IRE, iron-responsive element; snRNP, small nuclear ribonucleoprotein particles.

binding. Likewise, an extensive mutagenic analysis of the human immunodeficiency virus *tar* site of transcriptional activation (*167–170a*) results in a recognition pattern reminiscent of the bacteriophage operators.

Why are RNA hairpins such common structural elements for recognition by proteins? To a certain extent, this question can be answered by noting the frequency with which hairpins occur in RNA structures. However, it is possible to identify at least four reasons that hairpins make particularly good sites for RNA binding. First, the size of an RNA hairpin is appropriate for recognition by an average protein. A typical RNA hairpin with a stem of seven base-pairs and five nucleotides in the loop is approximately $30 \times 20 \times 20$ Å, which is similar in size to a 10-kDa globular protein. Second, RNA hairpins contain enough information to ensure specific recognition within the cell. Since base-pairs are not generally recognized in a sequence-specific fashion, these nucleotides contribute less to the information content of the site. Thus, to ensure similar specificity, an RNA sequence will have to be somewhat longer than a corresponding DNA sequence. If all five nucleotides and seven canonical base-pairs are required for binding, the sample hairpin would be expected to occur once every 1.7×10^4 kb. Third, hairpin struc-

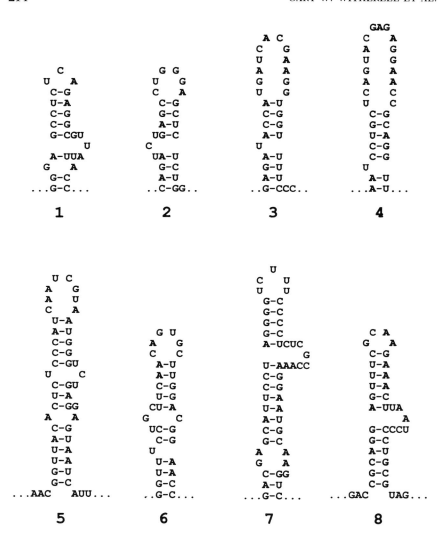

FIG. 11. RNA hairpins as recognition elements. Proposed secondary structures for RNAs bound by (1) ribosomal protein L1, (2) human immunodeficiency virus tat, (3) mammalian 70K protein, (4) α-sarcin, (5) ribosomal protein L4, (6) iron-responsive element binding protein, (7) mammalian p57, and (8) ribosomal protein L10. See Table II for details and references.

ture is dependent on the details of the sequence, thereby providing a unique shape for the protein to bind. Formation of a hairpin constrains the multiple degrees of freedom available to the RNA backbone. Since the RNA–protein complex is likely to have a defined structure, this will reduce the entropy change required upon protein binding. Finally, since a hairpin is formed from a contiguous RNA sequence, it is possible to fold the hairpin immediately after transcription or after its structure has been disrupted during translation. This permits activators, attenuators, or repressors to act on hairpins on nascent RNAs.

Many of the more complex protein binding sites on RNA also contain hairpin elements that are important for recognition. Perhaps the simplest of these is the RNA pseudoknot, where loop residues of a hairpin pair with residues immediately 3′ or 5′ to the stem, forming a second, co-axial helix (188). RNA pseudoknots therefore form a highly constrained RNA backbone and provide a limited number of single-stranded residues for potential protein binding. To date, ribosomal proteins S4 (189) and S15 (190) and the T4 gene-32 protein (191) have been shown to recognize RNA pseudoknots. However, since the pseudoknot has only recently been recognized as a structural motif, more such proteins are likely to emerge.

The tertiary structure of tRNA can be understood as a long RNA hairpin consisting of the acceptor stem and TΨCG hairpin interacting with a "dumbbell" resulting from the co-axial stacking of the anticodon and D hairpins. While a number of tertiary interactions are involved in keeping these two elements in a perpendicular arrangement to give tRNA its characteristic L shape, a number of tRNA enzymes can use simple RNA hairpins as substrates. ARS (192), RNase P (193), and tRNA m^5U_{54}-methyltransferase (194) all show considerable activity with the acceptor-T hairpin. The isolated anticodon stem–loop binds to mRNA-programmed 30-S ribosomes in a manner similar to intact tRNA (195, 196). Also, although other tRNA enzymes inspect a larger portion of the molecule, this may be done with different parts of the protein. For example, one domain of *E. coli* glutamyl-tRNA synthetase contacts the acceptor stem, while another contacts the anticodon loop (150). Thus, even in more complex protein binding sites, principles seen for simple hairpin binding proteins may be relevant.

ACKNOWLEDGMENTS

This work was supported by National Institutes of Health (NIH) grant GM36944 to O.C.U. J.M.G. is an NIH Postdoctoral Fellow (GM12452). We thank Dan Herschlag, Marty Fedor, Sarah Woodson, Jamie Williamson, Gary Stormo, and Craig Tuerk for their comments and Angela Padilla for preparing the manuscript.

REFERENCES

1. J. van Duin, *in* "The Bacteriophages" (R. Calendar, ed.), Vol. 1, p. 117. Plenum, New York, 1988.
2. W. Fiers, *in* "Comprehensive Virology" (H. Fraenkel-Conrat and R. Wagner, eds.), p. 69. Plenum, New York, 1979.
3. N. D. Zinder (ed.), "RNA Phages." CSHLab, Cold Spring Harbor, New York, 1975.
4. C. Vasquez, N. Granboulan and R. M. Franklin, *J. Bact.* **92**, 1779 (1966).
5. D. Casper and A. Klug, *CSHSQB* **27**, 1 (1962).

 6. D. W. Scott, *Virology* **26,** 85 (1965).
 7. I. Watanabe, T. Miyake, T. Sakurai, T. Shiba and T. Ohno, *PNAS* **43,** 204 (1967).
 8. I. Watanabe, T. Nishihara, H. Kaneko, T. Sakurai and S. Osawa, *PNAS* **43,** 210 (1967).
 9. R. G. Krueger, *J. Virol.* **4,** 567 (1969).
10. T. Miyake, I. Haruna, T. Shiba, Y. H. Itoh, K. Yamane and I. Watanabe, *PNAS* **68,** 2022 (1971).
11. K. Furuse, A. Hirashima, H. Harigai, A. Ando, K. Watanabe, K. Kurosawa, Y. Inokuchi and I. Watanabe, *Virology* **97,** 328 (1979).
12. W. Min Jou, G. Haegeman, M. Ysebaert and W. Fiers, *Nature* **237,** 82 (1972).
13. W. Fiers, R. Contreras, F. Duerinck, G. Haegeman, J. Merregaert, W. Min Jou, A. Raeymakers, G. Volckaert, M. Ysebaert, J. Van de Kerckhove, F. Nolf and M. Van Montagu, *Nature* **256,** 273 (1975).
14. W. Fiers, R. Contreras, F. Duerinck, G. Haegeman, D. Iserentant, J. Merregaert, W. Min Jou, F. Molemans, A. Raeymaekers, A. Van den Berghe, G. Volckaert and M. Ysebaert, *Nature* **260,** 500 (1976).
15. Y. Inokuchi, R. Takahashi, T. Hirose, S. Inayama, A. Jacobson and A. Hirashima, *J. Biochem.* **99,** 1169 (1986).
16. P. Mekler, Ph.D. thesis. University of Zurich, Zurich, Switzerland, 1981.
17. Y. Inokuchi, A. B. Jacobson, T. Hirose, S. Inayama and A. Hirashima, *NARes* **16,** 6205 (1988).
18. M. R. Adhin, Ph.D. thesis. University of Leiden, Leiden, The Netherlands, 1989.
19. J. Steitz, *Nature* **224,** 957 (1969).
20. M. R. Adhin, A. Hirashima and J. van Duin, *Virology* **170,** 238 (1989).
21. T. Shiba and T. Miyake, *Nature* **254,** 157 (1975).
22. K. Horiuchi, R. E. Webster and S. Matsuhashi, *Virology* **45,** 429 (1971).
23. A. M. Weiner and K. Weber, *Nature NB* **234,** 206 (1971).
24. A. M. Weiner and K. Weber, *JMB* **80,** 837 (1973).
25. H. Hofstetter, H. J. Monstein and C. Weissmann, *BBA* **374,** 238 (1974).
26. R. I. Kamen, *Nature* **228,** 527 (1970).
27. M. Kondo, R. Gallerani and C. Weissmann, *Nature* **228,** 525 (1970).
28. J. F. Atkins, J. A. Steitz, C. W. Anderson and P. Model, *Cell* **18,** 247 (1979).
29. M. N. Beremand and T. Blumenthal, *Cell* **18,** 257 (1979).
30. P. Model, R. E. Webster and N. D. Zinder, *Cell* **18,** 235 (1979).
31. S. Karnik and M. Billeter, *EMBO J.* **2,** 1521 (1983).
32. R. B. Winter and L. Gold, *Cell* **33,** 877 (1983).
33. C. Weissmann, *FEBS Lett.* **40,** S10 (1974).
34. W. Paranchych, S. K. Ainsworth, A. J. Dick and P. M. Krahn, *Virology* **45,** 615 (1971).
35. J. H. Cramer and R. L. Sinsheimer, *JMB* **62,** 189 (1971).
36. E. Viñuela, I. D. Algranati and S. Ochoa, *EJB* **1,** 3 (1967).
37. T. Blumenthal, T. A. Landers and K. Weber, *PNAS* **69,** 1313 (1972).
38. H. Inouye, Y. Pollack and J. Petre, *EJB* **45,** 109 (1974).
39. J. J. Wahba, M. J. Miller, A. Niveleau, T. A. Landers, G. G. Carmichael, K. Weber, D. A. Hawley and L. I. Slobin, *JBC* **249,** 3314 (1974).
40. M. T. Franz de Fernandez, W. S. Hayward and J. T. August, *JBC* **247,** 824 (1972).
41. R. Kamen, M. Kondo, W. Romer and C. Weissmann, *EJB* **31,** 44 (1972).
42. H. D. Robertson and H. F. Lodish, *PNAS* **67,** 710 (1970).
43. J. W. Roberts and J. A. Steitz, *PNAS* **58,** 1416 (1967).
44. C. M. Ling, P. P. Hung and L. R. Overby, *Bchem* **8,** 4464 (1969).
45. C. M. Ling, P. P. Hung and L. R. Overby, *Virology* **40,** 920 (1970).
46. T. Hohn, *EJB* **8,** 552 (1969).

47. K. Eggen, M. Oeschger and D. Nathans, *BBRC* **28**, 587 (1967).
48. J. Hindley and D. H. Staples, *Nature* **224**, 964 (1969).
49. B. Berkhout and J. van Duin, *NARes* **13**, 6955 (1985).
50. B. Berkhout, B. F. Schmidt, A. van Strien, J. van Boom, J. van Westrenen and J. van Duin, *JMB* **195**, 517 (1987).
51. D. H. Staples, J. Hindley, M. A. Billeter and C. Weissmann, *Nature NB* **234**, 202 (1971).
52. F. Meyer, H. Weber and C. Weissmann, *JMB* **153**, 631 (1981).
53. H. Weber, M. A. Billeter, S. Kahane, C. Weissmann, J. Hindley and A. Porter, *Nature NB* **237**, 166 (1972).
54. D. Kolakofsky and C. Weissmann, *BBA* **246**, 596 (1971).
55. D. Kolakofsky and C. Weissmann, *Nature NB* **231**, 42 (1971).
56. T. Shiba and Y. Suzuki, *BBA* **654**, 249 (1981).
57. H. F. Lodish and N. D. Zinder, *JMB* **19**, 333 (1966).
58. E. Vinuela, I. D. Algranati, G. Feix, D. Garwes, C. Weissmann and S. Ochoa, *BBA* **155**, 558 (1968).
59. D. Nathans, M. P. Oeschger, S. K. Polmar and K. Eggen, *JMB* **39**, 279 (1969).
60. K. Horiuchi and S. Matsuhashi, *Virology* **42**, 49 (1970).
61. A. Palmenberg and P. Kaesberg, *J. Virol.* **11**, 603 (1973).
62. M. R. Capecchi and G. N. Gussin, *Science* **149**, 417 (1965).
63. T. Sugiyama, R. R. Hebert and K. A. Hartman, *JMB* **25**, 455 (1967).
64. P. F. Spahr, M. Farber and R. F. Gesteland, *Nature* **222**, 455 (1969).
65. K. Eggen and D. Nathans, *JMB* **39**, 293 (1969).
66. T. Sugiyama and D. Nakada, *PNAS* **57**, 1744 (1967).
67. T. Sugiyama and D. Nakada, *JMB* **31**, 431 (1968).
68. R. Ward, M. Strand and R. C. Valentine, *BBRC* **30**, 310 (1968).
69. H. F. Lodish, *Nature* **220**, 345 (1968).
70. L. Skogerson, D. Roufa and P. Leder, *PNAS* **68**, 276 (1971).
71. A. Bernardi and P. F. Spahr, *PNAS* **69**, 3033 (1972).
72. H. Weber, *BBA* **418**, 175 (1976).
73. V. Berzin, G. P. Borisova, I. Cielens, V. A. Gribanov, I. Jansone, G. Rosenthal and E. J. Gren, *JMB* **119**, 101 (1978).
74. I. E. Cielens, I. V. Jansone, V. A. Gribanov, I. Vishnevskii, V. M. Berzin and E. J. Gren, *Mol. Biol.* **16**, 1109 (1982).
75. J. A. Steitz, *Nature* **248**, 223 (1974).
76. F. Jacob and J. Monod, *JMB* **3**, 318 (1961).
77. E. Remaut, P. De Waele, A. Marmenout, P. Stanssens and W. Fiers, *EMBO J.* **1**, 205 (1982).
78. R. A. Kastelein, B. Berkhout, G. P. Overbeek and J. van Duin, *Gene* **23**, 245 (1983).
79. G. W. Witherell and O. C. Uhlenbeck, *Bchem* **28**, 71 (1989).
80. P. Shafranski, V. Zagorski, Y. Khrobochek and L. Zagorski, *Mol. Biol.* **9**, 78 (1975).
81. D. Beckett and O. C. Uhlenbeck, *JMB* **204**, 927 (1988).
82. H. Takamatsu and K. Iso, *Nature* **298**, 819 (1982).
83. T. Hohn, *BBRC* **36**, 7 (1969).
84. D. Schubert and H. Frank, *Virology* **43**, 41 (1971).
85. P. J. Oriel and P. H. Cleveland, *Virology* **42**, 1007 (1970).
86. K. S. Matthews and R. D. Cole, *JMB* **65**, 1 (1972).
87. K. S. Matthews and R. D. Cole, *JMB* **65**, 17 (1972).
88. K. Weber and W. Konigsberg, *JBC* **242**, 3563 (1967).
89. K. Weber, *Bchem* **6**, 3144 (1967).
90. W. Konigsberg, T. Maita, J. Katze and K. Weber, *Nature* **227**, 271 (1970).

91. G. J. Thomas, Jr., B. Prescott, P. E. McDonald-Ordzie and K. A. Hartman, *JMB* **102**, 103 (1976).
92. M. G. Rossmann and J. E. Johnson, *ARB* **58**, 533 (1989).
93. K. Valegård, L. Liljas, K. Fridborg and T. Unge, *Nature* **345**, 36 (1990).
94. J. Gralla, J. A. Steitz and D. M. Crothers, *Nature* **248**, 204 (1974).
95. M. Krug, P. L. de Haseth and O. C. Uhlenbeck, *Bchem* **21**, 4713 (1982).
96. J. F. Milligan, D. R. Groebe, G. W. Witherell and O. C. Uhlenbeck, *NARes* **15**, 8783 (1987).
97. H. N. Wu and O. C. Uhlenbeck, *Bchem* **26**, 8221 (1987).
98. H. N. Wu, K. A. Kastelic and O. C. Uhlenbeck, *NARes* **16**, 5055 (1988).
99. J. Carey, P. T. Lowary and O. C. Uhlenbeck, *Bchem* **22**, 4723 (1983).
100. J. Carey, V. Cameron, M. Krug, P. L. de Haseth and O. C. Uhlenbeck, *JBC* **259**, 20 (1984).
101. I. C. Deckman and D. E. Draper, *JMB* **196**, 323 (1987).
102. J. Normanly and J. Abelson, *ARB* **58**, 1029 (1989).
103. J. Carey, V. Cameron, P. L. de Haseth and O. C. Uhlenbeck, *Bchem* **22**, 2601 (1983).
104. C. W. Hilbers, R. G. Schulman, T. Yamane and J. A. Steitz, *Nature* **248**, 225 (1974).
105. D. R. Groebe and O. C. Uhlenbeck, *Bchem* **28**, 742 (1989).
106. H. F. Noller, *ARB* **53**, 119 (1984).
107. D. R. Groebe and O. C. Uhlenbeck, *NARes* **16**, 11725 (1988).
108. C. A. G. Haasnoot, C. W. Hilbers, G. A. van der Marel and J. H. van Boom, *J. Biosci.* **8**, 767 (1985).
109. R. R. Guttell, B. Weiser, C. R. Woese and H. F. Noller, *This Series* **32**, 155 (1985).
110. D. J. Patel, S. A. Kozlowski, L. A. Marky, J. A. Rice, C. Broka, K. Itakura and K. J. Breslauer, *Bchem* **21**, 445 (1982).
111. D. Hare, L. Shapiro and D. J. Patel, *Bchem* **25**, 7456 (1986).
112. S. A. Woodson and D. M. Crothers, *Biopolymers* **28**, 1149 (1989).
113. S. A. Woodson and D. M. Crothers, *Bchem* **27**, 3130 (1988).
114. K. M. Morden, Y. G. Chu, F. H. Martin and I. Tinoco, Jr., *Bchem* **22**, 5557 (1983).
115. L. Joshua-Tor, D. Rabinovich, H. Hope, F. Frolow, E. Appella and J. L. Sussman, *Nature* **334**, 82 (1988).
116. M. Miller, R. W. Harrison, A. Wlodawer, E. Appella and J. L. Sussman, *Nature* **334**, 85 (1988).
117. S. A. White and D. E. Draper, *NARes* **15**, 4049 (1987).
118. S. A. White and D. E. Draper, *Bchem* **28**, 1892 (1989).
119. L. Zagórska, J. Chroboczek and W. Zagórski, *J. Virol.* **15**, 509 (1975).
120. P. Giacomoni, *Biochem. Int.* **2**, 389 (1981).
121. H. S. Strauss, R. R. Burgess and M. T. Record, Jr., *Bchem* **19**, 3504 (1980).
122. J. Carey and O. C. Uhlenbeck, *Bchem* **22**, 2610 (1983).
123. R. B. Winter, O. G. Berg and P. H. von Hippel, *Bchem* **20**, 6960 (1981).
124. M. M. Garner and A. Revzin, *NARes* **9**, 3047 (1981).
125. M. Fried and D. M. Crothers, *NARes* **9**, 6505 (1981).
126. H. N. Wu, Ph.D. thesis. University of Illinois, Champaign, Illinois, 1988.
127. P. T. Lowary and O. C. Uhlenbeck, *NARes* **15**, 10483 (1987).
128. D. S. Peabody, *NARes* **17**, 6017 (1989).
129. M. T. Record, Jr., T. M. Lohman and P. L. de Haseth, *JMB* **107**, 145 (1976).
130. T. M. Lohman, P. L. de Haseth and M. T. Record, Jr., *Bchem* **19**, 3522 (1980).
131. O. C. Uhlenbeck, J. Carey, P. J. Romaniuk, P. T. Lowary and D. Beckett, *J. Biomol. Struct. Dyn.* **1**, 539 (1983).
132. P. J. Romaniuk, P. Lowary, H. N. Wu, G. Stormo and O. C. Uhlenbeck, *Bchem* **26**, 1563 (1987).

133. T. D. Schneider, G. D. Stormo, L. Gold and A. Ehrenfeucht, *JMB* **188**, 415 (1986).
134. D. A. Peattie, S. Douthwaite, R. A. Garrett and H. F. Noller, *PNAS* **78**, 7331 (1981).
135. S. Stern, T. Powers, L. M. Changchien and H. F. Noller, *Science* **244**, 783 (1989).
136. H. J. P. Schoemaker and P. R. Schimmel, *Bchem* **16**, 5454 (1977).
137. A. L. Pogolotti, Jr., and D. V. Santi, *in* "Bioorganic Chemistry" (E. E. van Tamilen, ed.), p. 277. Academic Press, New York, 1977.
138. J. C. Wu and D. V. Santi, *JBC* **262**, 4778 (1987).
139. D. V. Santi and L. W. Hardy, *Bchem* **26**, 8599 (1987).
140. D. V. Santi, Y. Wataya and A. Matsuda, *in* "Proceedings of the International Symposium on Substrate-Induced Irreversible Inhibition of Enzymes" (N. Seiler, M. J. Jung and J. Koch-Weser, eds.), p. 291. Elsevier, Amsterdam, 1978.
141. M. G. Kunitani and D. V. Santi, *Bchem* **19**, 1271 (1980).
142. Y. C. Yeh and G. R. Greenberg, *JBC* **242**, 1307 (1967).
143. V. M. Berzin, A. Y. Tsimanis, E. Y. Gren, W. Zagorski and P. Szalranski, *Bioorg. Khim.* **7**, 894 (1981).
144. J. F. Milligan, Ph.D. thesis. University of Illinois, Champaign, Illinois, 1988.
145. D. Santi and P. Danenberg, *in* "Folates and Pterins" (R. Blakely and S. Benkovic, eds.), Vol. 1, p. 344. Wiley, New York, 1984.
146. P. J. Romaniuk and O. C. Uhlenbeck, *Bchem* **24**, 4239 (1985).
147. R. M. Starzyk, S. W. Koontz and P. Schimmel, *Nature* **298**, 136 (1982).
148. S. W. Koontz and P. R. Schimmel, *JBC* **254**, 12277 (1979).
149. Y. Wataya, K. Negishi and H. Hayatsu, *Bchem* **12**, 3992 (1973).
150. M. A. Rould, J. J. Perona, D. Soll and T. A. Steitz, *Science* **246**, 1135 (1989).
151. T. Hohn, *JMB* **43**, 191 (1969).
152. D. Beckett, H. N. Wu and O. C. Uhlenbeck, *JMB* **204**, 939 (1988).
153. N. R. Pace, *in* "Processing of RNA" (D. Apirion, ed.), p. 2. CRC Press, Boca Raton, Florida, 1984.
154. J. Normanly, R. C. Ogden, S. J. Horvath and J. Abelson, *Nature* **321**, 213 (1986).
155. Y. M. Hou and P. Schimmel, *Nature* **333**, 140 (1988).
156. W. H. McClain and K. Foss, *JMB* **202**, 697 (1988).
157. J. F. Milligan and O. C. Uhlenbeck, *Bchem* **28**, 2849 (1989).
158. R. L. Stavis and J. T. August, *ARB* **39**, 527 (1970).
159. P. P. Hung, C. M. Ling and R. Overby, *Science* **166**, 1638 (1969).
160. G. W. Witherell, H. N. Wu and O. C. Uhlenbeck, *Bchem*, **29** (1990).
161. R. A. Driedonks, P. C. J. Krijgsman and J. E. Mellema, *JMB* **113**, 123 (1977).
162. P. Pfeiffer, M. Herzog and L. Hirth, *Philos. Trans. R. Soc. London, Ser. B* **276**, 99 (1976).
163. K. W. Adolph and P. J. G. Butler, *Philos. Trans. R. Soc. London, Ser. B* **276**, 113 (1976).
164. G. Baughman and M. Nomura, *Cell* **34**, 979 (1983).
165. G. Baughman and M. Nomura, *PNAS* **81**, 5389 (1984).
166. M. A. Muesing, D. H. Smith and D. J. Capon, *Cell* **48**, 691 (1987).
167. S. Feng and E. C. Holland, *Nature* **334**, 165 (1985).
168. M. J. Selby, E. S. Bain, P. A. Lucieo and B. M. Peterlin, *Genes Dev.* **3**, 547 (1989).
169. J. A. Garcia, D. Harrick, E. Soultanakis, F. Wu, R. Mitsuyasu and R. B. Gaynor, *EMBO J.* **8**, 765 (1989).
170. B. Berkhout and K.-T. Jeang, *J. Virol.* **63**, 5501 (1989).
170a. R. A. Marciniak, M. A. Garcia-Blanco and P. A. Sharp, *PNAS* **87**, 3624 (1990).
171. J. R. Patton and T. Pederson, *PNAS* **85**, 747 (1988).
172. C. C. Query, R. C. Bentley and J. D. Keene, *MCBiol* **9**, 4872 (1989).
173. J. Hamm, M. Kazmaier and I. W. Mattaj, *EMBO J.* **6**, 3479 (1979).
174. Y. Endo, Y.-L. Chan, A. Lin, K. Tsurugi and I. G. Wool, *JBC* **263**, 7917 (1988).
175. Y. Endo, A. Glück, Y.-L. Chan, K. Tsurugi and I. G. Wool, in press.

176. J. L. Yates and M. Nomura, *Cell* **21**, 517 (1980).
177. L. P. Freedman, J. M. Zengel, R. H. Archer and L. Lindahl, *PNAS* **84**, 6516 (1987).
178. P. Shen, J. M. Zengel and L. Lindahl, *NARes* **16**, 8905 (1988).
179. M. T. Murray, K. White and H. N. Munro, *PNAS* **84**, 7438 (1987).
180. E. W. Müllner and L. C. Kühn, *Cell* **53**, 815 (1988).
181. J. L. Casey, M. W. Hentze, D. M. Koeller, S. W. Caughman, T. A. Rouault, R. D. Klausner and J. B. Harford, *Science* **240**, 924 (1988).
182. T. A. Rouault, M. W. Hentze, S. W. Caughman, J. B. Harford and R. D. Klausner, *Science* **241**, 1207 (1988).
183. L. F. Dickey, Y.-H. Wang, G. E. Shull, I. A. Wortman III and E. C. Theil, *JBC* **263**, 3071 (1988).
183a. H. A. Barton, R. S. Eisenstein, A. Bomford and H. N. Munro, *JBC* **265**, 7000 (1990).
183b. E. A. Leibold, A. Laudano and Y. Yu, *NARes* **18**, 1819 (1990).
184. S. K. Jang and E. Wimmer, *Genes Devel.* **4**, 1560 (1990).
185. J. L. Yates, D. Dean, W. A. Strycharz and M. Nomura, *Nature* **294**, 190 (1981).
186. T. Christensen, M. Johnsen, N. P. Fiil and J. D. Friesen, *EMBO J.* **3**, 1609 (1984).
187. S. C. Climie and J. D. Friesen, *JMB* **198**, 371 (1987).
188. C. W. A. Pleij, K. Rietveld and L. Borsch, *NARes* **13**, 1717 (1985).
189. C. K. Tang and D. E. Draper, *Cell* **57**, 531 (1989).
190. C. Philippe, C. Portier, M. Mougel, M. Grunberg-Manago, J. P. Ebel, B. Ehresmann and C. Ehresmann, *JMB* **211**, 415 (1990).
191. D. S. McPheeters, G. D. Stormo and L. Gold, *JMB* **201**, 517 (1988).
192. C. Francklyn and P. Schimmel, *Nature* **337**, 478 (1989).
193. W. H. McClain, C. Guerrier-Takada and S. Altman, *Science* **238**, 527 (1987).
194. X. Gu and D. V. Santi, in press.
195. S. J. Rose, P. T. Lowary and O. C. Uhlenbeck, *JMB* **167**, 103 (1983).
196. D. Moazed and H. F. Noller, *Cell* **47**, 985 (1986).

Superoxide Dismutases

WAYNE BEYER,
JAMES IMLAY
AND IRWIN FRIDOVICH[1]

Department of Biochemistry
Duke University Medical Center
Durham, North Carolina 27710

I. Superoxide and Superoxide Dismutases

A. Brief History

Enzymes are usually discovered and subsequently isolated on the basis of their catalytic activities. Physicochemical characterization, which follows isolation, thus lags behind discovery of the activity. In the case of SOD,[2] this sequence of events was reversed. David Keilin had embarked on the isolation of carbonic anhydrase, which he suspected might contain copper. All of the protein fractions obtained from the hemolysate were therefore being assayed both for catalysis of the hydration of CO_2 and for copper content. Given that carbonic anhydrase contains zinc, not copper, it was inevitable

---

[1] To whom correspondence may be addressed.

[2] Superoxide dismutase (EC 1.15.1.1), which catalyzes the conversion of superoxide (O_2^-) to O_2 and H_2O_2. [Eds.]

Progress in Nucleic Acid Research
and Molecular Biology, Vol. 40

that the copper and the catalytic activity should part company. The copper-containing protein, which had been encountered during these fractionations, was isolated on the basis of enrichment for copper. Since it had no known activity, it was named hemocuprein and tentatively assigned the function of copper storage (1). Virtually identical proteins were subsequently isolated from a variety of sources and were given names that reflected their tissue of origin and copper content. Hence, the literature dealing with erythrocuprein, hepatocuprein, cerebrocuprein, and cytocuprein (2–9) burgeoned.

Independent studies of the peculiar oxygen-dependent properties of milk xanthine oxidase led to the realization that this enzyme produces O_2^- as well as H_2O_2. Having an enzymatic source of O_2^-, which was demonstrably responsible for several easily measurable chemical changes, led to the discovery of SOD activity, and this activity guided the isolation of the enzyme from bovine erythrocytes (10, 11). Once the enzyme was in hand, its physicochemical similarities to the cupreins were obvious.

The availability of a spectrophotometric assay for SOD activity and of an activity stain applicable to polyacrylamide gels (12) facilitated the isolation of SODs from a variety of sources. A manganese-containing SOD (Mn-SOD) was rather quickly isolated from Escherichia coli (13) and from chicken liver mitochondria (14), and an iron-containing SOD (Fe-SOD) was isolated from E. coli (15). The history of these events has been described in considerable detail (16–18). These SODs are widely distributed, abundant, and stable, and thus are well-suited to studies of structure, function, and evolution.

B. Dangers of the Substrate O_2^-

The ubiquity and abundance of SODs among aerobes suggest that their substrate, O_2^-, is frequently encountered and potentially damaging. In fact, the barrier to divalent reduction of O_2, which is raised by the spin restriction (19), leaves univalent reduction as the most facile pathway. Although predominant in abiotic O_2 reduction, this univalent free-radical pathway is usually minimized in living cells by enzymes that accomplish two- or four-electron reductions of O_2, without the release of intermediates. Nevertheless, O_2^- is produced in cells during both enzymatic and spontaneous oxidations. Moreover, its rate of production can be markedly increased by photosensitizers in the light, and by viologens, quinones, and arylnitro compounds in the dark. These and related compounds undergo cycles of enzymatic reduction followed by auto-oxidation and thus mediate net O_2^- production. Biological sources of O_2^- have been described (20, 21).

Free radicals are usually reactive, and their reactions with diamagnetic molecules always produce new radicals. We may therefore anticipate the possibility of direct attack of O_2^- on cellular targets, as well as indirect effects due to other radicals engendered by O_2^-. Several $(Fe–S)_n$-containing enzymes appear to be subject to direct attack by O_2^-. Among these is the *E. coli* dihydroxy-acid dehydratase (EC 4.2.1.9), which is on the pathway of biosynthesis of branched-chain amino acids and which is exquisitely sensitive to O_2^- (22, 23). Other enzymes directly inactivated by O_2^- include catalases and peroxidases (24).

Small molecules can also serve as targets for O_2^-, which can initiate and sometimes also propagate free-radical oxidations of sulfite, enediolates, polyphenols, catecholamines, and tetrahydropterins. The ability of O_2^- to act as an oxidant can be markedly augmented by association with cationic centers, such as protons or the metals Mn(II) or V(V). Thus, O_2^- per se does not oxidize NADH, but does so in the presence of Mn(II) or V(V), due to the formation of $Mn(I)O_2$ or $V(IV)O_2$. In the presence of V(V), O_2^- initiates a free-radical chain oxidation of NAD(P)H, which results in the oxidation of many molecules of NAD(P)H per O_2^- introduced (25). Similarly, O_2^- does not directly oxidize polyunsaturated fatty acids, but protonation ($pK_a = 4.7$) yields HO_2, which does so (26).

H_2O_2 is produced by the dismutation of O_2^- and is therefore present whenever O_2^- is being made in aqueous media. This sets the stage for the generation of devastatingly powerful oxidants. Thus, O_2^- can reduce transition metals, such as Fe(III) or Cu(II), whose reduced forms can, in turn, reduce H_2O_2, yielding HO· or metal derivatives of HO·. This process, which is sometimes called the metal-catalyzed Haber–Weiss reaction, can be represented as follows:

$$Fe(III) + O_2^- \; \rightleftharpoons \; Fe(II) + O_2 \tag{a}$$
$$Fe(II) + HOOH \; \rightleftharpoons \; Fe(I)-OOH + H^+ \tag{b}$$
$$Fe(I)-OOH \; \rightleftharpoons \; Fe(II)=O + HO^- \tag{c}$$
$$Fe(II)O + H^+ \; \rightleftharpoons \; Fe(III)-OH \; \rightarrow \; Fe(III) + HO· \tag{d}$$

Since the metal reduced in reaction (a) is reoxidized during reactions (b)–(d), its role is catalytic. This allows low levels of the metal to mediate substantial production of HO·. Indeed, an early report (27) of the production of HO· by an enzymatic source of O_2^- and H_2O_2 failed to recognize the catalytic role of the metal, which was present as an impurity in the phosphate buffer.

HO· and Fe(II)O are extremely reactive and would not survive many collisions with cellular constituents without reacting. This leads to the expectation that HO·, generated in free solution, would not be very damaging because it would expend itself on easily replaced sugar phosphates, amino acids, nucleotides, or metabolic intermediates. However, since the catalytic metals are likely to be bound onto the polyanionic DNA or cell membranes, the HO· or Fe(II)O would be generated adjacent to, and would preferentially attack, these critical targets. This has been called the site-specific Haber–Weiss reaction (28, 29). Metals such as Zn(II), which can compete with Fe(III) or Cu(II) for binding sites, but which cannot participate in redox reactions, should protect. This has been demonstrated (30), as has the anticipated protection by SOD or catalase, or by chelating agents, which would displace the bound metal (31). Desferal, because of its selective affinity for Fe(III), hinders redox cycling of iron and thus prevents this metal from catalyzing HO· production from O_2^- plus H_2O_2 (32). Diethylenetriamine pentaacetic acid (pentetic acid) exerts a similar effect (33).

Metal-catalyzed production of HO· from O_2^- plus H_2O_2 appears to occur *in vivo*. DNA scissions within fibroblasts, caused by H_2O_2, can be prevented by the chelating agents *o*-phenanthroline or α,α′-bipyridyl. Moreover, HO· scavengers, such as thiourea, also protect, whereas inactivation of the intracellular Cu,Zn-SOD with diethyldithiocarbamate augments the DNA damage (34). Similar studies of the effect of H_2O_2 on the viability of hepatocytes established that Desferal, SOD, catalase, and thiourea protect, in accord with the view that HO· generated from O_2^- + H_2O_2 is the lethal species (35).

Mutants of *E. coli* with defects in both SOD genes were hypersensitive to aerobic H_2O_2, even though they contained normal levels of catalases, an indication that O_2^- can augment the damaging effect of H_2O_2 (36). Hydroxylated purines and pyrimidines are among the products of attack on DNA by HO· (37). These products are normally excreted in urine and can be found in both nuclear and mitochondrial DNA (38, 39). Their rate of production appears to be inversely related to life span (40). All of this supports the view that the metal-catalyzed Haber–Weiss reaction occurs *in vivo*. The theoretical basis of this reaction has been considered (41).

C. SODs: Varieties and Distributions

Common selection pressures applied to varied biotas are apt to elicit multiple solutions to the same problem. One need only consider the manifold types of protective coloration, mimicry, and other forms of camouflage evolved in response to the pressures of predation in order to appreciate the validity of this statement. The oxygenation of the earth, by the earliest water-splitting photosynthetic organisms, must have imposed such a selection pressure on a biota composed of anaerobes. It is thus not surprising that we now find more than one type of SOD.

We know of two independently evolved groups of SODs, the Cu,Zn-SODs, on the one hand, and the Mn-SODs/Fe-SODs, on the other. Similar multiplicity is seen with other enzymes providing antioxidative defense. There are catalases based on heme and others based on binuclear clusters of manganese ions, and some lactobacilli are capable of producing one or the other, depending on conditions of growth. There are also peroxidases based on heme and others that contain selenocysteine at the active site.

In some cases, the distribution of SODs provides a clear indication of evolutionary history, while other cases remain enigmatic. Mitochondria contain a Mn-SOD, while the cytosols of eukaryotic cells contain a Cu,Zn-SOD. The mitochondrial Mn-SOD is strikingly homologous to the Mn-SODs/Fe-SODs found in prokaryotes, but bears no resemblance to the cytosolic Cu,Zn-SOD, which supports the idea of an endosymbiotic origin for this organelle (42, 43). Among the enigmas is why a few bacteria contain Cu,Zn-SODs, which are typically found in eukaryotic cytosols. These bacterial Cu,Zn-SODs, usually referred to as bacteriocupreins, do show homology to their eukaryotic counterparts (44), but contain a leader peptide indicative of a periplasmic localization (45). Another puzzle is the occurrence of Fe-SODs in certain plants (46, 47).

1. Cu,Zn-SODs

Although found most often in the cytosols of eukaryotic cells, Cu,Zn-SODs have been identified in, and isolated from, several bacteria, including *Photobacter leiognathi* (48), *Caulobacter crescentis* (49), two pseudomonads (50), and *Paracoccus denitrificans* (51). There is, moreover, a tetrameric, glycosylated Cu,Zn-SOD found in mammalian extracellular fluids (52). Cu,Zn-SODs have been thoroughly reviewed (43, 53–55) and are not described here in further detail.

2. Mn-SODs and Fe-SODs

Mn-SODs and Fe-SODs were first isolated from *E. coli* (13, 15) and have since been found in, and isolated from, a variety of prokaryotes. Table I summarizes the properties of the Mn-SOD and Fe-SOD of *E. coli*. Although most frequently encountered as homodimers with a subunit M_r of ~22,000, some bacterial Mn-SODs (56, 57) and Fe-SODs (58–60) occur as tetramers. Mitochondria contain a homotetrameric Mn-SOD (61–63) with extensive sequence homology to the corresponding bacterial enzymes (42), in keeping with a prokaryotic ancestry and an endosymbiotic origin for this organelle (64).

Anaerobes, or anaerobically grown facultative bacteria, usually contain a Fe-SOD, while aerobic growth is often associated with induction of a Mn-SOD. In spite of extensive sequence homologies, Mn-SODs and Fe-SODs are usually active only when the catalytic site is occupied with the metal found in the native enzyme. Nevertheless, a few species of *Bacteroides* produce a single SOD protein which contains, and is active with, Fe when grown anaerobically and with Mn when grown in the presence of O_2 (65–68).

TABLE I

COMPARISON OF *E. coli* Mn- AND Fe-SODs

Property	Fe-SOD	Mn-SOD
Oligomeric state	Dimeric	Dimeric
Subunit M	21,100	22,900
Number of amino acids	192	205
Isoelectric point	4.45, 4.93	6.64, 6.90
Metal content (per subunit)	0.8–1.2 (Fe)	0.6–0.9 (Mn)
Absorption		
Visible (λmax $[\epsilon]^a$	350 nm (1850 M^{-1}cm^{-1}	470 nm (610 M^{-1}cm^{-1})
UV (λ, [A$^{1\%}$]^b	280 nm (25.4)	282 nm (18.9)
Inhibitors	H_2O_2, N_3^- (~2 mM) 50%	N_3^- (~30 mM) 50%
Specific activity (U/mg)	4200–5000	2800–3800
Stokes radius (Å)	28.5 ± 1.3	29.0 ± 1.7
S^{20} ($\times 10^{-13}$)	3.22 ± 0.3	3.55 ± 0.3
v (partial specific volume)	0.733	0.735

^{a}Based on metal.
^{b}Based on protein.

A few species of plants contain Fe-SODs (69–71). There is, as yet, no adequate explanation for the presence of Cu,Zn-SODs in some bacteria, and of Fe-SODs in a few plants.

D. X-Ray Crystallography of Mn-SODs and Fe-SODs

Mn-SODs from yeast (72), *E. coli* (72), *Thermus thermophilus* (73), and *Bacillus stearothermophilus* (74) have been examined by X-ray crystallography, in the latter two cases to a resolution of 2.4 Å. Studies of the *B. stearothermophilus* Mn-SOD were actually initiated in the mid-1970s (75), but were discontinued because of the report of preliminary studies of the *E. coli* Mn-SOD (72). The latter studies have not yet been carried to fruition, but structural analysis of the *B. stearothermophilus* enzyme was subsequently pursued to 2.4 Å resolution (74). X-ray crystallographic analysis has also been applied to the Fe-SODs from *Thermoplasma acidophilus* (76), *Pseudomonas ovalis* (77), and *E. coli* (78).

The Fe-SODs from *P. ovalis* and *E. coli* exhibit practically identical structures. Crystals of the *P. ovalis* Fe-SOD were unstable in the x-ray beam. This problem was overcome by using the azide or fluoride derivatives. The instability may have been due to radiochemical production of H_2O_2, which is known to inactivate Fe-SODs (79, 80). That Fe-SODs and Mn-SODs also exhibit similar structures might be expected from their sequence homologies (81). Comparison of the tetrameric Mn-SOD from *T. thermophilus* with the dimeric *E. coli* Fe-SOD revealed one metal atom per subunit in comparable binding sites (82). The tetrameric enzyme showed two sets of subunit contacts. One of these corresponded with the dimer interface of the *E. coli* Fe-SOD, while the other involved an inserted peptide segment absent from the *E. coli* Fe-SOD. The conformations of the Mn-SOD/Fe-SOD family of enzymes is unrelated to that of the Cu,Zn-SOD enzyme family (78), as expected from the lack of sequence homology between these families of SODs. The structure of one subunit of the Mn-SOD from *B. stearothermophilus* (74) is shown in Fig. 1.

Fitting amino-acid sequences to electron-density maps allowed detailed structural analysis, which shows that both Mn-SOD (73) and Fe-SOD (81) ligate the metal at the active site through three histidine imidazoles and one

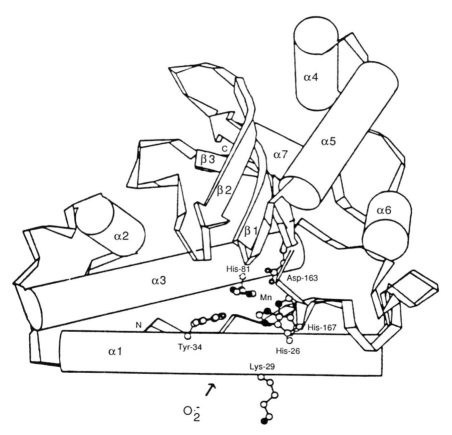

FIG. 1. The *B. stearothermophilus* Mn-SOD monomer. α-Helices are labeled α1–α7 and β-strands β1–β3. The active-site manganese and its ligands are indicated. A probable pathway of approach of the O_2^- ion and the proximity of Tyr-34 and Lys-29 are shown. (Reproduced from 74.)

aspartate carboxylate, as specified in Table II. A liganding water molecule was also evident in the *E. coli* Fe-SOD and the *T. thermophilus* Mn-SOD, but not in the *B. stearothermophilus* Mn-SOD (*74, 81*). The coordination geometry was described as tetrahedral, with distortion toward either a trigonal bipyramid (*73, 81*) or a trigonal pyramid (*74*). It is a curious coincidence that the Zn(II) in the structurally unrelated Cu,Zn-SOD is also ligated to three histidines and one aspartate (*83*).

The active site in Mn-SOD and Fe-SOD is surrounded by hydrophobic residues, including three Tyr, three Trp, and two Phe within 10 Å of the metal center, with extensive aromatic stacking. Mn(III) is potentially a strong oxidant; in water it dismutes to Mn(II) plus MnO_2. The electrodative ligand field and the surrounding shell of hydrophobic residues may serve to stabilize Mn(III) at the active site of Mn-SOD. The importance of the residues in the hydrophobic shell around the active site is supported by their conservation in all Mn-SODs and Fe-SODs for which sequence data are available (*84*). It should be noted that Fe-SODs contain a Tyr at position 76, whereas in Mn-SODs we find a corresponding Phe (*74, 81, 85*).

Fe-SOD and Mn-SOD subunits exhibit a two-domain structure in which one domain contains α-helices while the second is composed of both α-helices and β-sheets. The metal binding site occurs between these two domains. The hinge region exhibits both insertions and deletions (*74*). In the case of the Mn-SOD from *B. stearothermophilus*, each subunit approximates a triangular prism, whose dimensions are $43 \times 53 \times 45$ Å. One domain of this subunit contains a pair of long, antiparallel α-helices, designated α1 and α3 in Fig. 1, which diverge at a 35° angle. A kink in α1, in a histidine-rich

TABLE II

GEOMETRY OF THE MANGANESE-BINDING SITE IN *B. stearothermophilus* Mn-SOD[a]

Bond	Distance (Å)
His-26 ($N\epsilon_2$)-Mn	2.08
His-81 ($N\epsilon_2$)-Mn	2.38
His-167 ($N\epsilon_2$)-Mn	1.94
Asp-163 ($O\delta_1$)-Mn	1.94

Bond	Angle
His-26 ($N\epsilon_2$)-Mn-His-81 ($N\epsilon_2$)	96°
His-26 ($N\epsilon_2$)-Mn-Asp-163 ($O\delta_1$)	88°
His-26 ($N\epsilon_2$)-Mn-His-167 ($N\epsilon_2$)	97°
His-81 ($N\epsilon_2$)-Mn-His-167 ($N\epsilon_2$)	134°
His-81 ($N\epsilon_2$)-Mn-Asp-163 ($O\delta_1$)	92°
His-163 ($N\epsilon_2$)-Mn-His-167 ($N\epsilon_2$)	133°

[a]From *74*.

region, has the effect of positioning a conserved tyrosine residue (Tyr-34) closer to the metal center (73, 74). A two-turn helical segment, designated α2, is found in Mn-SODs, but not in Fe-SODs (73, 74, 81). In the *T. thermophilus* Mn-SOD, α2 supplies residues that stabilize the tetrameric structure. The human and mouse tetrameric Mn-SODs, however, exhibit seven residue deletions in this region. This has led to the suggestion that α2 and the basis of tetramer assembly are species-specific (73, 74).

Both α1 and α3 each contribute one histidine ligand to the metal center, while the second domain provides one histidine and one aspartate. The second domain may be described as a sandwich, with three helices (α4, α5, and α6) on one side, a β-sheet in the middle, and an extended non-helical chain on the other side. The interdomain hinge joins α3 to α4 and follows an unusual path that may constrain the manner of folding (73). Ligation of the metal by residues from both domains allows the metal to provide for both stabilization and catalysis.

The active-site metals are 18 Å apart in the dimeric Mn-SODs/Fe-SODs. There is no main-chain interpenetration across the dimer interface of the dimeric Mn-SOD from *B. stearothermophilus*, but in the corresponding tetrameric enzyme from *T. thermophilus*, Tyr-172 and Glu-168 from one subunit penetrate into the active-site region of the neighboring subunit, perhaps contributing to stability. Table III (74) summarizes intersubunit contacts. *E. coli* Mn-SOD and Fe-SOD must have subtle differences in their dimer contact regions. Thus, removal of the metal leaves the apo-Mn-SOD as a dimer, whereas the apo-Fe-SOD dissociates into subunits (85). The suggestion that insertion of metal into the apoenzymes requires dissociation

TABLE III

MONOMER–MONOMER CONTACTS OBSERVED IN THE *B. stearothermophilus* Mn-SOD[a]

Monomer 1		Monomer 2		
Atom	Residue	Atom	Residue	Distance (Å)
$N\epsilon_2$	His-30[b]	OH	Try-170[b]	2.66
$O\gamma$	Ser-128[b]	$O\gamma$	Ser-128[b]	3.06
$O\epsilon_1$	Glu-166[b]	N	His-167[c]	2.86
$O\epsilon_2$	Glu-166[b]	$N\delta_1$	His-167[c]	3.02
N	His-167[c]	$O\epsilon_1$	Glu-166[b]	2.86
$N\delta_1$	His-167[c]	$O\epsilon_2$	Glu-166[b]	3.02
OH	Tyr-170[b]	$N\epsilon_2$	His-30[b]	2.66
	Phe-126		Trp-165[b]	
	Trp-165[b]		Phe-126	

[a] From 74.

[b] Invariant residue.

[c] Manganese ligand.

of subunits (86) can be questioned on the grounds that native, dimeric apo-
Mn-SOD can be reconstituted by the addition of Mn(II) salts in the absence
of chaotropic agents (87).

A tyrosine residue (Tyr-36 in the *T. thermophilus* Fe-SOD or Tyr-34 in
the *B. stearothermophilus* Mn-SOD) places a phenolic hydroxyl within 5 Å
of the metal center (73, 74). Ionization of this phenolic hydroxyl may account
for the activity-limiting ionization ($pK_a \approx 9.5$) responsible for a decline in
activity with increasing pH (88–92). Electrostatic facilitation of the dismutation reaction has been demonstrated (93, 94) and may be provided by the
preponderance of cationic residues around the entrance to the active-site
pocket.

The effects of dithionite reduction of crystals of Mn-SOD (95) and of
ascorbate reduction of crystals of Fe-SOD (95) were examined by difference
Fourier methods. No significant conformational changes in the active-site
region were noted upon reduction. It is possible that crystal lattice forces
constrained changes which might otherwise take place upon reduction in
free solution (95).

E. Evolutionary Relationships

Figure 2 presents sequence data for Mn-SODs and Fe-SODs from a
variety of sources. Much homology, suggesting a common evolutionary origin, is evident. Approximately 28 residues are invariant throughout, and
many instances of conservative replacements at other positions indicate retention of conformation. Table IV summarizes the degrees of homology between pairs of Mn-SODs and Fe-SODs. The amino-terminal regions are
particularly highly conserved, 21% of the invariant residues being found in
residues 1–20. Possible explanations for this concentration of conserved residues in the amino-terminal region have been offered (74, 96). In spite of
considerable sequence homology, the Mn-SOD and Fe-SOD of *E. coli* are
not immunologically cross-reactive (97, 98), presumably because epitopes
involve the least conserved surface residues.

Most Fe-SODs are active only with iron at the active site and most Mn-
SODs are correspondingly activity-specific for manganese, even though
other metals can compete for occupancy of the active site (101). This specificity must depend on subtle structural differences (74, 96, 99, 100). The *Bacteroides* enzyme, which is active with either Mn or Fe at the active site (65–
68), may hold the key to this puzzle and should be carefully studied.

Increasing ionic strength decreases the activities of all SODs, in keeping
with an electrostatically facilitated catalytic process (93, 94, 102–104).
Chemical modifications that eliminate positive charges in the active-site
region also diminish activity (93, 94, 105). Numerous cationic residues are
clustered near the entrance to the active-site pocket, including histidines 17,

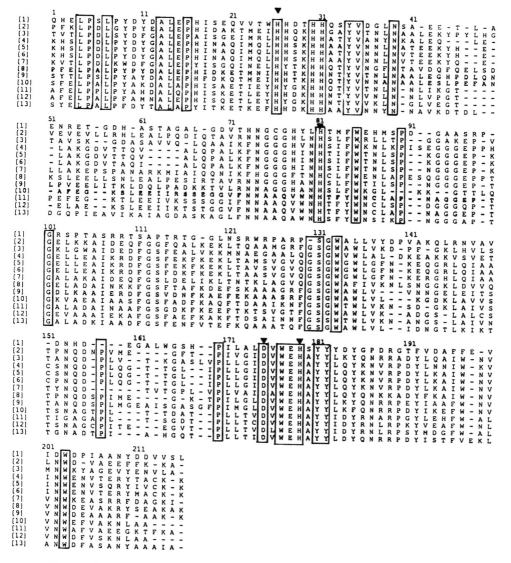

FIG. 2. Aligned amino-acid sequences of nine Mn-SODs and four Fe-SODs. The metal ligands His-26, His-81, Asp-175, and His-179 are indicated by ▼. Invariant regions in the aligned sequences are indicated by boxed areas. The references (metal ion utilized and host organism) are [1] Mn *H. halobium* (204), [2] Mn *T. thermophilus* (205), [3] Mn maize (206), [4] Mn mouse (207), [5] Mn rat (208), [6] Mn human (209–211), [7] Mn *S. cerevisiae* (212, 213), [8] Mn *B. stearothermophilus* (121), [9] Mn *E. coli* (176, 214), [10] Fe *E. coli* (81, 215), [11] Fe *Ps. ovalis* (216), [12] Fe *P. leiognathi* (217), and [13] Fe *Anacystic nidulans* R2 (218). (Reproduced from 84.)

TABLE IV

DEGREE OF AMINO-ACID SEQUENCE IDENTITY BETWEEN SODS[a]

	Human	Mouse	S. cerevisiae	B. stearothermophilus	T. thermophilus	E. coli	E. coli	Ps. ovalis	P. leiognathi
				Mn				Fe	
Mn									
Human	X								
Mouse	94	X							
S. cerevisiae	44	43	X						
B. stearothermophilus	50	48	39	X					
T. thermophilus	49	48	42	62	X				
E. coli	43	42	39	60	52	X			
Fe									
E. coli	40	40	34	49	40	42	X		
Ps. ovalis	42	42	34	52	41	43	65	X	
P. leiognathi	37	38	34	49	37	40	74	65	X

[a]The degree of sequence identity is expressed as a percentage. (From 96.)

27, 30, 31, and 78; lysines 20, 28, and 172; and arginines 125, 176, and 189 (74). Lys-28, thought to guide the approach of O_2^- to the active site (96), is conserved in all Mn-SODs and Fe-SODs except the Mn-SOD from *Halobacterium halobium*, which functions at an ionic strength high enough to greatly weaken electrostatic interactions (106). Chan *et al.* (84) found that an arginine residue, most likely the conserved Arg-189, is important for the activities of Mn-SODs and Fe-SODs. The one exception was the Mn-SOD of *Saccharomyces cerevisiae*, in which Arg-189 is replaced by a lysine. As expected, this enzyme was very sensitive to lysine-modifying reagents.

1. HYBRID SODs

Given that the Mn-SOD and Fe-SOD from *E. coli* are homodimers with considerable sequence homologies, it is not surprising that a hybrid (Hy-SOD) occurs. When first isolated (107), this *E. coli* Hy-SOD was found to contain 0.8 atoms of Fe per dimer and to be sensitive to H_2O_2. Its specific activity was low (350 U/mg protein). Because of their very different isoelectric points (4.9 for Fe-SOD and 6.6 for Mn-SOD), electrophoresis of the native *E. coli* enzymes readily separates Mn-SOD, Fe-SOD, and Hy-SOD. The isolated hybrid enzyme was unstable because of resegregation of the subunits. Reinvestigation of Hy-SOD (108) resulted in a preparation whose specific activity was 1900 U/mg and that contained 2.3 atoms Fe plus 0.41 of Mn per dimer. This Hy-SOD was inactivated to a limit of 70% by H_2O_2, whereas the corresponding figure for Fe-SOD is 90% and for Mn-SOD, 0%. Streptomycin, which had previously been seen to bind tightly to the *E. coli* Mn-SOD and Fe-SOD without eliminating catalytic activity (109), similarly associated with Hy-SOD. Treatment of Hy-SOD with H_2O_2 was accompanied by resegregation of the subunits and the formation of active Mn-SOD and inactive Fe-SOD (108). As expected for a hybrid, apo-Hy-SOD regained activity when treated with either Mn(II) or Fe(II). Separation of the subunits and the formation of hybrid molecules have also been reported for Cu,Zn-SODs (110–112).

2. ACTIVITY WITH EITHER MN OR FE

A few SODs appear to be active with either Mn or Fe at the active site (65–68, 113, 114). *Propionibacterium shermanii* make either a Mn-SOD or an Fe-SOD, depending on the relative abundance of these two metals in the culture medium (114). The Mn-SOD, isolated from cells grown in Fe-poor medium, and the Fe-SOD, obtained from cells grown in Mn-poor medium, had identical amino-acid compositions and amino-terminal sequences (12 residues). The subunit M_r of the *P. shermanii* enzyme was reported to be ~32,000, and the specific activity was 900 U/mg for the Mn-SOD and 400 U/mg for the Fe-SOD (115). These are aberrant in that well-characterized

Mn-SODs and Fe-SODs have subunit M_rs of ~22,000 and specific activities in the range 4000–5000 U/mg. Re-examination of the properties of the *P. shermanii* enzyme is clearly in order.

Bacteroides fragilis produces an Fe-SOD when grown anaerobically. This Fe-SOD is a homodimer with a specific activity of 1200 U/mg. It has a M_r of ~42,000 and contains 1.8–1.9 atoms of Fe per dimer (65). The *B. fragilis* apo-SOD could be reactivated with either Mn(II) or Fe(II), and its electrophoretic mobility was not influenced by which metal it contained. Exposure of anaerobically grown cells to low levels of O_2 caused the appearance of a Mn-SOD whose polypeptide appeared identical to that of the Fe-SOD (66). Similar results have been obtained with other species of *Bacteroides* (67, 68).

Streptococcus mutans produces a Mn-SOD or an Fe-SOD, depending on which metal was most abundant in the culture medium, and the name "cambialistic" was suggested for enzymes capable of being active with more than one prosthetic group (113). Unfortunately, the data for this enzyme suggest that further study is also required. Thus, the Fe-SOD had a specific activity of only 176 U/mg, whereas that of the Mn-SOD was 4500 U/mg. Moreover, earlier work (116) found only a Mn-SOD in *S. mutans*. It remains possible that a small impurity of active Mn-SOD could have been responsible for the low activity reported for the Fe-SOD of *S. mutans* (113). One must also allow for the frequent cross-contamination of iron salts with manganese; only ultrapure salts should be used for reconstitution of apoproteins prepared from "cambialistic" SODs. A useful diagnostic is sensitivity to H_2O_2, since Fe-SODs are inactivated by H_2O_2 but Mn-SODs are not. This test was applied in the case of the *Bacteroides* enzymes, but not in the other cases reported.

Table V summarizes metal contents for SODs reported to contain multiple metals. Since many metals compete with the native metal for occupancy of the active site (101), it seems likely that reports of SODs containing Fe + Mn + Zn, or even Cu, are the result of such competition. In no case has the functional significance of these multiple metals been evaluated.

F. Reversible Resolution

Specific procedures have been developed for the removal and restoration of the metal center from Mn-SOD and from Fe-SOD (80, 85, 101, 117, 118). Iron is removed from Fe-SOD, with loss of activity, by anaerobic treatment with dithiothreitol plus EDTA at alkaline pH (80, 85, 117, 118). Subsequent dialysis against Fe(II), but not Fe(III), restored ~80% of the original activity. Other procedures for the reversible resolution of Fe-SOD have been tried, but with a much lower restoration of activity (85, 113, 114, 119).

Treatment of Mn-SOD with urea or guanidinium chloride, plus a chelat-

TABLE V
METAL CONTENT[a]

Source	M_r	Subunits	Specific activity (U/mg)	Fe	Mn	Zn	Reference
Mycobacterium phlei	80,000	4		1.2	1.7	0.7	Y. Chikata, E. Kusonose, K. Ichihara and M. Kusunose, *Osaka City Med J.* **21**, 127 (1975)
Thermoplasma acidophilum	82,000	4	294	2.0	NR	1.0	58
Methanobacterium bryantii	91,000	4	2060	2.7	0.2	1.7	60
Norcardia asteroides	100,000	4		1.2	1.2	1.2	B. L. Beaman, S. M. Scaks, S. E. Moring, P. Deem and H. P. Misra, *JBC* **258**, 91 (1983)
Bacteroides fragilis	42,000	2	1200	1.8–1.9	NR	0.2	65
Plectonema boryanum	42,000	2	7600	2.0	NR	0.2	K. Asada, K. Yoshikawa, M. A. Takahashi, Y. Magday and K. Enmanji, *JBC* **250**, 2801 (1975)
Bacteroides thetaiotaomicron	46,000	2	1200	1.1	0.05	0.6	67
Bacteroides fragilis	43,000	2	1760	0.3	1.1	0.2	65
Rhodococcus bronchialis	80,000	4		0.9	2.2	NR	K. Ichihara, I. Kasaoka, E. Kusonose and M. Kusunose, *J. Gen. Appl. Microbiol.* **26**, 387 (1980)
Ginko biloba	47,000	2	500	1.4	0.22	2.2, 2.2 (Cu)	69
Halobacterium halobium	38,500	2		1.5	1.5	0.5, 1.5 (Cu)	106

[a] NR, Not reported.

ing agent at low pH, removes the metal and causes loss of activity (120–123). The apo-Mn-SOD is then reconstituted by treatment with Mn(II), with a regain of ~60–80% of the initial activity. In most of the procedures devised to date, the apo-Mn-SOD is kept in the presence of the chaotrope until dialyzed against the reconstituting metal (101, 120, 122–124). We have noted that the apo form of *E. coli* Mn-SOD is stable in the absence of chaotropes only in dilute solutions (<0.5 mg/ml); it polymerizes and precipitates at higher concentrations.

   With the exceptions already discussed, activity is restored to apo-Fe-SOD only by Fe and to apo-Mn-SOD only by Mn. Reconstitution with Co(II), Fe(II), Ni(II), Cu(II), Zn(II), Mn(II), Cr(II), or Cd(II) resulted in tight binding of 0.8–1.0 atom of the metal per subunit (80, 101, 117, 118, 120, 125). Metals other than the native metal could compete for binding and in so doing could prevent the restoration of activity. In some cases, an enzyme that was inactive by virtue of binding of a foreign metal could be reconverted to the apo form and then reactivated with the native metal. Placement of Cu(II) into the Mn-binding site of *B. stearothermophilus* generated an epr signal (124) virtually identical to that associated with Cu(II) bound at the Zn(II) site of Cu,Zn-SOD (11). This is not surprising, since the Zn(II)-binding site of Cu,Zn-SOD and the Fe/Mn-binding sites of Mn-SODs/Fe-SODs are composed of three histidines and one aspartate with similar geometries. This observation does establish that when Cu(II) binds to the *B. stearothermophilus* apo-Mn-SOD, it does so at the active site. Another indication of metal occupancy of the active site is the quenching of tryptophan fluorescence (85, 117, 118).

G. Catalytic Mechanism

   Pulse radiolysis has been used to generate bursts of O_2^- and, when combined with spectrophotometry, to show that interaction with O_2^- causes partial bleaching of the metal center in Cu,Zn-SOD (126, 127), Fe-SOD (128), and Mn-SOD (129). This leads to the following mechanism:

$$Me^n + O_2^- \quad \rightleftharpoons Me^{n-1} + O_2 \qquad \text{(e)}$$
$$Me^{n-1} + O_2^- + 2H^+ \rightleftharpoons Me + H_2O_2 \qquad \text{(f)}$$

The degree of reductive bleaching of the metal in the steady state of catalysis depends on the rate constants for these two half-reactions of the catalytic cycle. Since the rate constants for reactions (e) and (f) are nearly identical, 50% of bleaching is expected and has been observed. The activity of Cu,Zn-SOD is independent of pH in the range 5–9, whereas those of Fe-SOD and Mn-SOD decrease above neutrality, defining an activity-limiting ionization with $pK_a \approx 9$. Evidence for saturation of *E. coli* Fe-SOD with O_2^- has been reported using stopped-flow methods (89, 91), whereas more complex kinetics were seen with Mn-SOD (129, 130).

The pH independence of the catalytic activity of Cu,Zn-SOD, and its nearly diffusion-limited rate, indicate an efficient mechanism for proton conduction. The imidazolate, which bridges the Cu(II) and the Zn(II), was thought to provide for proton conduction by being released from the copper center, while binding a proton during reaction (e), and then donating that proton to O_2^- and re-establishing bridging to copper during reaction (f) (131). Data supporting this involvement of the bridging imidazolate in proton conduction during the catalytic cycle of Cu,Zn-SOD have been reported (132, 133).

Studies with the E. coli Fe-SOD may indicate a role for Tyr-34 in proton conduction. Reduction of this enzyme is linked to uptake of one proton per active site over the pH range 6–10 (91). Moreover, replacement of H_2O by D_2O slows the catalytic process and indicates that proton transfer is rate-limiting. Tyr-34 is totally conserved, and the phenolic hydroxyl is directed toward, and is only 5 Å from, the metal center (74).

H. Reactions with H_2O_2

Cu,Zn-SOD and Fe-SOD, but not Mn-SOD, are subject to inactivation by H_2O_2. Although of interest for what they can reveal about the structure and reactivity of the metals at the active site, these reactions with H_2O_2 would not be significant at the low concentrations of H_2O_2 achievable within living cells. H_2O_2 rapidly bleaches the visible absorption of Cu,Zn-SOD and more slowly inactivates the enzyme, while causing the oxidation of one histidine per subunit (131). Mn-SOD, in contrast, is bleached, but not inactivated, by H_2O_2 (134). Fe-SOD is also rapidly bleached by H_2O_2 (128, 135), and it is inactivated (80, 136).

Inactivation of the Fe-SOD from P. ovalis is accompanied by the loss of 1.6 Trp, 1.1 His, and 0.9 Cys per subunit (136), whereas with the E. coli enzyme only tryptophan was lost along with iron (80). The second-order rate constants for inactivation of Fe-SOD by H_2O_2 range from 1.1 $M^{-1}sec^{-1}$ for the P. leiognathi enzyme (128), to 1.5 $M^{-1}sec^{-1}$ for the P. ovalis Fe-SOD (136), to 4.6 $M^{-1}sec^{-1}$ for the E. coli enzyme (80). Saturation of rate with respect to $[H_2O_2]$ has been reported for the P. ovalis Fe-SOD (136), but not for the E. coli (94) or P. leiognathi (128) enzymes.

apo-Fe-SOD and Mn-substituted Fe-SOD were unaffected by H_2O_2 (80), as was a Cr-substituted Fe-SOD (136). This indicates a critical role for iron in the inactivation process. Treatment of E. coli Fe-SOD with H_2O_2 causes inactivation to a limit of 90%. The H_2O_2-resistant residual activity differs from that of the native enzyme in heat stability and sensitivity to inhibition by N_3^- and to inactivation by rose bengal plus light, or by N-bromosuccinimide (80). Inactivation of Fe-SOD by H_2O_2 thus modifies, but does not obliterate, the active site.

We have proposed (80) that H_2O_2 first reduces Fe(III) at the active site of Fe-SOD to Fe(II), which then reacts with H_2O_2 in a Fenton-like process, yielding a potent oxidant. This oxidant, generated at the iron center, takes an electron from one of its histidine ligands that, in turn, takes an electron from one of the several tryptophan residues that surround the active site. The net effect is oxidation of tryptophan, rather than of histidine. This mechanism is supported by the finding that H_2O_2, equimolar to active-site Fe(III), causes neither inactivation of Fe-SOD nor loss of tryptophan (135). The rate constant for reduction of the Fe(II) of Fe-SOD by H_2O_2 is $1.7 \times 10^2 \, M^{-1}sec^{-1}$ (128), which exceeds the rate of inactivation by nearly an order of magnitude. This also supports a mechanism in which reduction by H_2O_2 precedes inactivation by H_2O_2.

Fe(III) at the active site of Fe-SOD quenches fluorescence of tryptophan residues, and reduction by H_2O_2 increases this fluorescence. This suggests transfer of excitation energy between tryptophan and Fe(III) (135). In accord with the quenching effect of Fe(III) is the greater fluorescence of the apo- compared with the holo-Fe-SOD (80, 136). N_3^-, which inhibits Fe-SOD, also slows both the reductive and inactivating effects of H_2O_2 (135).

II. Superoxide and Oxidative DNA Damage

There is ample evidence that superoxide can contribute to the production of DNA damage *in vivo*. Drugs, such as paraquat, that generate high levels of superoxide in bacteria mutate DNA (137) and induce DNA-repair systems (138), and strains that lack SOD exhibit an elevated rate of oxygen-dependent spontaneous mutagenesis (139). Analysis of DNA damage systems both *in vivo* and *in vitro* indicates that O_2^- does not directly attack DNA, but, rather, exerts its toxic effect by driving the production of powerful oxidants by the Haber–Weiss cycle (140) [reactions (a)–(d)]. The removal of either catalytic metals or H_2O_2, through the addition of excess metal chelators or catalase, respectively, can fully protect DNA from the ill effects of O_2^-

Electron transfer to H_2O_2 [the Fenton reaction, (b)–(d)], creating a strong DNA oxidant, can be effected *in vitro* by reduced species of iron, copper, cobalt, and titanium. Iron, the predominant transition metal in biological systems, plays this role *in vivo*. Cell-permeable iron chelators prevent the DNA damage that otherwise occurs upon exposure of cells to H_2O_2 (140, 141). O_2^- is not necessarily the agent directly responsible for reducing the iron *in vivo*. Investigators have used a variety of reductants other than O_2^- in *in vitro* Fenton systems, including NADH, ascorbate, and some chemotherapeutic drugs *(142)*. Although many of these agents are capable of reducing iron directly, SOD can be inhibitory since the free-radical chain reactions which these agents can initiate are often at quasi-equilibrium with, or even propagated by, O_2^- *(143)*. Furthermore, once reduced, some forms of bound iron rapidly autoxidize and initiate a quasi-equilibrium with O_2^-:

$$Fe^{2+} + O_2 \rightarrow Fe^{3+} + O_2^-$$

Accordingly, SOD can act as a free-radical sink and prevent the reaction of DNA-bound iron with H_2O_2. Consistent with this notion, *E. coli* that are either SOD-deficient or anaerobic are extremely sensitive to the DNA-damaging effects of added H_2O_2, while cells that are both aerobic and SOD-proficient are relatively resistant *(142)*. In this light, molecular oxygen and SOD can act in concert as a trap for electron-donating free radicals.

A. DNA Damage Products

The destruction of DNA by radiation-generated hydroxyl radicals has been studied for 40 years, and the damage products have been extensively characterized. Until recently, it was assumed that the oxidant generated by the Fenton reaction was also a hydroxyl radical and that it would produce an identical spectrum of lesions. However, *in vitro* Fenton systems can generate damage in a manner that cannot be blocked by hydroxyl-radical scavengers *(142)*. The Fenton-derived oxidant has been termed a "crypto-hydroxyl radical," and its ability to elude scavengers has been ascribed to either of two possibilities.

First, because metal atoms bind to cellular macromolecules such as DNA, hydroxyl radicals generated on their surface do not have to diffuse to reach their target. By reacting immediately at the site of their formation, the hydroxyl radicals have a negligible lifetime and are not easy prey for scavengers. Consistent with this idea, oxidants produced on EDTA-chelated iron, which is therefore not bound to the target molecule, can be intercepted by scavengers *(144)*. Because the DNA-bound iron atoms are presumably complexed to the phosphodiester backbone, hydroxyl radicals generated on their surface may be sterically constrained, or at least prone, to react preferentially with those parts of the nucleotides to which they are immediately exposed. This could bias the spectrum of lesions such that attacks on the ribose moiety, for example, predominate, whereas base lesions are the major products of ionizing radiation.

An alternative explanation for the scavenger-resistant behavior of some Fenton oxidants is that the reduction of H_2O_2 by ferrous iron produces an iron–oxygen species having oxidative character similar to, but distinct from, that of the hydroxyl radical. This oxidant has been postulated to be an Fe(II)=O, or an iron(IV), species (145), and its reactivity toward various substrates may be expected to differ somewhat from that of the hydroxyl radical.

It is not yet clear whether Fenton-derived oxidants produce the same DNA damage products as does ionizing radiation, although the available data indicate great similarities. Workers using *in vitro* systems have primarily monitored the appearance of DNA strand-breaks due to oxidative cleavage of the deoxyribose. Base modifications also occur. A recent study of DNA base products from DNA exposed to the oxidative burst of neutrophils noted the appearance of thymine and cytosine glycols, 8-hydroxyguanosine and 8-hydroxyadenine, and 4,6-diamino-5-formamidopyrimidine (146); these products can also be obtained by ionizing radiation through hydroxyl-radical attack on the 5,6-double bonds of pyrimidines and the 7,8-double bonds of purines (147).

Analysis of the initial damage products in intact cells is made difficult both by the presence of rapidly acting DNA-repair systems and by limits on the amount of damage that can be produced. In these studies, H_2O_2 is usually added to a cell suspension, and endogenous iron and reductants are relied on to participate in the Haber–Weiss cycle. Large quantities of H_2O_2 cannot be used to generate large yields of lesions, since excessive H_2O_2 inactivates the metabolic pathways that produce the reductants needed to drive the Fenton chemistry. The analytical methods in current use are most sensitive to the appearance of DNA strand-breaks and alkali-labile sites, and both have been observed in the extracted DNA. Both the frank and alkali-induced strand-breaks could be either products of oxidation of deoxyriboses or intermediates in the repair of oxidized bases. Double-strand-breaks appear not to be common initial lesions; this is in contrast to the case with ionizing radiation, which can produce a cluster of radicals at a single site of energy deposition (148).

B. Enzymatic Repair of Oxidative DNA Damage

Some idea of the nature of *in vivo* DNA oxidation can be deduced from the lesion specificities of DNA-repair enzymes and the consequences of their absence through mutation. Not surprisingly, the absence of either DNA polymerase I or recombinational-repair enzymes (which address an apparently limitless domain of DNA damage) sensitizes *E. coli* to killing by H_2O_2 (149–151). More informatively, mutants deficient in exonuclease III have sensitivity to H_2O_2 as their most notable phenotype (152). Exonuclease III incises baseless or urea-containing sites and can remove the remnants of fractured deoxyribose rings from the 5' side of a strand-break, a necessary step to permit subsequent closure of the break by DNA polymerase I.

Exposure of exonuclease-III-deficient cells to H_2O_2 results in the accumulation of strand-breaks containing a blocking group, presumably the phosphoglycolate fragments at the 5' side of the break (153). A minor endonuclease, endonuclease IV, also can remove these fragments (153); although endonuclease IV single mutants are not especially peroxide-sensitive, double mutants lacking both exonuclease III and endonuclease IV are exquisitely so (154). This evidence strongly suggests that strand breakage through deoxyribose oxidation and fracture is a major consequence of the intracellular Fenton reaction. A DNA diesterase that similarly removes deoxyribose fragments from nicks has been purified from yeast (155).

Several enzymes that can repair oxidative base lesions have been purified, but the genetic evidence does not yet certify that their role is essential in resisting oxidative damage. Endonuclease III from *E. coli* can remove thymine-glycol residues and their decomposition products and then incise the phosphodiester backbone at the resultant baseless site, the logical first step in excision repair of oxidized thymines (156). Similar enzymes have been isolated from mammalian cells (157, 158). However, strains lacking endonuclease III are not particularly sensitive to killing or mutagenesis by oxidants (159), suggesting that thymine-glycol residues are not produced in significant quantities, can be tolerated, or can be repaired by an alternative pathway. It has been suggested that the (A)BC exonuclease complex can also excise thymine-glycol residues (160), although strains lacking this nuclease are resistant to oxidants (151). Double mutants deficient in both endonuclease III and the (A)BC exonuclease must be constructed to determine whether the resistant phenotypes of the single mutants are merely due to the redundancy of the two repair pathways.

Formamidopyrimidine–DNA glycosylase has been identified in extracts from both *E. coli* and mammalian cells (161), but mutants have not been isolated. Hydroxymethyluracil–DNA glycosylase, which removes thymine residues that have been hydroxylated by oxidative attack on the methyl group, has been purified from mammalian cells (158). Despite extensive searches, no analogous activity has been found in *E. coli*.

At least two DNA-repair systems can be induced by oxidative stress. The SOS regulon is induced in *E. coli* upon treatment with H_2O_2 (151, 162). Mutants that cannot induce the many SOS-regulated functions are sensitive to killing by H_2O_2, and this sensitivity can be wholly ascribed to the loss of SOS-stimulated recombinational DNA repair. Endonuclease IV is induced up to 20-fold by treatments that produce intracellular O_2^-, including exposure to paraquat and hyperbaric oxygen (163). Because H_2O_2 does not similarly induce the enzyme, the inducing signal is likely to be O_2^- per se, rather than the DNA damage to which it contributes. Because the lesions recognized by endonuclease IV are generated by the Fenton reaction, the logic of its regulation is strong evidence that O_2^- drives the intracellular Fenton reaction.

C. How Prevalent Is Oxidative DNA Damage?

The detection of oxidative DNA damage in most experiments is contingent on an artificial source of H_2O_2 or O_2^-, which leads one to wonder whether this damage occurs at any significant frequency in the physiological environment. The universal presence of catalases, SODs, and DNA-repair enzymes indicates that aerobic organisms evolved in an environment in which oxidative stress was at least occasionally life-threatening. Additional data support this. Ames' group has developed assays that detect in urine a variety of oxidized DNA bases (164), presumably byproducts of routine repair of DNA that is damaged by endogenous oxidants. Mutants of *E. coli* deficient in pairs of enzymes that repair oxidative DNA damage—exonuclease III and recA protein, DNA polymerase I and recBC nuclease, exonuclease III and endonuclease IV—exhibit severe difficulties in replicating their DNA when grown under routine aerobic, but not anaerobic, conditions (142, 165, 166).

Mutagenesis rates have often been used as measures of sublethal DNA damage. *E. coli* strains devoid of SOD or depleted in H_2O_2-scavenging activities mutate spontaneously at a high rate when grown aerobically (139). Interesting, the enhanced mutagenesis of the SOD mutants is dependent on the presence of functional exonuclease III. One interpretation is that the exonuclease-III-dependent pathway of DNA repair is error-prone, while a competing pathway is not. This result further substantiates the proposal that an intracellular Fenton reaction, which generates substrate lesions for exonuclease III, can be driven by O_2^-.

It is not clear whether sufficient oxidative DNA damage persists in scavenger-proficient, repair-proficient *E. coli* to contribute to the observed rate of spontaneous mutagenesis. Mutation is lessened slightly by anaerobiosis (139, 167, 168), but this may be an indirect consequence of a reduction in growth rate.

III. Cellular Regulation of SOD

A. Inductions

The rate of SOD biosynthesis increases at high oxygen tension in many organisms, including bacteria, yeast, plants, and mammals (20). The complex phenomenology of SOD regulation has been most extensively documented in *E. coli*, which is well-suited to such studies by its amenability to wide variations in growth conditions. The patterns of synthesis that have emerged suggest the existence of multiple levels of control. It is anticipated that the regulatory mechanisms will soon be clarified by genetic analysis.

Shortly after their discovery, it was noted that Mn-SOD levels in *E. coli* are much more sensitive to oxygen tension than are Fe-SOD levels (169). Mn-SOD is undetectable in extracts of cells grown anaerobically in traditional media, while Fe-SOD activity is not significantly different from that of aerobically grown cells. Hyperbaric oxygen further induces Mn-SOD, as does the addition of drugs that stimulate intracellular O_2^- production (170). These observations were the most persuasive early evidence that the physiological role of SOD is indeed to scavenge O_2^-. By contrast, Fe-SOD synthesis is unresponsive to environmental stimuli. This difference in regulation remains the major distinction between the *E. coli* enzymes, which otherwise are structurally and kinetically similar and are not known to differ in intracellular location.

The early supposition that O_2^- concentrations per se dictate Mn-SOD levels were challenged by the observation that seven-fold Fe-SOD overproduction, which must accordingly diminish O_2^- accumulation, had no quantitative effect on the induction of Mn-SOD by normobaric and hyperbaric oxygen (171). Furthermore, the provision of either anaerobic oxidants, such as nitrate or ferricyanide, or iron chelators can induce anaerobic Mn-SOD expression (87, 172). (The analysis is complicated by the fact that Mn-SOD synthesized under some anaerobic conditions is inactive, probably due to the lack of the appropriate prosthetic metal at the active site.)

The cloning of *sodA*, the gene that encodes Mn-SOD as a single-gene operon, has helped to establish that dissolved oxygen, O_2^--generating drugs, and metal chelators all affect Mn-SOD expression at the level of transcription (173). (Additionally, some competition between manganese and iron for the metal-binding site may occur.) Several workers have attempted to combine these modifiers of Mn-SOD expression into a single, economical regulatory scheme. It has been suggested that an iron-binding, redox-sensitive repressor molecule may govern Mn-SOD synthesis (174). If so, chelators could relieve repression by removing the metal, and an oxidative environment could inactivate the repressor through modulation of the metal redox state. The identification of a nearly consensus binding sequence for Fur protein (an iron-containing protein known to be a repressor of the genes involved in iron uptake) within the promoter region of the *sodA* gene lends support to this idea (175). But Fur protein is not known to be redox-sensitive and in fact can use a variety of divalent metals, including manganese, cobalt, and cadmium, as cofactors. Thus, if Fur protein does confer the metal sensitivity of Mn-SOD expression, an independent regulatory mechanism may impart the redox sensitivity. In fact, the Mn-SOD activity of *fur* mutants is still negligible during anaerobiosis.

It is also dubious whether a single effector molecule could sense anaerobic respiration, normobaric oxygen, hyperbaric oxygen, and drug-induced O_2^- as a continuum of increasing oxidative stress. Although the inductive effects of anaerobic oxidants are clearly due to their action as respiratory electron sinks, the Michaelis constant of cytochrome oxidase ($\sim 1\ \mu M$) is such that hyperbaric oxygen is no greater a sink than is normobaric oxygen. An alternative is that high oxygen concentrations, like redox-cycling drugs, owe their excess inducing capability to the chemical oxidation of cellular constituents and the consequent production of O_2^-, with an additional regulatory element detecting an increase in O_2^- levels. The promoter region of the *sodA* gene contains a 19-base-pair inverted repeat apart from the putative Fur-binding site (176), suggesting an additional locus for the binding of regulatory proteins. Site-specific mutagenesis of part of this region results in high-level constitutive synthesis of Mn-SOD, indicating that it is indeed a binding site for repressor molecules (177). The engineering of fusions between the *sodA* promoter and genes that produce easily scored phenotypes is expected to facilitate the isolation of regulatory mutants and the elucidation of biosynthetic controls.

In eukaryotic cells, two SODs are constitutively present: a cytoplasmic Cu,Zn-SOD and a mitochondrial Mn-SOD. Their compartmentalization is a necessary consequence of the inability of O_2^- to traverse membranes, as a cytoplasmic SOD cannot reduce the steady-state O_2^- concentration in mitochondria. It is less clear why *E. coli* needs two SODs, but the advantage must lie in their different patterns of regulation. The presence of Fe-SOD during anaerobic growth ensures the cell against oxidative stress that would ensue upon any transition to aerobiosis. The natural niche of *E. coli*, the gut, is anaerobic, but the excretion of the bacterium in feces would rapidly shift it to an aerobic environment. The cell cannot rely on a subsequent induction of SOD for protection, since protein synthesis would be rapidly inhibited by oxidative inactivation of amino-acid biosynthesis (see Section III,B).

The induction of Mn-SOD under conditions of iron starvation ensures that SOD activity is present when Fe-SOD synthesis would only produce an inactive apoenzyme. Although Mn-SOD can be induced by the provision of anaerobic electron sinks, this may be an inadvertent consequence of the mechanism used by the cell to sense an oxygen-containing environment, a shift in the redox status of the nicotinamide–adenine dinucleotide pool, perhaps. Further induction may be necessary to maintain a low steady-state O_2^- concentration in the face of agents that exacerbate O_2^- formation; these may include drugs manufactured as bacteriocides by higher organisms. It is not to the benefit of *E. coli* to constitutively synthesize SOD at a high rate, since the fully induced promoter rivals the *tac* promoter in activity and would divert much of the cells' resources and metal pool to the synthesis of an unnecessary protein. In fact, strains of *E. coli* bearing multiple copies of the gene fare poorly under highly inducing growth conditions (*178*, *179*).

B. SOD Mutant Phenotypes

Early speculation on the physiological role of SOD could not be considered definitive because SOD levels could not be varied within an organism without the possibility of influencing other properties as well. Recently, however, strains genetically deficient in SOD have been developed in the model organisms *E. coli*, yeast, and *Drosophila*. In each case, the results establish that SOD is essential in conferring oxygen tolerance.

Drosophila and yeast, like most eukaryotes, contain both a cytoplasmic Cu,Zn-SOD and a mitochondrial Mn-SOD. Because membranes are generally impervious to O_2^-, these enzymes function in isolation and neither can compensate for a defect in the other. *Drosophila* homozygotes that lack the Cu,Zn-SOD (*180*) are viable as larvae, although the larvae are acutely sensitive to paraquat. The adult flies, however, are sterile and live an average of only 12 days (versus ~60 days for the wild type or heterozygotes). The specific sites of lethal injury have not been determined.

Mutants of yeast that are unusually sensitive to paraquat have been isolated and are devoid of Cu,Zn-SOD (*181*). These strains cannot grow in air unless supplemented with lysine and cysteine, probably indicating that O_2^--sensitive enzymes are participants in the biosynthesis of these amino acids. Growth does not occur under 100% oxygen even with amino-acid supplementation; the target(s) resulting in this growth inhibition is not known. These strains are hypersensitive to killing by H_2O_2, indicating that H_2O_2 and O_2^- act synergistically in generating the toxic oxidant. Yeasts that have no Mn-SOD have been generated by *in vitro* disruption of the cloned gene and transformation to effect chromosomal gene replacement (*182*). The Mn-SOD-deficient haploid cells can grow in air on glucose, but fail in pure oxygen. Nonfermentable carbon sources impose a greater burden on mitochondrial respiration; accordingly, Mn-SOD-deficient strains exhibit severe growth difficulties on such media at normobaric oxygen levels. Somewhat surprisingly, although the more rapid divergence of mitochondrial DNA relative to nuclear DNA in higher organisms has been postulated to be a result of its constant exposure to respiration-produced oxy radicals, no increase in the mutation rates of mitochondrial DNA has been observed in the Mn-SOD mutants.

Mutants of *E. coli* that are devoid of SOD have been generated and characterized (*36*). Such strains exhibit an O_2-dependent auxotrophy for branched-chain and aromatic amino acids and bradytrophy for several others. Cells grow slowly in aerobic-rich media and exhibit a high rate of spontaneous mutagenesis. As with SOD-deficient yeast, the increase in steady-state O_2^- levels in these cells results in sensitivity to iron-dependent killing by H_2O_2, consistent with a role for O_2^- in driving the Fenton reaction. Paraquat and hyperbaric oxygen are growth-inhibitory in concentrations that are innocuous to SOD-proficient strains.

Analysis of the nutritional requirements of the SOD-deficient *E. coli* mutants has allowed the confirmation of one intracellular target of O_2^-. Earlier studies with hyperbaric oxygen and redox-cycling drugs had suggested that the dihydroxy-acid dehydratase of the biosynthetic pathway for branched-chain amino acids is sensitive to oxidative inactivation (183, 184). The enzyme is destabilized by the selective removal (in aerobic extracts) of SOD, while catalase affords no protection (22). Flint and Emptage have purified the enzyme anaerobically and have determined that its instability is due to destruction of a catalytic 4Fe–4S center by O_2^- (23). They and others (185) conjecture that O_2^- may oxidize bound metals, possibly prompting the metal to oxidize adjacent ligands in turn.

The mutant phenotypes of SOD-deficient yeast and *E. coli* can be reversed by the addition of SOD genes cloned from diverse sources (186, 187). These studies confirm suspicions regarding the *in vivo* effectors of oxidative stress. First, O_2^- may be the oxidative agent that directly causes damage due to normobaric and hyperbaric oxygen. Second, physiological levels of O_2^- can promulgate Fenton-mediated DNA damage. Third, O_2^- can rapidly inactivate enzymes without recourse to Fenton chemistry. And finally, endogenous O_2^- production, in normally cultured *E. coli*, yeast, and *Drosophila*, is sufficient to require the presence of SOD activity.

C. Additional Regulons Pertinent to Oxy-radical Damage

Catalase, like SOD, is a nearly ubiquitous enzyme activity in the aerobic biota. Its presence minimizes the accumulation of H_2O_2, a direct product of several oxidases as well as of SOD, and thereby lessens the frequency of the Fenton reaction. Catalase activity is frequently represented by multiple isozymes within a single organism; the distribution and expression of these isozymes are responsive to signals that are not well-understood (188).

E. coli synthesizes two catalases, designated hydroperoxidase-I and -II (HP-I and HP-II). HP-I, encoded by the *katG* gene, is secreted to the periplasm; HP-II, from the *katE* locus, is cytoplasmic (189). Although mechanistic differences between the two isozymes exist, there is no evidence that either has any function other than the clearance of H_2O_2. Treatment of *E. coli* with low concentrations of H_2O_2 confers resistance to subsequent doses that would otherwise be lethal (190). This phenomenon is due to the induction of a regulon under the positive control of the *oxyR* gene product (191). The redox-sensitive oxyR protein binds upstream at *oxyR*-regulated genes and, in its oxidized form, stimulates their transcription (191a). The resistance to H_2O_2 is entirely due to an increase in the synthesis of HP-I (151), although at least eight other oxyR-regulated and perhaps 30 oxyR-independent proteins are also induced. Although most of these inducible proteins are known only by their migration behavior on two-dimensional gels, two of them comprise subunits of alkylhydroperoxide reductase, a flavin-containing NAD(P)H-utilizing enzyme that reduces a wide variety of organic hydroperoxides (192). Strains from which the oxyR gene is deleted exhibit a high rate of spontaneous mutagenesis (167). Although the oxyR-regulated proteins are non-inducible in such strains, they appear to be present at wild-type levels during routine growth, leaving open the question of why a high spontaneous mutation rate ensues.

The other catalase, HP-II, is non-inducible by H_2O_2, but is present at higher titers in aerobic than in anaerobic cells (193). The biosynthetic rate also rises dramatically during late log-phase growth in glucose-containing medium, possibly in conjunction with a conversion from glycolytic to purely aerobic metabolism. A genetic locus, katF, has been identified that is necessary for transcription of the katE structural gene (194). Intriguingly, mutations in katF also eliminate exonuclease-III synthesis. Since exonuclease III and HP-II are both critical elements in the cell's defense against H_2O_2, it is tempting to speculate that a single regulatory system combines scavenging and DNA-repair enzymes.

Analogously, O_2^-, but not H_2O_2, induces both Mn-SOD and endonuclease IV (163, 170). It is not yet known whether these enzymes share a common regulatory system. The synthesis of glucose-6-phosphate dehydrogenase is also stimulated by O_2^--generating drugs (195). Two-dimensional gel analysis of protein synthesis indicates that up to several dozen polypeptides may be induced by redox-cycling agents, with some overlap with those induced by H_2O_2 (195, 196). Several responsive loci have been localized by protein fusions, but the functions of the proteins they encode are not yet known (197). Some of these proteins may be members of the SOS regulon, which can be induced both by H_2O_2 and by redox-cycling drugs (138, 151).

Glutathione has been implicated as an important effector of resistance to oxidative stress in mammalian cells (198). In theory, at least, its antioxidant benefits could be mediated by any of several functions: by its activity as a chemical reductant of DNA or protein radicals, the immediate products of oxy-radical attack; by its reduction of oxidized cysteine residues on proteins; or by its function as a substrate for glutathione peroxidase, which plays a major role in the removal of hydroperoxides. In contrast, glutathione seems not to be an important defense against oxidative stress in E. coli. Glutathione-less cells are not particularly sensitive to either ionizing radiation or H_2O_2 (199). The latter observation is consistent with the apparent absence of glutathione peroxidase from E. coli. Furthermore, since ionizing radiation exerts its lethality by damaging DNA, the failure of glutathione deficiency to sensitize cells indicates that glutathione rarely reduces primary DNA radicals. It remains possible, however, that glutathione does relieve the cells of less acute oxidative stresses that are merely growth-inhibitory, rather than lethal.

IV. Epilogue

It is predictable that newly discovered enzymes will be examined by a variety of physicochemical techniques that will reveal molecular weights, subunit compositions, prosthetic groups, amino-acid sequences, three-dimensional structures, and mechanisms of action. All of this is both interesting and useful information, and the efforts expended in ferreting it out are laudable. Others will seek to explore the biological importance of the enzymes by manipulating the level of the enzymes and their substrate by chemical and genetic techniques. This, too, is useful and commendable.

More exciting still are the unforeseen correlations and explanations, for diverse physiological and pathological processes, that flow from awareness of the new enzymes. These provide the strongest justification for basic research, and we close this review by mentioning a few of these unanticipated fallouts from studies of the SODs. These include: the production of O_2^- during the respiratory burst of phagocytic leukocytes (200); the role of O_2^- in the inflammatory process (201) and in reperfusion injury (202); and the role of O_2^- in the dioxygen-dependent toxicities of viologens, quinones, and aromatic nitro compounds (203). The level of investigative activity in these areas is high, the relevant literature is burgeoning, and practical solutions to long-standing problems seem close at hand.

ACKNOWLEDGMENT

We thank C. L. Borders, Jr., for providing us with a preprint of 84 and Fig. 2.

REFERENCES

1. T. Mann and D. Keilin, *Proc. R. Soc. London, Ser. B* **126**, 303 (1939).
2. H. Markowitz, G. E. Cartwright and M. M. Wintrobe, *JBC* **234**, 40 (1959).
3. J. R. Kimmel, H. Markowitz and D. M. Brown, *JBC* **234**, 46 (1959).
4. H. Porter and J. Folch, *J. Neurochem.* **1**, 260 (1957).
5. M. S. Mohamed and D. M. Greenberg, *J. Gen. Physiol.* **37**, 433 (1953).
6. M. J. Stansell and H. F. Deutsch, *JBC* **240**, 4299 (1965).
7. J. W. Hartz and H. F. Deutsch, *JBC* **244**, 4565 (1969).
8. R. J. Carrico and H. F. Deutsch, *JBC* **244**, 6087 (1969).
9. R. J. Carrico and H. F. Deutsch, *JBC* **245**, 723 (1970).
10. J. M. McCord and I. Fridovich, *JBC* **243**, 5753 (1968).
11. J. M. McCord and I. Fridovich, *JBC* **244**, 6049 (1969).
12. C. Beauchamp and I. Fridovich, *Anal. Biochem.* **44**, 276 (1971).

13. B. B. Keele, Jr., J. M. McCord and I. Fridovich, *JBC* **245**, 6176 (1970).
14. R. A. Weisiger and I. Fridovich, *JBC* **248**, 3582 (1973).
15. F. J. Yost, Jr., and I. Fridovich, *JBC* **248**, 4905 (1973).
16. J. M. McCord and I. Fridovich, *Free Radicals Biol. Med.* **5**, 363 (1988).
17. W. H. Bannister and J. V. Bannister, *Free Radicals Biol. Med.* **5**, 371 (1988).
18. W. H. Bannister, *Free Radical Res. Commun.* **5**, 35 (1988).
19. H. Taube, *J. Gen. Physiol.* **49**, 29 (1965).
20. J. DiGuiseppi and I. Fridovich, *CRC Crit. Rev. Toxicol.* **12**, 315 (1984).
21. I. Fridovich, *Annu. Rev. Pharmacol. Toxicol.* **23**, 239 (1983).
22. C. F. Kuo, T. Mashino and I. Fridovich, *JBC* **262**, 4724 (1987).
23. D. H. Flint and M. H. Emptage, *in* "Biosynthesis of Branched Chain Amino Acids" (Z. Barak, D. Chipman and J. V. Schloss, eds.), pp. 288–314. Weinheim/Deerfield Borch and Balaban, Rehovot/Philadelphia, 1988.
24. I. Fridovich, *ABB* **247**, 1 (1986).
25. S. I. Liochev and I. Fridovich, *Free Radicals Biol. Med.* **6**, 617 (1989).
26. B. H. J. Bielski, R. L. Arudi and M. W. Sutherland, *JBC* **258**, 4759 (1983).
27. C. Beauchamp and I. Fridovich, *JBC* **245**, 4641 (1970).
28. A. Samuni, M. Chevion and G. Czapski, *Radiat. Res.* **99**, 562 (1984).
29. G. Czapski, *Isr. J. Chem.* **24**, 29 (1984).
30. J. P. Thomas, G. J. Bachowski, and A. W. Girotti, *BBA* **884**, 448 (1986).
31. A. W. Girotti and J. P. Thomas, *BBRC* **118**, 474 (1984).
32. J. M. C. Gutteridge, R. Richmond and B. Halliwell, *BJ* **184**, 469 (1979).
33. G. Cohen and P. M. Sinet, *FEBS Lett.* **138**, 258 (1982).
34. A. C. Mello Filho and R. Meneghini, *BBA* **781**, 56 (1984).
35. P. E. Starke and J. L. Farber, *JBC* **260**, 10099 (1985).
36. A. Carlioz and D. Touati, *EMBO J.* **5**, 623 (1986).
37. L. R. Karam, M. Dizdaroglu and M. G. Simic, *Radiat. Res.* **116**, 210 (1988).
38. R. Cathcart, E. Schwiers, R. L. Saul and B. N. Ames, *PNAS* **81**, 5633 (1984).
39. C. Richter, J.-W. Park and B. N. Ames, *PNAS* **85**, 6465 (1988).
40. R. Adelman, R. L. Saul and B. N. Ames, *PNAS* **85**, 2706 (1988).
41. S. Goldstein and G. Czapski, *J. Free Radicals Biol. Med.* **2**, 3 (1986).
42. H. M. Steinman and R. L. Hill, *PNAS* **70**, 3725 (1973).
43. H. M. Steinman, *in* "Superoxide Dismutase" (L. W. Oberley, ed.), Vol. 1, p. 11. CRC Press, Boca Raton, Florida, 1982.
44. H. M. Steinman, *in* "Oxy Radicals and Their Scavenger System," Proceedings of the Third International Conference on Superoxide, Superoxide Dismutase, 1982 (G. Cohen and R. A. Greenwald, eds.), p. 167. Elsevier, New York, 1983.
45. H. M. Steinman, *JBC* **262**, 1882 (1987).
46. S. M. Bridges and M. L. Salin, *Plant Physiol.* **68**, 275 (1981).
47. J. Kwiatkowski and Z. Kaniuga, *Acta Physiol. Plant.* **6**, 197 (1985).
48. K. Puget and A. M. Michelson, *BBRC* **58**, 830 (1974).
49. H. M. Steinman, *JBC* **257**, 10283 (1982).
50. H. M. Steinman, *J. Bact.* **162**, 1255 (1985).
51. P. M. Vignais, A. Terech, C. M. Meyer and M. F. Henry, *BBA* **701**, 305 (1982).
52. S. Marklund, *PNAS* **79**, 7634 (1982).
53. J. V. Bannister, W. H. Bannister and G. Rotilio, *CRC Crit. Rev. Biochem.* **22**, 111 (1987).
54. I. Fridovich, *Adv. Enzymol.* **58**, 62 (1986).
55. J. S. Valentine and M. W. Pantoliano, *in* "Copper Protein" (T. G. Spiro, ed.), p. 292. Wiley, New York, 1981.
56. S. Sato and K. Nakazawa, *J. Biochem.* **83**, 1165 (1978).

57. S. Sato and J. I. Harris, *EJB* **73**, 373 (1977).
58. K. B. Searcy and D. C. Searcy, *BBA* **670**, 39 (1981).
59. E. Kusunose, K. Ichinara, Y. Noda and M. Kusunose, *J. Biochem.* **80**, 1343 (1976).
60. T. W. Kirby, J. L. Lancaster and I. Fridovich, *ABB* **210**, 140 (1981).
61. Y. Abe and T. Okazaki, *ABB* **253**, 241 (1987).
62. S. Marklund, *Int. J. Biochem.* **9**, 299 (1978).
63. S. D. Ravindranath and I. Fridovich, *JBC* **250**, 6107 (1975).
64. M. W. Gray, R. Cedergren, Y. Abel and D. Sankoff, *PNAS* **86**, 2267 (1989).
65. E. M. Gregory and C. H. Dapper, *ABB* **220**, 293 (1983).
66. E. M. Gregory, *ABB* **238**, 83 (1985).
67. C. D. Pennington and E. M. Gregory, *J. Bact.* **166**, 528 (1986).
68. A. Amano, S. Shizukuishi, H. Tamagawa, R. Iwakura, S. Tsunasawa and A. Tsunemitsu, *J. Bact.* **172**, 1457 (1990).
69. M. V. Duke and M. L. Salin, *ABB* **243**, 305 (1985).
70. J. Kwiatowski, A. Safianowska and Z. Kaniuga, *EJB* **146**, 459 (1985).
71. S. Kanematsu and K. Asada, *ABB* **195**, 535 (1979).
72. K. M. Beem, J. S. Richardson and D. C. Richardson, *JMB* **105**, 327 (1976).
73. W. C. Stallings, K. A. Pattridge, R. K. Strong and M. L. Ludwig, *JBC* **260**, 16429 (1985).
74. M. W. Parker and C. C. F. Blake, *JMB* **199**, 649 (1988).
75. J. Bridgen, J. I. Harris and E. Kolb, *JMB* **105**, 333 (1976).
76. D. C. Morris, D. G. Searcy and B. F. Edwards, *JMB* **186**, 213 (1985).
77. D. Ringe, G. A. Petsko, F. Yamakura, K. Suzuki and D. Ohmori, *PNAS* **80**, 3879 (1983).
78. W. C. Stallings, T. B. Powers, K. A. Pattridge, J. A. Fee and M. L. Ludwig, *PNAS* **80**, 3884 (1983).
79. F. Yamakura and K. Suzuki, *BBA* **874**, 23 (1986).
80. W. F. Beyer, Jr., and I. Fridovich, *Bchem* **26**, 1251 (1987).
81. A. Carlioz, M. L. Ludwig, W. C. Stallings, J. A. Fee, H. M. Steinman and D. Touati, *JBC* **263**, 1555 (1988).
82. W. C. Stallings, K. A. Pattridge, P. K. Strong and M. L. Ludwig, *JBC* **259**, 10695 (1984).
83. J. A. Tainer, E. D. Getzoff, K. M. Beem, J. S. Richardson and D. C. Richardson, *JMB* **160**, 181 (1982).
84. V. W. F. Chan, M. J. Bjerrum and C. L. Borders, Jr., *ABB* **279**, 195 (1990).
85. W. F. Beyer, Jr., J. A. Reynolds and I. Fridovich, *Bchem* **28**, 4403 (1989).
86. C. J. Brock, J. I. Harris and S. Sato, *JMB* **107**, 175 (1976).
87. C. T. Privalle, W. F. Beyer, Jr., and I. Fridovich, *JBC* **264**, 2758 (1989).
88. M. E. McAdam, E. M. Fielden, F. Lavelle, L. Calabrese, C. Coco and G. Rotilio, *BJ* **167**, 271 (1977).
89. J. A. Fee, G. J. McClune, P. O. O'Neill and E. M. Fielden, *BBRC* **100**, 377 (1981).
90. J. A. Fee, G. J. McClure, A. L. Lees, R. Zidovetzki and I. Recht, *Isr. J. Chem.* **21**, 54 (1981).
91. C. Bull and J. A. Fee, *JACS* **107**, 3295 (1985).
92. A. Terech, J. Purcheault and C. Ferredini, *BBRC* **113**, 114 (1983).
93. J. Benovic, T. Tillman, A. Cudd and I. Fridovich, *ABB* **221**, 329 (1983).
94. C. L. Borders, Jr., P. J. Horton and W. F. Beyer, Jr., *ABB* **268**, 74 (1989).
95. W. C. Stallings, K. A. Pattridge and M. L. Ludwig, *in* "Superoxide and Superoxide Dismutase in Chemistry, Biology and Medicine" (G. Rotilio, ed.), p. 195. Elsevier, New York, 1986.
96. M. W. Parker and C. C. F. Blake, *FEBS Lett.* **229**, 377 (1988).
97. D. Touati, *J. Bact.* **155**, 1078 (1983).
98. W. F. Beyer, Jr., D. C. Clare and I. Fridovich, unpublished.

99. M. W. Parker, C. C. F. Blake, D. Barra, F. Bossa, M. E. Schinina, W. H. Bannister and J. V. Bannister, *Protein Eng.* 1, 393 (1987).

100. T. Isobe, I. Fang, D. Muno, T. Okuyama, D. Ohmori and F. Yamakura, *Biochem. Int.* 16, 495 (1988).

101. D. E. Ose and I. Fridovich, *JBC* 251, 1217 (1976).

102. J. A. Tainer, E. D. Getzoff, J. S. Richardson and D. C. Richardson, *Nature* 306, 284 (1983).

103. W. H. Koppenol, *in* "Oxygen and Oxy Radicals in Chemistry and Biology" (M. J. A. Rodgers and E. L. Powers, eds.), p. 671, Academic Press, New York, 1981.

104. A. Cudd and I. Fridovich, *JBC* 257, 11443 (1982).

105. D. P. Malinowski and I. Fridovich, *Bchem* 18, 5909 (1979).

106. M. L. Salin and D. Oesterhet, *ABB* 260, 806 (1988).

107. H. W. Dougherty, S. J. Sadowski and T. T. Baker, *JBC* 253, 5220 (1978).

108. D. A. Clare, J. Blum and I. Fridovich, *JBC* 259, 5932 (1984).

109. L. Britton and I. Fridovich, *ABB* 191, 198 (1978).

110. G. Beckman, *Hereditas* 73, 305 (1973).

111. P. M. Kahn, *ABB* 145, 470 (1971).

112. H. Tegelstrom, *Hereditas* 81, 185 (1975).

113. M. E. Marlin, B. R. Byers, M. O. J. Olson, M. L. Salin, J. E. L. Aruneaux and C. Tolbert, *JBC* 261, 9361 (1986).

114. B. Meier, D. Barra, F. Bossa, L. Calabrese and G. Rotilio, *JBC* 257, 13977 (1982).

115. H. Twilfer, K. Gersonde, B. Meier and A. C. Schwartz, *in* "Chemical and Biochemical Aspects of Superoxide and Superoxide Dismutase" (J. V. Bannister and H. A. O. Hill, eds.), Vol. 11A, p. 168. Elsevier/North-Holland, New York, 1980.

116. P. G. Vance, B. B. Keele, Jr., and K. V. Rajagopalan, *JBC* 247, 4782 (1972).

117. F. Yamakura and K. Suzuki, *BBRC* 72, 1108 (1976).

118. F. Yamakura, *J. Biochem.* 83, 849 (1978).

119. A. Anastasi, J. V. Bannister and W. H. Bannister, *Int. J. Biochem.* 7, 541 (1976).

120. D. E. Ose and I. Fridovich, *ABB* 194, 360 (1979).

121. C. J. Brock and J. G. Walker, *Bchem* 19, 2873 (1980).

122. C. J. Brock, J. I. Harris and S. Sato, *JMB* 107, 175 (1976).

123. S. Sato and J. I. Harris, *EJB* 73, 373 (1977).

124. J. V. Bannister, A. Desideria and G. Rotilio, *FEBS Lett.* 188, 91 (1985).

125. K. Puget, F. Lavelle and A. M. Michelson, *in* "Superoxide and Superoxide Dismutase" (A. M. Michelson, J. M. McCord and I. Fridovich, eds.), p. 139. Academic Press, New York, 1977.

126. D. Klug-Roth, I. Fridovich and I. Rabani, *JACS* 95, 2786 (1973).

127. E. M. Fielden, P. B. Roberts, R. C. Bray, D. J. Lowe, G. N. Mautner, G. Rotilio and L. Calabrese, *BJ* 139, 49 (1974).

128. F. Lavelle, M. G. McAdam, E. M. Fielden and P. B. Roberts, *BJ* 161, 3 (1977).

129. M. G. McAdam, R. A. Fox, F. Lavelle and E. M. Fielden, *BJ* 165, 71 (1977).

130. M. Pick, J. Rabani, F. Yost and I. Fridovich, *JACS* 96, 7329 (1974).

131. E. K. Hodgson and I. Fridovich, *Bchem* 14, 5294 (1975).

132. N. J. Blackburn, S. S. Hasnain, N. Binstead, G. P. Diakun, G. D. Garner and P. F. Knowles, *BJ* 219, 985 (1984).

133. E. D. Getzoff and J. A. Tainer, *in* "Proceedings of the Fifth International Symposium on Superoxide and Superoxide Dismutases" (G. Czapski, ed.). Harwood Academic Publ., London, in press.

134. C. V. Bugrii and V. V. Kukhlin, *J. Theor. Biol.* 90, 161 (1981).

135. D. M. Dooley, J. F. Koras, T. F. Jones, C. E. Coti and S. B. Smith, *Inorg. Chem.* 25, 4761 (1986).

136. F. Yamakura, *BBRC* **122**, 635 (1984).
137. C. S. Moody and H. M. Hassan, *PNAS* **79**, 2855 (1982).
138. M. K. Brawn and I. Fridovich, *J. Bact.* **260**, 922 (1985).
139. S. B. Farr, R. d'Ari and D. Touati, *PNAS* **83**, 8268 (1986).
140. J. A. Imlay, S. M. Chin and S. Linn, *Science* **240**, 640 (1988).
141. A. C. de Mello Filho and R. Meneghini, *BBA* **847**, 82 (1985).
142. J. A. Imlay and S. Linn, *Science* **240**, 1302 (1988).
143. C. C. Winterbourn, J. K. French and R. F. C. Claridge, *FEBS Lett.* **94**, 269 (1978).
144. C. C. Winterbourn, *Free Radicals Biol. Med.* **3**, 33 (1987).
145. M. J. D. Rush, Z. Maskos and W. H. Koppenol, *FEBS Lett.* **1**, 121 (1990).
146. J. H. Jackson, E. Gajewski, I. U. Schraufstatter and P. A. Hyslop, *J. Clin. Invest.* **84**, 1644 (1989).
147. F. Hutchinson, *This Series* **32**, 115 (1985).
148. J. F. Ward, W. F. Blakely and E. I. Joner, *Radiat. Res.* **103**, 383 (1985).
149. H. N. Ananthaswamy and A. Eisenstark, *J. Bact.* **130**, 187 (1977).
150. J. Carlsson and V. S. Carpenter, *J. Bact.* **142**, 319 (1980).
151. J. A. Imlay and S. Linn, *J. Bact.* **169**, 2967 (1987).
152. B. Demple, J. Halbrook and S. Linn, *J. Bact.* **153**, 1079 (1983).
153. B. Demple, A. Johnson and D. Fung, *PNAS* **83**, 7731 (1986).
154. R. P. Cunningham, S. M. Saporito, S. G. Spitzer and B. Weiss, *J. Bact.* **168**, 1120 (1986).
155. A. W. Johnson and B. Demple, *JBC* **263**, 18009 (1988).
156. B. Demple and S. Linn, *Nature* **296**, 773 (1982).
157. D. E. Helland, P. W. Doetsch and W. A. Haseltine, *MCBiol* **6**, 1983 (1986).
158. M. C. Hollstein, P. Brooks, S. Linn and B. N. Ames, *PNAS* **81**, 4003 (1984).
159. R. P. Cunningham and B. Weiss, *PNAS* **82**, 474 (1985).
160. J.-J. Lin and A. Sancar, *Bchem* **28**, 7979 (1989).
161. L. H. Breimer and T. Lindahl, *Mutat. Res.* **150**, 85 (1985).
162. O. Goerlich, P. Quillardet and M. Hofnung, *J. Bact.* **171**, 6141 (1989).
163. E. Chan and B. Weiss, *PNAS* **84**, 3189 (1987).
164. M. K. Shigenaga, C. J. Gineno and B. N. Ames, *PNAS* **86**, 9697 (1989).
165. J. A. Imlay and S. Linn, *J. Bact.* **166**, 519 (1986).
166. M. Morimyo, *J. Bact.* **152**, 208 (1982).
167. G. Storz, M. F. Christman, H. Sies and B. N. Ames, *PNAS* **84**, 8917 (1987).
168. H. E. Schellhorn and H. M. Hassan, *Can. J. Microbiol.* **34**, 1171 (1988).
169. E. M. Gregory and I. Fridovich, *J. Bact.* **114**, 543 (1973).
170. H. M. Hassan and I. Fridovich, *J. Bact.* **129**, 1574 (1977).
171. C. J. Nettleton, C. Bull, T. O. Baldwin and J. A. Fee, *PNAS* **81**, 4970 (1984).
172. J. R. Schiavone and H. M. Hassan, *JBC* **263**, 4269 (1988).
173. D. Touati, *J. Bact.* **170**, 2511 (1988).
174. C. S. Moody and H. M. Hassan, *JBC* **259**, 12821 (1984).
175. E. C. Niederhoffer, C. M. Nairanjo and J. A. Fee, *in* "Metal Ion Homeostasis: Molecular Biology and Chemistry" (D. H. Hamer and D. R. Winge, eds.), p. 149. Liss, New York, 1989.
176. Y. Takeda and H. Avila, *NARes* **14**, 4577 (1986).
177. S. M. Naik and H. M. Hassan, *PNAS* **87**, 2618 (1990).
178. M. D. Scott, S. R. Meshnick and J. W. Eaton, *JBC* **262**, 3640 (1987).
179. C. A. Bloch and F. M. Ausubel, *J. Bact.* **168**, 795 (1986).
180. J. P. Phillips, S. D. Campbell, D. Michaud, M. Charbonneau and A. J. Hilliker, *PNAS* **86**, 2761 (1989).
181. T. Bilinski, Z. Krawiec, A. Liczmanski and J. Litwinska, *BBRC* **130**, 533 (1985).

182. A. P. G. M. van Loon, B. Pesold-Hurt and G. Schatz, *PNAS* **83**, 3820 (1986).
183. D. E. Boehme, K. Vincent and O. R. Brown, *Nature* **262**, 418 (1976).
184. O. E. Brown and R. L. Seither, *Fund Appl. Toxicol.* **3**, 209 (1983).
185. G. Czapski, S. Goldstein and D. Meyerstein, *Free Radical Res. Commun.* **4**, 231 (1988).
186. D. O. Natvig, K. Imlay, D. Touati and R. A. Hallewell, *JBC* **262**, 14697 (1987).
187. C. Bowler, T. Alliotte, M. Van den Bulcke, G. Bauw, J. Vandekerckhove, M. Van Montagu and D. Inze, *PNAS* **86**, 3239 (1989).
188. P. Chary and D. O. Natvig, *J. Bact.* **171**, 2646 (1989).
189. A. Heimberger and A. Eisenstark, *BBRC* **154**, 392 (1988).
190. B. Demple and J. Halbrook, *Nature* **304**, 466 (1983).
191. M. F. Christman, R. W. Morgan, F. S. Jacobson and B. N. Ames, *Cell* **41**, 753 (1985).
191a. G. Storz, L. A. Tartaglia and B. N. Ames, *Science* **248**, 189 (1990).
192. F. S. Jacobson, R. W. Morgan, M. F. Christman and B. N. Ames, *J. Bact.* **171**, 2049 (1989).
193. H. E. Schellhorn and H. M. Hassan, *J. Bact.* **170**, 4286 (1988).
194. B. D. Sak, A. Eisenstark and D. Touati, *PNAS* **86**, 3271 (1989).
195. J. T. Greenberg and B. Demple, *J. Bact.* **171**, 3933 (1989).
196. L. K. B. Walkup and T. Kogoma, *J. Bact.* **171**, 1476 (1989).
197. T. Kogoma, S. B. Farr, K. M. Joyce and D. O. Natvig, *PNAS* **85**, 4799 (1988).
198. A. Meister and M. E. Anderson, *ARB* **52**, 711 (1983).
199. J. T. Greenberg and B. Demple, *J. Bact.* **168**, 1026 (1986).
200. B. M. Babior, *Can. J. Physiol. Pharmacol.* **60**, 1353 (1982).
201. J. M. McCord, S. H. Stokes and K. Wong, *Adv. Inflammation Res.* **1**, 273 (1979).
202. J. M. McCord, *FP* **46**, 2402 (1987).
203. H. M. Hassan and I. Fridovich, *ABB* **196**, 385 (1979).
204. M. L. Salin, M. V. Duke, D. Oesterhelt and D. P. Ma, *Gene* **70**, 153 (1988).
205. S. Sato, Y. Nakoda and K. Nakazawa-Tomizawa, *BBA* **912**, 178 (1987).
206. J. A. White and J. G. Scandalios, *BBA* **951**, 61 (1988).
207. R. A. Hallewell, G. T. Mullenbach, M. M. Stempien and G. I. Bell, *NARes* **14**, 9539 (1986).
208. Y. S. Ho and J. D. Crapo, *NARes* **15**, 10070 (1987).
209. D. Barra, M. E. Schinia, M. Simmaco, J. V. Bannister, W. H. Bannister, G. Rotilio and F. Bossa, *JBC* **259**, 12595 (1984).
210. Y. Beck, R. Oren, B. Amit, A. Levanon, M. Gorecki and J. R. Hartman, *NARes* **15**, 9076 (1987).
211. Y. S. Ho and J. D. Crapo, *FEBS Lett.* **229**, 256 (1988).
212. C. Ditlow, J. T. Johansen, B. M. Martin and I. Svendsen, *Carlsberg Res. Commun.* **47**, 81 (1982).
213. C. A. M. Marres, A. P. G. M. Van Loon, P. Oudshoorn, H. Van Steig, L. A. Grivell and E. C. Salter, *EJB* **147**, 153 (1985).
214. H. M. Steinman, *JBC* **253**, 8708 (1978).
215. M. G. Schinina, L. Maffey, D. Barra, F. Bossa, K. Puget and A. M. Michelson, *FEBS Lett.* **221**, 87 (1987).
216. T. Isobe, Y. I. Fang, D. Muro, T. Okuyama, D. Ohmori and F. Yamakura, *FEBS Lett.* **223**, 92 (1987).
217. D. Barra, M. G. Schinina, W. H. Bannister, J. V. Bannister and F. Bossa, *JBC* **262**, 1001 (1987).
218. D. E. J. Laudenbach, C. G. Trick and N. A. Straus, *MGG* **216**, 455 (1989).

Genetics of Human Alcohol-Metabolizing Enzymes

Akira Yoshida,
Lily C. Hsu
and Michio Yasunami

Department of Biochemical Genetics
Beckman Research Institute of the City
of Hope
Duarte, California 91010

Large numbers of alcohol dehydrogenase isozymes and aldehyde dehydrogenase isozymes have been found in humans and other mammals. These enzymes oxidize various biogenic and exogenic alcohols and aldehydes. More than 80% of ethanol administered is oxidized by alcohol dehydrogenase (alcohol:NAD$^+$ oxidoreductase, EC 1.1.1.1), and most of the acetaldehyde thus formed is further oxidized to acetate by aldehyde dehydrogenase (aldehyde:NAD$^+$ oxidoreductase, EC 1.2.1.3) in the liver. In recent years, several genes that govern the synthesis of some of these enzymes have been cloned and characterized. Genetic variants, polymorphisms, and modes of gene expression have also been studied. Relationships between the genetic variations and alcohol-related physiological problems have become apparent. We review here our current knowledge of the molecular genetics of human alcohol dehydrogenase and aldehyde dehydrogenase.

I. Alcohol Dehydrogenase

Alcohol dehydrogenases (ADH; EC 1.1.1.1) are enzymes catalyzing the conversion of various alcohols to the corresponding aldehydes by means of an NAD$^+$-dependent oxidation. The human ADH isozyme system is extremely complex and varied among individuals. Based on analyses of electrophoretic variations and the mode of inheritance of isozyme patterns, it was proposed (1–3) that: (1) three non-allelic loci (ADH_1, ADH_2, and ADH_3)

Progress in Nucleic Acid Research
and Molecular Biology, Vol. 40

are involved in the synthesis of three types of subunits, α, β, and γ, respectively; (2) The ADH_2 and ADH_3 loci are dimorphic, that is, there are two common alleles, ADH_2^1 and ADH_2^2, and ADH_3^1 and ADH_3^2, respectively, in each locus; and (3) the catalytically active ADH isozymes are homo- and heterodimers of these wild-type and variant-type subunits. Later, an additional common variant allele (ADH_2^3) in the ADH_2 locus was found in American blacks (4). The model proposed has been confirmed by cloning and by characterization of cDNAs and genes.

The isozymes produced by these three loci exhibit high catalytic activity for the oxidation of short-chain aliphatic alcohols, e.g., ethanol, and are strongly inactivated by pyrazole. These isozymes are grouped as class-I ADH (5).

Another type of ADH, which exhibits high catalytic activity for the oxidation of long-chain aliphatic alcohols and aromatic alcohols and is less sensitive to pyrazole, is classified as class-II ADH (6). The subunit of this enzyme was named π, and the gene is designated ADH_4. Still another type of ADH, which has virtually no activity for ethanol oxidation, but which exhibits high activity for the oxidation of long-chain alcohols and is completely insensitive to pyrazole, is classified as class-III ADH (7). This isozyme consists of a χ subunit controlled by the ADH_5 locus.

These three classes of ADH isozymes are found in other mammals as well.

A. Biochemistry of the ADH Enzyme System

1. DISTRIBUTION OF ISOZYMES

The class-I ADHs are most abundant in liver, but exist also in other tissues: e.g., the β subunit in fetal and adult lungs and in adult intestine, and the γ subunit in fetal kidney and in fetal and adult gastrointestinal tracts (1). The class-I ADH activity is not detectable in brain, skin fibroblasts, and erythrocytes.

The class-II ADH (ππ enzyme) is found primarily in liver (6). A similar activity is also detectable in the gastrointestinal tract (2). It remains to be elucidated whether or not the latter isozyme(s) is identical to the liver ππ enzyme. The class-III ADH (χχ enzyme) is found in all tissues examined, including brain, testis, and red blood cells (8, 9).

2. EXOGENOUS AND ENDOGENOUS SUBSTRATES

Ingested ethanol is oxidized mainly by the class-I ADH in liver. The class-II ADH (ππ enzyme), which has a higher K_m for ethanol than does the class-I ADH, may also play some role in ethanol oxidation when the tissue ethanol level exceeds 20 mM (6). It has long been known that females are more susceptible to alcoholic liver injury than are males. Recently, it was reported that a significant amount of orally administered ethanol was metabolized in the stomach of males, but not of females, and ADH activity of stomach mucous membrane is substantially higher in males than in females (10). The nature of this ADH isozyme remains to be examined.

Liver metabolizes biologically active amines, e.g., dopamine by class-I ADH (11), norepinephrine by class-II ADH (12), and serotonin by both (13). The facts suggest relationships between alcoholism and the metabolism of neurotransmitters. ADH consisting of γ subunits exhibits 3β-hydroxy-5β-steroid dehydrogenase activity (14). Testosterone is an allosteric regulator for ADH consisting of the γ subunit, and may thus play a role in the metabolism of androgens (15). 16-Hydroxyhexadecanoic acid is a "good" substrate for class-I ADHs; hence, these enzymes may take part in fatty acid oxidation (16). The deficiency of other fatty alcohol oxidation system(s) causes the neurological disorder Sjögren–Larsson syndrome (17).

Rat liver class-I ADH can convert the endogenously generated toxic aldehyde 4-hydroxynonenal to the less toxic alcohol form (18). Human class-I ADH may have the same activity. Ingested ethanol would compete with the physiological substrates and disturb the above-mentioned detoxification by ADH.

The molecular identity of rat class-III ADH and glutathione-dependent formaldehyde dehydrogenase (EC 1.2.1.1) was recently reported (19). By analogy, the human class-III ADH (χχ enzyme) may also exhibit a similar aldehyde dehydrogenase activity, e.g., oxidation of S-hydroxymethylglutathione into S-formylglutathione in the presence of NAD^+. A significant amount of S-hydroxymethylglutathione exists in most tissues, and the class-III ADH (formaldehyde dehydrogenase; EC 1.2.1.1) may be involved in glutathione metabolism (19).

Rat retina and hamster testis contain ADH that catalyzes the conversion of trans-retinol to retinaldehyde (20, 21). This ADH may play a role in the activation of vitamin A. Analogous ADH isozymes may exist also in humans.

3. STRUCTURE

The amino-acid sequences of five human ADH subunits (α, β, γ, π, and χ) have been determined by direct protein sequencing and also deduced from the nucleotide sequences of the corresponding cDNAs (22–29) (Fig. 1).

The best-studied ADH is the horse ADH-EE isozyme. The three-dimensional structure and detailed kinetic mechanism of this ADH have been well documented. The degree of resemblance (positional identity) between horse E subunit (consisting of 374 amino-acid residues) and the human class-I ADH subunits (consisting of 374 amino-acid residues) is about 87%. Thus,

```
          1                                                                                              29
α     (Met)Ser Thr Ala Gly Lys Val Ile Lys Cys Lys Ala Ala Val Leu Trp Glu Leu Lys Lys Pro Phe Ser Ile Glu Glu Val Glu Val Ala
β     (Met)Ser Thr Ala Gly Lys Val Ile Lys Cys Lys Ala Ala Val Leu Trp Glu Leu Lys Lys Pro Phe Ser Ile Glu Asp Val Glu Val Ala
γ     (Met)Ser Thr Ala Gly Lys Val Ile Lys Cys Lys Ala Ala Val Leu Trp Glu Leu Lys Lys Pro Phe Ser Ile Glu Glu Val Glu Val Ala
π     (Met)Gly Thr Lys Gly Lys Val Ile Lys Cys Lys Ala Ala Ile Ala Trp Glu Ala Gly Lys Pro Leu Cys Ile Glu Glu Val Glu Val Ala
χ     --- ---(Met)Ala Asn Glu Val Ile Lys Cys Lys Ala Ala Ile Ala Trp Glu Ala Gly Lys Pro Leu Ser Ile Glu Glu Ile Glu Ile Ala
ADH6  (Met)Ser Thr Thr Gly Gln Val Ile Arg Cys Lys Ala Ala Ile Leu Trp Lys Pro Gly Ala Pro Phe Ser Ile Glu Glu Val Glu Val Ala

          30                                                                                             59
α     Pro Pro Lys Ala His Glu Val Arg Ile Lys Met Val Ala Val Gly Ile Cys Gly Thr Asp Asp His Val Val Ser Gly Thr Met Val Thr
β     Pro Pro Lys Ala Tyr Glu Val Arg Ile Lys Met Val Ala Val Gly Ile Cys Arg Thr Asp Asp His Val Val Ser Gly Asn Leu Val Thr
γ     Pro Pro Lys Ala His Glu Val Arg Ile Lys Met Val Ala Val Gly Ile Cys Arg Thr Asp Asp His Val Val Ser Gly Ala His Val Thr
π     Pro Pro Lys Ala His Glu Val Arg Ile Gln Ile Ile Ala Thr Ser Leu Cys His Thr Asp Ala Ser Val Ile Asp Ser Lys Phe Glu Gly
χ     Pro Pro Lys Ala His Glu Val Arg Ile Lys Ile Ile Ala Thr Ala Leu Cys His Thr Asp Ala Tyr Thr Leu Ser Gly Ala Asp Pro Glu
ADH6  Pro Pro Lys Ala Gly Glu Val Arg Ile Lys Val Val Ala Thr Ala Leu Cys Gly Thr Glu Met Lys Val Leu Gly Ser Lys His Leu Glu

          60  61                                                                                         88
α     Pro --- Leu Pro Val Ile Leu Gly His Glu Ala Ala Gly Ile Val Glu Ser Val Gly Glu Gly Val Thr Thr Val Lys Pro Gly Asp Lys
β     Pro --- Leu Pro Val Ile Leu Gly His Glu Ala Ala Gly Ile Val Glu Ser Val Gly Glu Gly Val Thr Thr Val Lys Pro Gly Asp Lys
γ     Pro --- Leu Pro Val Ile Leu Gly His Glu Ala Ala Gly Ile Val Glu Ser Val Gly Glu Gly Val Thr Thr Val Lys Pro Gly Asp Lys
π     Leu Ala Phe Pro Val Ile Leu Gly His Glu Ala Ala Gly Ile Val Glu Ser Ile Gly Pro Gly Val Thr Asn Val Lys Pro Gly Asp Lys
χ     Gly Cys Phe Pro Val Ile Leu Gly His Glu Gly Ala Gly Ile Val Glu Ser Ile Gly Glu Gly Val Thr Ser Val Lys Leu Ala Gly Asp Thr
ADH6  Val Leu Tyr Pro Thr Ile Leu Gly His Glu Gly Ala Gly Ile Val Glu Ser Ile Gly Glu Gly Val Thr Ser Val Lys Pro Gly Asp Lys

          89                                                                                             118
α     Val Ile Pro Leu Ala Ile Pro Gln Cys Gly Lys Cys Arg Ile Cys Lys Asn Pro Glu Ser Asn Tyr Cys Leu Lys Asn Asp Leu Gly Asn
β     Val Ile Pro Leu Phe Thr Pro Gln Cys Gly Lys Cys Arg Val Cys Lys Asn Pro Glu Ser Asn Tyr Cys Leu Lys Asn Asp Leu Gly Asn
γ     Val Ile Pro Leu Phe Thr Pro Gln Cys Gly Lys Cys Arg Val Cys Lys Asn Pro Glu Ser Asn Tyr Cys Leu Lys Asn Asp Val Ser Asn
π     Val Ile Pro Leu Tyr Ala Pro Leu Cys Arg Lys Cys Lys Phe Cys Leu Ser Pro Leu Thr Asn Leu Cys Gly Lys Ile Ser Asn Leu Lys
χ     Val Ile Pro Leu Tyr Thr Pro Gln Cys Gly Glu Cys Thr Ser Cys Leu Asn Ser Glu Gly Asn Phe Cys Ile Gln Phe Lys Gln Ser Lys
ADH6  Val Ile Thr Leu Phe Leu Pro Gln Cys Gly Glu Cys Thr Ser Cys Leu Asn Ser Glu Gly Asn Phe Cys Ile Gln Phe Lys Gln Ser Lys

          119 121             122                                                                        144
α     Pro Gln Gly --- --- --- --- Thr Leu Gln Asp Gly Thr Ser Arg Phe Thr Cys Arg Arg Lys Pro Ile His His Phe Leu Gly Ile Ser
β     Pro Arg Gly --- --- --- --- Thr Leu Gln Asp Gly Thr Arg Arg Phe Thr Cys Arg Gly Lys Pro Ile His His Phe Val Gly Thr Ser
γ     Pro Arg Gly --- --- --- --- Thr Leu Gln Asp Gly Thr Arg Arg Phe Thr Cys Ser Gly Lys Pro Ile His His Phe Val Gly Thr Ser
π     Ser Pro Ala Ser Asp Gln Gln Leu Met Glu Asp Lys Thr Ser Arg Phe Thr Cys Lys Gly Lys Pro Val Tyr His Phe Met Gly Thr Ser
χ     Gly Lys Lys Gly --- --- --- --- Leu Met Pro Asp Gly Thr Ser Arg Phe Thr Cys Lys Gly Lys Ser Ile Tyr His Phe Gly Asn Thr Ser
ADH6  Thr Gln --- --- --- --- --- Leu Met Ser Asp Gly Thr Ser Arg Phe Thr Cys Lys Gly Lys Ser Ile Tyr His Phe Gly Asn Thr Ser

          145                                                                                            174
α     Thr Phe Ser Gln Tyr Thr Val Val Asp Glu Asn Ala Val Ala Lys Ile Asp Ala Ala Ser Pro Leu Glu Lys Val Cys Leu Ile Gly Cys
β     Thr Phe Ser Gln Tyr Thr Val Val Asp Glu Asn Ala Val Ala Lys Ile Asp Ala Ala Ser Pro Leu Glu Lys Val Cys Leu Ile Gly Cys
γ     Thr Phe Ser Gln Tyr Thr Val Val Asp Glu Asn Ala Val Ala Lys Ile Asp Ala Ala Ser Pro Leu Glu Lys Val Cys Leu Ile Gly Cys
π     Thr Phe Ser Gln Tyr Thr Val Val Ser Asp Ile Ser Ala Val Ala Lys Ile Asp Ala Ala Ser Pro Leu Glu Lys Val Cys Leu Ile Gly Cys
χ     Thr Phe Ser Glu Tyr Thr Val Val Ala Asp Ile Ser Val Ala Lys Ile Asp Pro Leu Ala Pro Leu Asp Lys Val Cys Leu Leu Gly Cys
ADH6  Thr Phe Cys Glu Tyr Thr Val Ile Lys Glu Ile Ser Val Ala Lys Ile Asp Ala Val Ala Pro Leu Glu Lys Val Cys Leu Ile Ser Cys

          175                                                                                            204
α     Gly Phe Ser Thr Gly Tyr Gly Ser Ala Val Asn Val Ala Lys Val Thr Pro Gly Ser Thr Cys Ala Val Phe Gly Leu Gly Gly Val Gly
β     Gly Phe Ser Thr Gly Tyr Gly Ser Ala Val Asn Val Ala Lys Val Thr Pro Gly Ser Thr Cys Ala Val Phe Gly Leu Gly Gly Val Gly
γ     Gly Phe Ser Thr Gly Tyr Gly Ser Ala Val Lys Val Ala Lys Val Thr Pro Gly Ser Thr Cys Ala Val Phe Gly Leu Gly Gly Val Gly
π     Gly Phe Ser Thr Gly Tyr Gly Ala Ala Ile Asn Asn Ala Lys Val Thr Pro Gly Ser Thr Cys Ala Val Phe Gly Leu Gly Gly Val Gly
χ     Gly Ile Ser Thr Gly Tyr Gly Ala Ala Ile Asn Thr Ala Lys Leu Glu Pro Gly Ser Thr Cys Ala Val Phe Gly Leu Gly Gly Val Gly
ADH6  Gly Phe Ser Thr Gly Phe Gly Ala Ala Ile Asn Thr Ala Lys Val Thr Pro Gly Ser Thr Cys Ala Val Phe Gly Leu Gly Gly Val Gly

          205                                                                                            234
α     Leu Ser Ala Ile Met Gly Cys Lys Ala Ala Gly Ala Ala Arg Ile Ile Ala Val Asp Ile Asn Lys Asp Lys Phe Ala Lys Ala Lys Glu
β     Leu Ser Ala Val Met Gly Cys Lys Ala Ala Gly Ala Ala Arg Ile Ile Ala Val Asp Ile Asn Lys Asp Lys Phe Ala Lys Ala Lys Glu
γ     Leu Ser Val Val Met Gly Cys Lys Ala Ala Gly Ala Ala Arg Ile Ile Ala Val Asp Ile Asn Lys Asp Lys Phe Ala Lys Ala Lys Glu
π     Leu Ser Val Ile Met Gly Cys Lys Ala Ala Gly Ala Ala Arg Ile Ile Gly Ile Asp Ile Asn Ser Glu Lys Phe Val Lys Ala Lys Glu
χ     Leu Ala Val Ile Met Gly Cys Lys Val Ala Gly Ala Ala Arg Ile Ile Gly Val Asp Ile Asn Lys Asp Lys Phe Lys Arg Ala Lys Glu
ADH6  Leu Ser Val Val Met Gly Cys Lys Ala Ala Gly Ala Ala Arg Ile Ile Gly Val Asp Val Asn Lys Glu Lys Phe Lys Lys Ala Gln Glu

          235                                                                                            264
α     Leu Gly Ala Thr Glu Cys Ile Asn Pro Gln Asp Tyr Lys Lys Pro Ile Gln Glu Val Leu Lys Glu Met Thr Asp Gly Gly Val Asp Phe
β     Leu Gly Ala Thr Glu Cys Ile Asn Pro Gln Asp Tyr Lys Lys Pro Ile Gln Glu Val Leu Lys Glu Met Thr Asp Gly Gly Val Asp Phe
γ     Leu Gly Ala Thr Glu Cys Ile Asn Pro Gln Asp Tyr Lys Lys Pro Ile Gln Glu Val Leu Lys Glu Met Thr Asp Gly Gly Val Asp Phe
π     Leu Gly Ala Thr Asp Cys Leu Asn Pro Arg Asp Leu Lys Lys Pro Ile Gln Glu Val Ile Ile Glu Leu Thr Lys Gly Gly Val Asp Phe
χ     Leu Gly Ala Thr Glu Cys Ile Asn Pro Gln Asp Phe Ser Lys Pro Ile Gln Glu Val Leu Ile Glu Met Thr Asp Gly Gly Val Asp Tyr
ADH6  Leu Gly Ala Thr Glu Cys Leu Asn Pro Gln Asp Phe Lys Lys Pro Ile Gln Glu Val Leu Phe Asp Met Thr Asp Ala Gly Ile Asp Phe

          265                                                                                            294
α     Ser Phe Glu Val Ile Gly Arg Leu Asp Thr Met Met Ala Ser Leu Leu Cys Cys His Glu Ala Cys Gly Thr Ser Val Ile Val Gly Val
β     Ser Phe Glu Val Ile Gly Arg Leu Asp Thr Met Met Ala Ser Leu Leu Cys Cys His Glu Ala Cys Gly Thr Ser Val Ile Val Gly Val
γ     Ser Phe Glu Val Ile Gly Arg Leu Asp Thr Met Met Ala Ser Leu Leu Cys Cys His Glu Ala Cys Gly Thr Ser Val Ile Val Gly Val
π     Ala Leu Asp Cys Ala Gly Gly Ser Glu Thr Met Lys Ala Ala Leu Asp Cys Thr Thr Ala Gly Trp Gly Ser Cys Thr Phe Ile Gly Val
χ     Ser Phe Glu Ala Ile Gly Asn Leu Asp Val Leu ... ... ... ... ... ... ... ... ... ... ... ... ... ... ... ... ... ...
ADH6  Cys Phe Glu Ala Ile Gly Asn Leu Asp Val Leu ... ... ... ... ... ... ... ... ... ... ... ... ... ... ... ... ... ...

          295                                                                                            324
α     Pro Pro Asp Ser Gln Asn Leu Ser Met Asn Pro Met Leu Leu Leu Thr Gly Arg Thr Trp Lys Gly Ala Ile Leu Gly Gly Phe Lys Ser
β     Pro Pro Ala Ser Gln Asn Leu Ser Ile Asn Pro Met Leu Leu Leu Thr Gly Arg Thr Trp Lys Gly Ala Ile Tyr Gly Gly Phe Lys Ser
γ     Pro Pro Asp Ser Gln Asn Leu Ser Ile Asn Pro Met Leu Leu Leu Thr Gly Arg Thr Trp Lys Gly Ala Ile Tyr Gly Gly Phe Lys Ser
π     Ala Ala Gly Glu Glu Ile Ala Thr Arg Pro Phe Gln Leu Val Thr Gly Arg Thr Trp Lys Gly Thr Ala Phe Gly Gly Trp Lys Ser
χ     Ala Ala Ser Gly Glu Glu Ile Ala Thr Arg Pro Phe Gln Leu Val Thr Gly Arg Thr Trp Lys Gly Thr Ala Phe Gly Gly Trp Lys Ser
ADH6  ... ... ... ... ... ... ... ... ... ... ... ... ... ... ... ... ... ... ... ... ... ... ... ... ... ... ... ... ...

          325                                                                                            354
α     Lys Glu Cys Val Pro Lys Leu Val Ala Asp Phe Met Ala Lys Lys Phe Ser Leu Asp Ala Leu Ile Thr His Val Leu Pro Phe Glu Lys
β     Lys Glu Gly Ile Pro Lys Leu Val Ala Asp Phe Met Ala Lys Lys Phe Ser Leu Asp Ala Leu Ile Thr His Val Leu Pro Phe Glu Lys
γ     Lys Glu Ser Val Pro Lys Leu Val Ala Asp Phe Met Ala Lys Lys Phe Ser Leu Asp Ala Leu Ile Thr His Asn Leu Pro Phe Glu Lys
π     Val Asp Ser Ile Pro Lys Leu Val Thr Asp Tyr Lys Asn Lys Lys Phe Asn Leu Asp Ala Leu Ile Thr His Thr Leu Pro Phe Asp Lys
χ     Val Glu Ser Val Pro Lys Leu Val Ser Glu Tyr Met Ser Lys Lys Ile Lys Val Asp Glu Phe Val Thr His Asn Leu Ser Phe Asp Glu
ADH6  ... ... ... ... ... ... ... ... ... ... ... ... ... ... ... ... ... ... ... ... ... ... ... ... ... ... ... ... ...

          355                                      374
α     Ile Asn Glu Gly Phe Asp Leu Leu His Ser Gly Lys Ser Ile Arg Thr Ile Leu Met Phe
β     Ile Asn Glu Gly Phe Asp Leu Leu His Ser Gly Lys Ser Ile Arg Thr Val Leu Thr Phe
γ     Ile Asn Glu Gly Phe Asp Leu Leu Arg Ser Gly Lys Ser Ile Arg Thr Ile Leu Thr Phe
π     Ile Ser Glu Gly Phe Glu Leu Leu Asn Ser Gly Gln Ser Ile Arg Thr Ile Leu Thr Phe
χ     Ile Asn Lys Ala Phe Glu Leu Met His Ser Gly Lys Ser Ile Arg Thr Val Val Lys Ile
ADH6  ... ... ... ... ... ... ... ... ... ... ... ... ... ... ... ... ... ... ...
```

FIG. 1. Amino-acid sequence of the ADH subunits. Amino-acid sequences determined by direct protein sequencing and deduced from nucleotide sequencing of the corresponding cDNA

the conformations of human class-I ADH isozymes are considered to be basically similar to that of the horse enzyme (30).

In the horse ADH-EE, a long cleft divides the subunit into two domains, i.e., a catalytic domain and a coenzyme binding domain. A pleated sheet and three α-helices, which consist of the amino-terminal half (residues 1–174) and the carboxy-terminal region (residues 319–374), form a catalytic domain. Two Zn atoms are bound in this domain, one close to the subunit border to stabilize the dimeric structure, the other located at the center of the active site to bear the catalytic activity. The three amino-acid residues, i.e., Cys-46, His-67, and Cys-174, are implicated in the ligation of this Zn atom and the formation of the active site.

The coenzyme binding domain is built up with six consecutive α and β structures of the carboxy-terminal half (residues 176–318). Coenzyme NAD$^+$ bound to this domain is located in the cleft between the catalytic domain and the coenzyme binding domain. The conformational changes thus induced convert the dimeric enzyme into an "active" form. Asp-223, which forms a hydrogen bond with adenosine ribose, determines the preference for NAD$^+$ to NADP$^+$ as a cofactor. Arg-271 is in contact with the adenine ring of NAD$^+$. Several amino-acid residues take part in the interaction with NAD$^+$ by hydrogen bonds: Asp-223 and Lys-228 with adenosine ribose; Arg-47 and Arg-369 with phosphate oxygens; and Ser-48 and His-51 with the nicotinamide ribose. The nicotinamide ring of NAD$^+$ is near the catalytic Zn and contacts Thr-178 and Val-203. Kinetic studies indicate that the release of a reduced coenzyme is a rate-limiting step in the ethanol oxidation by the horse ADH-EE.

The amino-acid sequences of the three types of human class-I ADH subunits, α, β, and γ, are very similar (93–95% positional identity) (23). However, distinct differences exist in the vicinity of the Zn-binding Cys-46: Cys–Gly–Thr in the α; Cys–Arg–Thr in the wild-type β$_1$; Cys–His–Thr in the Oriental-type β$_2$; and Cys–Arg–Ser in the γ. These differences can be correlated with their kinetic properties (23).

Most of the functionally important residues of the horse enzyme mentioned above are conserved in the human enzymes. Several notable differences in human enzymes, seen in the three-dimensional model, appear to influence enzymatic properties. The human γ subunit is very similar to the horse E subunit in the vicinity of the active-site Zn atom, except for a substitution of Leu-141 in the horse E by Val in the human γ subunit. The

---

clones are shown. Lines α (23, 24), β (22, 34), γ (23, 25), π (26), and χ (27–29) correspond to the respective subunits. ADH$_6$ indicates the sequence of the putative product of the *ADH$_6$* gene, the undetermined part of which is shown by dots (⋯). Gaps (———) are intentionally introduced to conserve positional matching among subunits. Numbering of residues is in accordance with that of the class-I isozymes.

substitution appears to allow the human γγ isozyme to accept bulky molecules, e.g., steroids, as substrates. A substitution of Ser-48 in the horse E by Thr in the human β makes the substrate binding pocket smaller, reducing the catalytic activity of human ββ enzyme for the oxidation of secondary alcohols and aromatic alcohols. Inversely, a substitution of Phe-93 in the horse E by Ala in the human α appears to make the human αα enzyme active for the oxidation of secondary alcohols.

4. EXPRESSION AND REGULATION

Class-I ADH Genes show development- and tissue-specific differences in expression. At embryonic and fetal stages, liver ADH activity and mRNA content are much lower than those in the adult (*31, 32*). The ADH_1 gene is expressed first and ADH_2 follows. Finally, ADH_3 is expressed after birth, i.e., the class-I ADH gene family is expressed from the downstream 3' end to the upstream 5' end (*33*). Individual α-, β-, and γ-mRNA components in adult and infant livers were examined using oligonucleotide probes highly specific for each mRNA (*32*). A marked size heterogeneity of β-mRNA, ranging from 1.6 kb to 5.2 kb, in which 2.4 kb and 3.5 kb are major components, was observed in adult liver. The γ-mRNA is homogeneous (~1.6 kb), and the α-mRNA contained a major 1.4-kb and minor 4.3-kb components. The amount of mRNA was much lower (~10% of adult), and mRNAs were less heterogeneous in infant liver, i.e., α-mRNA (1.6 kb) and the β-mRNA (1.6 kb and 3 kb), and no detectable γ-mRNA. The size heterogeneity of adult β-mRNA was generated by the utilization of multiple poly(A) signals of the ADH_2 gene (*22, 32, 34*).

Glucocorticoids and sex steroid hormones induce ADH activity in the mouse *in vivo* and in a rat hepatoma cell line *in vitro* (*35–37*). The elevation of ADH activity is accompanied by an increase in mRNA. It is conceivable that binding of a glucocorticoid receptor near the promoter region of the gene activates a transcription machinery. Indeed, several glucocorticoid-responsive elements (GRE-like sequence motifs) are found in human, mouse, and rat class-I ADH genes (*38–40*).

B. Genetics of Human ADH Isozymes

1. GENOMIC STRUCTURE

cDNAs and genes for all known ADH subunits (i.e., class-I α, β, and γ; class-II π; and class-III χ) have been cloned and characterized. In addition, a unique functional ADH cDNA and gene, which encode a hitherto-unclassified ADH isozyme, was recently cloned and analyzed. A non-functional, intronless pseudogene was also reported.

Full-length cDNAs for the α, β, and γ subunits have been cloned and characterized in our laboratory and others (22–26, 28, 29). The nucleotide sequences reported by these investigators are compatible with each other in the coding regions. However, several differences are noticeable in their non-coding regions. The differences could be due to sequence errors, poly-morphism, or even misprints.

Consensus nucleotide sequences of the α-, β-, and γ-cDNAs are shown in Fig. 2. A high degree of resemblance exists not only in their coding sequences, but also in their 3'-non-coding regions. The polyadenylation signal, AATAAA, is located at approximately the same position (~60 bp downstream from the termination codon), and the poly(A) sequence is also similarly located in α- and γ-cDNAs. β-cDNA, with a long 3'-non-coding sequence, contained three poly(A) signals, at ~110, ~210, and ~460 from the chain-termination codon (22). The existence of multiple poly(A) signals on the β-cDNA has been confirmed by other investigators (34).

The structure of the ADH_2 (β) gene was the first to be elucidated. The gene spans about 15 kb and contains nine coding exons interrupted by eight introns (38, 42, 43) (Fig. 3). The ADH_1 (α) gene also spans about 15 kb and contains nine comparable exons (41). The nucleotide sequences of all coding regions, and that of the intron–exon junctions of these two genes, have been determined. The ADH_3 (γ) gene is not yet well-analyzed. Judging from the high degree of resemblance (~95%) in the three types of cDNAs (Fig. 2), the genomic organization of the ADH_3 gene is presumably similar to those of the ADH_1 and ADH_2 genes.

The ADH_2 gene has several possible regulatory signals—such as GRE-like sequences, enhancer core-homology, TG3 motifs (inverted CACCC box), and CAAT box—in its upstream region (38). The rat and mouse class-I ADH genes also have some of these sequences in homologous regions (39, 40). The mouse class-I ADH gene contains two TG3 motifs, one with and the other without a palindromic CACGTG sequence, at a region from −468 to +53. TG3 motifs interact with nuclear proteins and direct the expression of a reporter gene (45). The same sequence motifs are found in the human ADH_2 gene at two regions, from −94 to −84 and from −72 to −64, from the initiation site (38). The fragment of ADH_2 gene that contains these two regions dictates accurate initiation of in vitro transcription in extracts of rat hepatoma cell lines (46).

Pulsed-field gel electrophoresis of genomic DNA digested by SfiI indicated that a 300-kb-long segment contains all three genes (33). Analysis of overlapping genomic clones revealed that the three genes are oriented in a head-to-tail fashion in the order 5'-ADH_3 (γ) → ADH_2 (β) → ADH_1 (α)-3' in the ADH cluster locus, which spans about 80 kb (33) (Fig. 3). The cluster locus was mapped on chromosome 4q21–23 by in situ hybridization (47).

A cDNA for the π subunit can encode 391 amino-acid residues, instead of

A

```
ADH2                    GAATTCCAGAGGCCGGGGGGGGGTGGGAAGTGAGGAAAAGAGA   AAGTGATTACAATTTATCACTTTAACTTAATATTTAAACTAATGAAAACAAAATCTTATC

ADH2   TAGAATTTGGAAGTCAATATTTTGATTGCTGGTTCAGTACCCTTTTATCTGTTTTGACAG   TCTGGGAATAATCCAGTGGGTGTGGCTTAAAGACATAGATCACGTGTGGAATTGGAATTG

α                                                     GATGCACTTGAG   CAGGGAAGAAATCCACAAGGACTCACCAGTCTCCTGGTCTGCAGAGAAGACAGAATCAAC
ADH2   GATGTTACACAAGCAAACAAAATAAATATCTGTGCAATATATCTGCTTTATGCACTCAAG   CAGAGAAGAAATCCACAAAGACTCACCAGTCTGCTGGTGGGCAGAGAAGACAGAAACGAC
β                                                     AGTGCACTCAAG   CAGAGAAGAAATCCACAAAGACTCACCAGTCTGCTGGTGGGCAGAGAAGACAGAAACGAC
γ                                                     ATGCACTCAAGC   AGAGAAAGAAATCCACAAGTACTCACCAGCCTCCTGGTCTGCAGAGAAGACAGAATCAAT
π                                                                C   GAGGAGTTTGAAGCTTTCTTAACTCAGAAAGAAACTTCCAACACAGTTTCCCAAAGAAAA
χ                                                                      GGGCATGGGCGCGGCCACCCCGGATGTCAGCCCCCCGCGCCGACCAGAATCCGTGAAC
ψADH5  CTCTACTCACAGATAAGCCAATCATGGAATGAGAATAGCAACAGTTCCTCTCAGACAGTA   ATAATCTAGGTTCTGCATTAATATACAGTCCATCCCTGGCGCCGACCAGAACCCGTGGAC
ADH6                                    CCTGTGTACCTTTGTACTTTCTACAG   TGAAAGTTTCTACAGGATCTCCCTTTCTCAATAAATTCATTTGCGGTGGAGAAAATCAGC

            1                                                                                            29
α      ATG AGC ACA GCA GGA AAA GTA ATC AAA TGC AAA GCA GCT GTG CTA TGG GAG TTA AAG AAA CCC TTT TCC ATT GAG GAG GTG GAG GTT GCA
β      ATG AGC ACA GCA GGA AAA GTA ATC AAA TGC AAA GCA GCT GTG CTA TGG GAG GTA AAG AAA CCC TTT TCC ATT GAG GAT GTG GAG GTT GCA
γ      ATG AGC ACA GCA GGA AAA GTA ATC AAA TGC AAA GCA GCT GTG CTA TGG GAG TTA AAG AAA CCC TTT TCC ATT GAG GAG GTA GAG GTT GCA
π      ATG GGC ACC AAG GGC AAA GTT ATT AAA TGC AAA GCA GCC ATC GCC TGG GAA GCA GGC AAG CCC CTT TGC ATT GAA GAG GTT GAA GTA GCT
χ      --- --- ATG GCG AAC GAG GTT ATC AAG TGC AAG GCT GCA GTT GCT TGG GAG GCT GGA AAG CCT CTC TCC ATA GAG GAG ATA GAG GTG GCA
ψADH5  --- --- ATG GTG AAC CAG GTT ATC AAG TGC AAG GCT GCA GTT GCC TGG GAG GCT GGA AAG CCT CTC TCC GTA GAG GAG ATA GAG GTG GCA
ADH6   ATG AGT ACT ACA GGC CAA GTC ATC AGA TGC AAA GCA GCC ATA CTC TGG AAG CCT GGT GCA CCA TTT TCT ATT GAG GAG GTA GAA GTG GCC

        30                                                                                                   59
α      CCT CCT AAG GCC CAT GAA GTT CGT ATT AAG ATG GTG GCT GTA GGA ATC TGT GGC ACA GAT GAC CAC GTG GTT AGT GGT ACC ATG GTG ACC
β      CCT CCT AAG GCT TAT GAA GTT CGC ATT AAG ATG GTG GCT GTA GGA ATC TGT CGC ACA GAT GAC CAC GTG GTT AGT GGC AAC CTG GTG ACC
γ      CCT CCT AAG GCT CAT GAA GTT CGC ATT AAG ATG GTG GCT GCA GGA ATC TGT CGT TCA GAT GAG CAT GTG GTT AGT GGC AAC CTG GTG ACC
π      CCC CCC AAG GCT CAT GAA GTT CGC ATT CAG ATC ATT GCT ACC TCC CTG TGC CAT ACT GAT GCC AGT GTT ATC GAT TCT AAA TTT GAG GGC
χ      CCC CCA AAG GCT CAT GAA GTT CGA ATC AAG ATC ATT GCC ACT GCG GTT TGC CAC ACC GAT GCC TAT ACC CTG AGT GGA GCT GAT CCT GAG
ψADH5  CCC CTA AAG GCT CGT GAA GTT TGA ATC AAG ATC ATT GCC ACT GCA GTT TGC CAT ACC AAT GCC TAT ACC CTG AGC AGA GCT GAT CCT GAG
ADH6   CCA CCA AAG GCA AAG GAG GTT CGC ATA AAG GTT GTG GCC ACC GGA CTG TGT GGT ACA GAG ATG AAA GTG TTG GGG AGT AAA CAC TTG GAG

        60      61                                                                                           88
α      CCA --- CTT CCT GTG ATT TTA GGC CAT GAG GCA GCC GGC ATC GTG GAG AGT GTT GGA GAA GGG GTG ACT ACA GTC AAA CCA GGT GAT AAA -
β      CCC --- CTT CCT GTG ATT TTA GGC CAT GAG GCA GCC GGC ATC GTG GAG AGT GTT GGA GAA GGG GTG ACT ACA GTC AAA CCA GGT GAT AAA -
γ      CCC --- CTT CCT GTG ATT TTA GGC CAT GAG GCA GCC GGC ATC GTG GAA AGT GTT GGA GAA GGG GTG ACT ACA GTC AAA CCA GGT GAT AAA -
π      CTA GCT TTC CCA GTG ATC GTT GGC CAT GAG GCT GCA GGT ATT GTG GAA AGT ATT GGG CCA GGA GTG ACC AAC GTC AAA CCA GGT GAC AAA -
χ      GGT TGT TTT CCA GTG ATC TTG GGA CAT GAA GGT GCT GGA ATT GTG GAA AGT GTT GGT GAG GGA GTT ACT AAG CTG AAG GCG GGT GAC ACT -
ψADH5  GGT TGT TTT CCA GTG ATC TTG GGA CAT GAA TTG GCT GGA ATT GTG GGA AGT GTT GGT GAG GGA GTT GCT AAG CTG AAG GCG GGT GAT AAC T
ADH6   GTG TTG TAT CCC ACC ATC TTG GGC CAT GAA GGG GCT GGA ATC GTT GAG AGT ATT GGA GAA GGA GTA AGC ACA GTG AAA CCA GGT GAC AAA -

        89                                                                                                  118
α      GTC ATC CCA CTC GCT ATT CCT CAG TGT GGA AAA TGC AGA ATT TGT AAA AAC CCG GAG AGC AAC TAC TGC TTG AAA AAC GAT GTA AGC AAT
β      GTC ATC CCG CTC TTT ACT CCT CAG TGT GGA AAA TGC AGA GTT TGT AAA AAC CCG GAG AGC AAC TAC TGC TTG AAA AAT GAT CTA GGC AAT
γ      GTC ATC CCG CTC TTT ACT CCT CAG TGT GGA AAA TGC AGA ATT TGT AAA AAC CCA GAA AGC AAC TAC TGC TTG AAA AAT GAT CTA GGC AAT
π      GTA ATT CCA CTT TAT GCA CCT CTA TGT AGA AAA TGC AAG TTT TGT CTG AGT CCA CTC ACA AAT TTG TGT GGG AAA ATC AGT AAT CTC AAA
χ      GTC ATC CCA CTT TAC ATC CCA CAG TGT GGA GAA TGC AAA TTT TGT CTA AAT CCT AAA ACT AAC CTT TGC CAG AAG ATA AGA GTC ACT CAA
ψADH5  GTC ATC CCA TTT TAC ATC CCA CAG TGT GGA GAA TGC AAA TTT TGT CTA AAT CCT AAA ACT AAC CT- TGC CAG AAT ATA AGA GTC ACT CAA
ADH6   GTT ATC ACA CTC TTT CTG CCA CAG TGT GGA GAA TGT ACC TCT TGC CTG AAT TCT GAG GGC AAT TTT TGT ATA CAA TTC AAA CAG TCA AAA

        119     121                     122                                                                 144
α      CCT CAG GGG --- --- --- --- ACC CTG CAG GAT GGC ACC AGC AGG TTC ACC TGC AGG AGG AAG CCC ATC CAC CAC TTC CTT GGC ATC AGC
β      CCT CGG GGG --- --- --- --- ACC CTG CAG GAT GGC ACC AGG AGG TTC ACC TGC AGG GGG AAG CCC ATT CAC CAC TTC CTT GGC ACC AGC
γ      CCT CGG GGG --- --- --- --- ACC CTG CAG GAT GGC ACC AGG AGG TTC ACC TGC AGC GGG AAG CCC ATC CAC CAC TTC GTC GGC GTC AGC
π      AGT CCT GCT AGT GAT CAA CAA CTA ATG GAA GAC AAA ACC AGC AGG TTT ACC TGC AAA GGA AAA CCA GTT TAC CAT TTC TTT GGA ACC AGT
χ      GGG AAA GGA --- --- --- --- TTA ATG CCA GAT GGT ACC AGC AGA TTT ACT TGC AAA GGA AAG ACA ATT TTG CAT TAC ATG GGA ACC AGC
ψADH5  GGG AAA GGA --- --- --- --- TTA GTG CCA GAT GGT ACC AGC AGA TTT ACT TGC AAA GGA AAG ACA ATT TTA CAT TAC ATG GGA ACC AGC
ADH6   ACC CAA --- --- --- --- --- CTG ATG TCT GAT GGT ACC AGC AGG TTT ACC TGC AAG GGA AAA TCA ATA TAT CAC TTT GGT AAT ACC AGC

        145                                                                                                 174
α      ACC TTC TCA CAG TAC ACA GTG GTG GAT GAA AAT GCA GTA GCC AAA ATT GAT GCA GCC TCG CCT CTA GAG AAA GTC TGT CTC ATT GGC TGT
β      ACC TTC TCC CAG TAC ACG GTG GTG GAT GAG AAT GCA GTG GCC AAA ATT GAT GCA GCC TCG CCC CTG GAG AAA GTC TGC CTC ATT GGC TGT
γ      ACC TTC TCC CAG TAC ACA GTG GTG GAT GAG AAT GCA GTG GCC AAA ATT GAT GCA GCC TCG CCC CTG GAG AAA GTC TGC CTC ATT GGC TGT
π      ACA TTC TCT CAG TAC ACT GTG GTG TCA GAT ATC AAT CTT GCC AAA ATA GAT GAT GAT GCA AAT TTA GAG AGA GTT TGT CTG CTT GGA TGT
χ      ACA TTT TCT GAA TAC ACA GTT GTG GCT GAT ATC TCT GTT GCT AAA ATA GAT CCT TTA GCA CCT TTG GAT AAA GTC TGC CTT CTA GGT TGT
ψADH5  ACA TTT TCT GAA TGC ACA GTT GTG GCT GAT ATC TCT GTT GCT AAA ATA GAT TCT TTA GCA CCT TTG GAT AAA GTC TGC CTT CTA GGT TGT
ADH6   ACC TTC TGT GAA TAC ACA GTG ATA AAG GAA ATC TCA GTT GCC AAG ATT GAT GCA GTC GCT CCT CTA GAG AAA GTA TGC CTA ATT AGC TGT

        175                                                                                                 204
α      GGA TTT TCA ACT GGT TAT GGG TCT GCA GTC AAT GTT GCC AAG GTC ACC CCA GGC TCT ACC TGT GCT GTG TTT GGC CTG GGA GGG GTC GGC
β      GGA TTC TCG ACT GGT TAT GGG TCT GCA GTT AAC GTT GCC AAG GTC ACC CCA GGC TCT ACC TGT GCT GTG TTT GGC CTG GGA GGG GTC GGC
γ      GGA TTT TCG ACT GGT TAT GGG TCT GCA GTC AAA GTT GCC AAG GTC ACC CCA GGG TCT ACC TGT GCT GTG TTT GGC CTG GGA GGG GTC GGC
π      GGG TTT TCA ACT GGC TAT GGG GCT GCA ATC AAC AAT GCC AAG GTC ACC CCT GGT TCG ACT TGT GCT GTC TTT GGC CTA GGA GGT GTG GGT
χ      GGC ATT TCA ACC GGT TAT GGT GCT GCT GTG AAC ACT GCC AAG TTG GAG CCT GGC TCT GTT TGT GCC GTC TTT GGT CTG GGA GGA GTC GGA
ψADH5  GGC ATT TCA GCT GGT TAT GGT GCT GCT GTG AAC ACT GTC AAG GTG GGG CCT GGC TCT GTT TGG GCC GTC TTT GGC CTG GGA GGA GTT GGA
ADH6   GGC TTT TCC ACT GGG TTT GGT GCT GCA ATC AAT ACT GCC AAG GTG ACT CCA GGT TCT ACC TGT GCT GTG TTT GGC CTG GGA GGA GTC GGC

        205                                                                                                 234
α      CTA TCT GCT ATT ATG GGC TGT AAA GCA GCT GGG GCA GCC AGA ATC ATT GCG GTG GAC ATC AAC AAG GAC AAA TTT GCA AAG GCC AAA GAG
β      CTA TCT GCT GTT ATG GGC TGT AAA GCA GCT GGA GCA GCC AGA ATC ATT GCG GTG GAC ATC AAC AAG GAC AAA TTT GCA AAG GCC AAA GAG
γ      CTA TCT GTT GTT ATG GGC TGT AAA GCA GCT GGA GCA GCC AGA ATC ATT GCT GTG GAC ATC AAC AAG GAC AAA TTT GCA AAG GCT AAA GAG
π      CTT TCT GCT GTA ATG GGT TGT AAA GCA GCA GGA GCT TCC AGA ATC ATA GGT ATT GAC ATC AAC AGT GAG AAG TTT GTG AAG GCT AAA GCC
χ      TTG GCA GTT ATC ATG GGC TGT AAA GTG GCT GGT GCT TCC CGG ATC ATT GGT GTG GAC ATC AAT AAA GAT AAA TTT GCA AGG GCC AAA GAG
ψADH5  TTG ACA GTT ATC GTG GGC GGT AAA GTG GCT GGT GCA TCC CGG ATC ATT GGT GTG GAC ATC CAT CAA GAT AAA TTT CCA AGG GCT AAA GAG
ADH6   TTG TCT GTT GTC ATG GGT TGT AAA GCA GCA GGA GCA GCC AGG ATC ATT GGA GTG GAT GTC AAC AAG GAG AAA TTT AAG AAG GCA CAG GAA

        235                                                                                                 264
α      TTG GGG GCC ACT GAA TGC ATC AAC CCT CAA GAC TAC AAG AAA CCC ATC CAG GAG GTG CTA AAG GAA ATG ACT GAT GGA GGT GTG GAT TTT
β      TTG GGG GCC ACT GAA TGC ATC AAC CCT CAA GAC TAC AAG AAA CCC ATC CAG GAA GTG CTA AAG GAA ATG ACT GAT GGA GGT GTG GAT TTT
γ      TTG GGG GCC ACT GAA TGC ATC AAC CCT CAA GAC TAC AAG AAA CCC ATT CAG GAA GTG CTA AAG GAA ATG ACT GAT GGA GGT GTG GAT TTT
π      CTG GGA GCC ACT GAC TGC CTC AAT CCT AGA GAC TTA CAT AAA CCG ATC CAG GAA GTT ATC ATT GAA TTG ACC AAG GGA GGT GTG GAT TTT
χ      TTT GGA GCC ACT GAA TGT ATT AAC CCT CAG GAT TTT AGT AAA CCC ATC CAG GAA GTG CTC ATT GAG ATG ACC GAT GGA GGA GTG GAC TAT
ψADH5  TTT GGA GCC ACT GAA TGT ATG AAC CGT CAG -AT TTT AGT CAA CCC ATC CAG GAA GTG CTC ATT GAG CGG ACT GAT GGA GGA GTG GAC TAC
ADH6   TTG GGT GCT ACT GAG TGC CTC AAC CCT CAG GAC TTA AAG AAA CCC ATT CAA GAA GTT TTA TTT GAT ATG ACA GAT GCT GGT ATA GAC TTC

        265                                                                                                 294
α      TCA TTT GAA GTC ATC GGT CGG CTT GAC ACC ATG ATG GCT TCC CTG TTA TGT TGT CAT GAG GCA TGT GGC ACA AGT GTC ATC GTA GGG GTA
β      TCG TTT GAA GTC ATC GGT CGG CTT GAC ACC ATG ATG GCT TCC CTG TTA TGT TGT CAT GAG GCA TGT GGC ACA AGC GTC ATC GTA GGG GTA
γ      TCG TTT GAA GTC ATC GGT CGG CTT GAC ACC ATG ATG GCT TCC CTG TTA TGT TGT CAT GAG GCA TGT GGC ACA AGT GTC ATT GTA GGG GTA
π      GCC CTT GAC TGT GCA GGT GGA TCT GAA ACC ATG AAA GCA GCC CTG GAC TGT ACA ACC GCA GGC TGG GGA TCA TGT ACT TTC ATT GGA GTA
χ      TCC TTT GAA TGT ATT GGT AAT GTG AAG GTC ATG AGA GCA GCA CTT GAG GCA TGT CAC AAG GGC TGG GGC GTC AGC GTC GTG GTT GGA GTA
ψADH5  TCC TTT GAA TGT ATT AGG AAT GTC AAG GTC GTG AGA GCA GCA CTT GAG GCA TGT CAG CAG GGC TGG GGC GTC AGT GTG GTG GTT GGA GTA
ADH6   TGC TTT GAG GCC ATT GGA AAT CTG GAC GTT CTG

        295                                                                                                 324
α      CCT CCT GAT TCC CAA AAC CTC TCA ATG AAC CCT ATG CTG CTA CTG ACT GGA CGT ACC TGG AAG GGA GCT ATT CTT GGT GGC TTT AAA AGT
β      CCT CCT GCT TCC CAG AAC CTC TCA ATA AAC CCT ATG CTG CTA CTG ACT GGA CGC ACC TGG AAG GGG GCT GTT TAT GGT GGC TTT AAG AGT
γ      CCT CCT GAT TCC CAG AAC CTC TCA ATA AAC CCT ATG CTG CTA CTG ACT GGA CGC ACG TGG AAA GGA GCT ATT TTT GGA GGC TTT AAG AGT
π      GCT GCT GGT AGC AAA GGA TTG ACT ATT TTT CCA GAG GAG CTA ATA ATC GGC CGT ACT ATA AAT GGA ACA TTC TTT GGT GGT TGG AAA AGT
χ      GCT GCT TCA GGT GAA GAA ATT GCC ACT CGT CCA TTC CAG CTG GTA ACA GGT CGC ACA TGG AAA GGC ACT GCC TTT GGA GGA TGG AAG AGT
ψADH5  GCT GCT TCA GGT CAA GAA ATT GCC ACT CAT CCA TTC CAG CTG GTA ACA GGT CGC ACA TGG AAA GGC ACT GCC TTT GGA GGG TGA AAG AGT
```

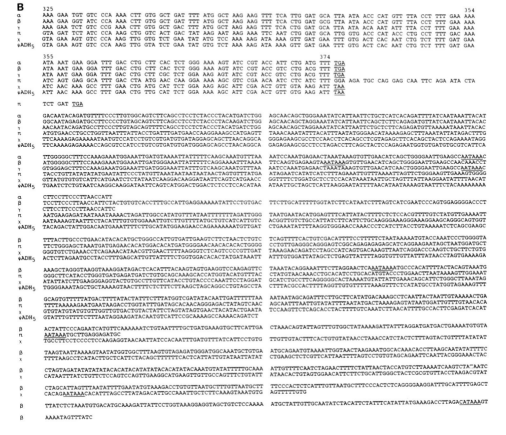

FIG. 2. Nucleotide sequence of cDNA and genomic clones for the ADH genes. Nucleotide sequences of the respective cDNA clones are shown in lines α (23, 24), β (22, 34), γ (23, 25), π (26), and χ (28, 29). The genomic upstream sequence of the ADH_2 gene is also shown in lines ADH_2 (38). ψADH_5 indicates the processed form of the pseudogene for the χ subunit (ADH_5 gene) (44). Lines ADH_6 are the partial sequence of cDNA for the ADH_6 gene. Gaps (———) are introduced to conserve positional matching among transcribed regions of the genes. Numbering is in accordance with that of the amino-acid residues of the class-I isozymes. Initiation ATG codons (including an additional upstream ATG codon found in χ-cDNA) and termination codons in-frame are underlined. In the lines for ADH_2, the transcriptional initiation site, the TATA box, and two conserved regions, which are considered to take part in the regulation of transcription, are underlined. Polyadenylation signals in downstream untranslated regions of each cDNA are also underlined.

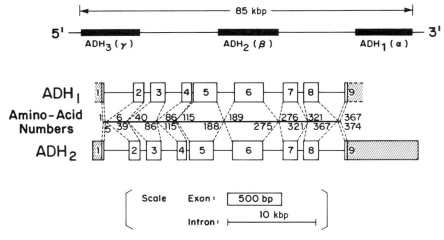

FIG. 3. Architectural configuration of the ADH cluster locus, and organization of ADH_1 and ADH_2 genes. Exons are boxed, and amino-acid sequences encoded by individual exons are indicated by dotted lines. Non-coding regions are shaded.

the 379 determined by protein sequencing, and contains four possible poly(A) signals in its extended 3′ region (25). There are two differences between the deduced and direct protein sequences. These differences could be due to the existence of polymorphism in the ADH_4 locus and post-translational cleavage of the COOH-terminal region (25). The ADH_4 gene has not yet been cloned, but it was mapped on chromosome 4q21–23 by *in situ* hybridization (48).

There are two reports on the isolation and characterization of χ-cDNA. One clone was in agreement with the 373 residues determined by direct protein sequencing (28), while the other differed by one residue at position 166 (Tyr instead of Asp) due to a single-base substitution, and could encode an additional 19 amino-acid residues, starting from an upstream initiation codon (29). It remains to be further examined whether or not post-translational cleavage of the NH_2-terminal occurred in the χ-subunit precursor.

The ADH_5 gene has not yet been well-analyzed. It has been reported that the ADH_5 gene has an intron at the position corresponding to the sixth intron of the ADH_1 and ADH_2 genes (44). The ADH_5 gene was mapped on chromosome 4q21–25 by segregation analysis (49).

A genomic DNA clone, which was hybridizable with a β-cDNA probe, contained no introns (44). It showed several structural defects, i.e., three frame shifts in the coding region with a total of 10 internal termination codons. Since the deduced amino-acid sequence is more similar to the class-III χ subunit (~89%) than to the class-I subunits (~57%) and the class-II subunit (~56%), it was proposed that the gene cloned is a non-functional pseudogene derived from the ADH_5 gene (44).

Recently, a genomic DNA segment with a high degree of homology to other ADH genes was cloned and analyzed (unpublished observation) (Figs. 1 and 2). The corresponding cDNA was obtained from a polymerase chain reaction (PCR)-amplified library prepared from the liver. A deduced amino-acid sequence indicated a positional identity of 68% with the class-I ADH subunits (α, β, and γ), 62% with the class-II subunit (π), and 63% with the class-III subunit (χ). Since this new gene cannot be put in any one of the three classes, it is designated ADH_6. The enzymatic property and physiological role of the ADH isozyme encoded by the ADH_6 gene remain to be studied.

2. Genetic Variants and Restriction-Fragment-Length Polymorphisms (RFLPs)

Three common alleles, i.e., ADH_2^1 for β_1, ADH_2^2 for β_2, and ADH_2^3 for β_3 exist in the ADH_2 locus, and two common alleles, i.e., ADH_3^1 for γ_1 and ADH_3^2 for γ_2, are found in the ADH_3 locus.

The molecular differences, at the protein level and at the gene level, of these genes and gene products have been elucidated (Table I).

The difference between the wild-type (β_1) and the Oriental atypical-type (β_2) subunit is a single amino-acid substitution, Arg $\rightarrow$ His, at the 47th position generated by the G·C $\rightarrow$ A·T base transition on exon 3 (22, 38, 50). These studies could not exclude the possibility of additional molecular differences between the β_1 and β_2 subunits, but determination of the nucleotide sequence of the cDNA for the β_2 subunit proved that the Arg $\rightarrow$ His substitution is the only difference between the two (51). The isozyme consisting of the atypical β_2 subunit exhibits about 100 times more catalytic activity for ethanol oxidation than the usual $\beta_1\beta_1$ isozyme at physiological pH (52).

The amino-acid substitution between the wild-type β_1 and the variant β_3 (β Indianapolis) is Arg $\rightarrow$ Cys at the 369th position (53). Deducing from the nucleotide sequence, this substitution was generated by the C·G $\rightarrow$ T·A base transition in exon 9. The catalytic activity of the isozyme consisting of a variant β_3 subunit is higher than that of usual $\beta_1\beta_1$ isozyme.

From the nucleotide sequences of cDNAs for the γ_1 and γ_2 subunits, two amino-acid differences, i.e., Arg $\rightarrow$ Glu at the 271st position and Ile $\rightarrow$ Val at the 349th position, were detected (24). The 276th position of the γ subunit was reported as Val, based on protein sequencing (54). From the cDNA sequence, this position should be Met (23). The difference is apparently an error in protein sequencing, not due to genetic polymorphism.

Discrepancies have been found between the amino-acid sequence of the π subunit and the nucleotide sequence of π-cDNA: position 303 is Arg in

TABLE I
ADH Genes and Gene Products

ADH class	Locus	Common allele	Subunit	Mutation site	Gene frequency
I	ADH_1	ADH_1	α		~100%
	ADH_2	ADH_2^1	β_1		Wild type, >90% in Caucasians
		ADH_2^2	β_2	Arg → His at position 47	Common in Orientals (~70%)
		ADH_2^3	β_3	Arg → Cys at position 369	Common in blacks (~16%)
	ADH_3	ADH_3^1	γ_1		Wild type, >90% in Orientals
		ADH_3^2	γ_2	Arg → Glu at position 271	Common in Caucasians (~40%)
				Ile → Val at position 349	
II	ADH_4	ADH_4^1	π_1		See text[a]
		ADH_4^2	π_2	Arg → Lys at position 302	
				Val → Ile at position 312	
III	ADH_5	$AIID_5$	χ		
	ADH_6	ADH_6		New gene and locus (see text)	

[a] From the discrepancies between the amino-acid sequence and the cDNA sequence (26).

cDNA but Lys in protein, and position 312 is Val in cDNA but Ile in protein (26). Two or more common alleles might exist in the ADH_4 locus.

Due to the high degree of similarity in the three class-I ADH loci, restriction-fragment patterns are very complex when Southern blot hybridization is carried out using cDNA probes or exon probes. Using a β-cDNA as probe, PvuII polymorphism was found in the cluster locus (55). Using less homologous intron sequences, one from the ADH_2 (β) gene and two from the ADH_3 (γ) gene as probes, RsaI polymorphism was found in the ADH_2 locus, and XbaI, MspI, and StuI polymorphisms were found in the ADH_3 locus (56). Frequencies of these polymorphisms differ widely between Caucasians and Orientals.

A tight linkage of ADH_3 and the epidermal growth factor gene (EGF) was detected in the study of RFLPs (57). The mutation, $G \cdot C \rightarrow A \cdot T$ on exon 3 of the ADH_2 locus, occurring in the Oriental atypical ADH_2^2 allele, creates a MaeIII cleavage site in the atypical allele. Thus, the MaeIII haplotype is polymorphic in Orientals (58).

The SacI haplotype is polymorphic in the ADH_5 locus (59), and the RFLP of the ADH_4 locus has not yet been reported.

3. GENETIC POLYMORPHISMS AND ALCOHOL-RELATED PROBLEMS

The class-I ADH exhibits high activity for ethanol oxidation, and is considered to play a major role in alcohol elimination. The class-II ADH and the ADH existing in stomach mucous membrane may also play a significant role when the tissue ethanol level reaches high concentrations (6, 10). The genetic differences in the ADH genes controlling the synthesis of these isozymes may affect the physiological reaction to ethanol. It has been suggested that the higher incidence of alcohol sensitivity (alcohol-flushing) in Orientals (50–90%) than in Caucasians (5–10%) (60) could be due to the rapid acetaldehyde formation by the more active $β_2$ enzyme produced by the Oriental atypical ADH_2^2 gene (61).

Genotypes of the ADH_2 locus can be determined by in-gel hybridization of endonuclease-digested DNA samples with allele-specific oligonucleotide probes (58, 62, 63), or dot hybridization of the targeted DNA region amplified by the PCR with the probes (64), or by digestion of amplified DNA samples with MaeIII.

Genotypes of the ADH_2 locus of Japanese "alcohol-flushers," "non-alcohol-flushers," patients with alcoholic liver diseases, and control subjects have been determined (62, 63) (Table II). No difference was found between the subjects with alcoholic liver diseases and controls in the frequency of the atypical ADH_2^2. Frequency of the ADH_2^2 was found to be higher in alcohol-flushers than in non-flushers, but statistical significance was not established in the sample size analyzed. As described in the following section, a strong

TABLE II
GENOTYPES OF ADH_2 AND $ALDH_2$ LOCI IN JAPANESE

ADH_2 locus	Genotype			Gene frequency	
	1/1	1/2	2/2	ADH_2^1	ADH_2^2
Controls ($n = 49$)	4	20	25	0.29	0.71
Patients with alcoholic liver disease ($n = 23$)	3	6	14	0.26	0.74
Alcohol-flushers ($n = 8$)	0	1	7	0.06	0.94
Non-flushers ($n = 6$)	0	3	3	0.25	0.75

$ALDH_2$ locus	Genotype			Gene frequency	
	1/1	1/2	2/2	$ALDH_2^1$	$ALDH_2^2$
Controls ($n = 49$)	21	22	6	0.65	0.35
Patients with alcoholic liver disease ($n = 23$)	20	3	0	0.93	0.07
Alcohol flushers ($n = 9$)	0	7	2	0.39	0.61
Non-flushers ($n = 6$)	5	1	0	0.92	0.08

correlation exists among alcohol-flushing, alcoholic liver diseases, and the genotypes of the mitochondrial aldehyde dehydrogenase $ALDH_2$. It can be concluded that the atypical ADH_2^2 gene has only a minor effect on the physiological reaction to alcohol.

A similar study has not yet been done on ADH_2^3, which is common in American blacks, on the two common alleles of the ADH_3 locus in Caucasians, and on the possible multiple alleles of the ADH_4 locus.

4. EVOLUTION OF THE ADH GENE FAMILY

The genes for ADH isozymes appear to have been generated by serial gene duplications and subsequent diversifications from a common ancestor gene for Zn-containing, NAD^+-dependent oxidoreductase. The following three major steps would occur in the course of the evolution of ADH isozymes. (1) A duplication and diversification that generated alcohol dehydrogenase and sorbitol dehydrogenase. The changes would have caused the differences in subunit conformation, Zn content, and specificities of reactions (65). (2) Duplications and diversifications that generated the different classes of ADH. The changes would lead to distinctive enzymatic preferences of each class for various substrates. Since every mammalian species examined has ADH isozymes of each of the three classes, the duplications should have taken place in a common ancestor dated before the differentiation of the mammalian species. (3) Duplications and diversifications that generated three members of class I in primates. The changes would have raised a distinctive mode of expression in the liver and other tissues. The insertion sites of interspersed, repetitive sequences of the $AluI$ family and the L1 family, both of which are thought to be a kind of movable genetic element referred to as "retroposons," suggest that duplications of the class-I genes occurred in the earlier phase of human/primate evolution (23). In fact, several primate species, including *Rhesus*, have three copies of the gene for the class-I isozyme (unpublished observation). Based on the nucleotide differences between human β-cDNA and baboon β-cDNA, it has been proposed (66) that the first ADH gene duplication and diversion of the α gene and the β–γ gene occurred 60 million years ago, and the subsequent duplication and diversion of the β gene and the γ gene occurred about 50 million years ago.

II. Aldehyde Dehydrogenase

Aldehyde dehydrogenases (ALDH; EC 1.2.1.3) are a group of enzymes catalyzing the conversion of aldehydes to the corresponding acids by means of an NAD^+-dependent, irreversible reaction. They display a relatively broad substrate specificity. However, they are usually identified with short-chain aliphatic aldehydes, acetaldehyde or propionaldehyde, as substrates. ALDH activity occurs in most tissues and organs, with the highest activity localized in the liver (67).

Bovine liver ALDH activity was first described about 40 years ago (68). During the past 20 years, the study of the biochemistry and genetics of the liver ALDH isozyme system was furthered mainly due to the recognition of its major role in the detoxification of alcohol-derived acetaldehyde, in the development of alcohol sensitivity, and in the alcohol-related disorders in humans (69–72). In the 1970s, the studies focused on the identification, characterization, and purification of the ALDH isozymes from the livers of human and other mammalian species. In the 1980s, more human ALDH isozymes were identified, and cDNAs and genes for the major liver ALDH isozymes were characterized.

Four nomenclature systems, based on different criteria, have been used in the ALDH system. (1) Arabic numbers were first used to distinguish ALDH isozymes (i.e., F_1, E_1, or $ALDH_1$, and F_2, E_2, or $ALDH_2$, etc.), based on the order of the elution profiles of the two major horse liver isozymes from DEAE-cellulose columns (73). (2) Roman numerals (i.e., ALDH-I, ALDH-II, etc.) were introduced later, based on the relative electrophoretic mobility of the human isozymes toward the anode (74). (3) The ALDH isozymes were also classified, based on subcellular distributions and/or kinetic properties, as cytosol/mitochondrial/microsomal ALDH and low-K_m/high-K_m ALDH toward short-chain aliphatic aldehydes (75). (4) Recently, class-I, -II, -III, etc., were proposed for the animal ALDH system, partly based on the molecular structures of the isozymes (76). We use the traditional nomenclature system (i.e., $ALDH_1$, $ALDH_2$, etc.) throughout this review.

A. Biochemistry of the ALDH Enzyme System

1. IDENTIFICATION, DISTRIBUTION, AND PURIFICATION OF ISOZYMES

Human liver ALDH isozymes can be differentiated by electrophoretic mobility, kinetic properties, subcellular localization, tissue distribution, disulfiram sensitivity, and molecular structures (74, 77–84) (Table III).

Cytosolic $ALDH_1$ and mitochondrial $ALDH_2$, the two major liver isozymes first identified, showed low K_m (micromolar range) toward acetaldehyde. Both isozymes are ubiquitously distributed among various tissues, with the highest level in liver, except that $ALDH_2$ is not present in erythrocytes (85–87). They were first purified from human liver in 1977 (78). $ALDH_1$ migrates slower toward the anode (pI = 5.1) on gel electrophoresis and is very sensitive to disulfiram inhibition in comparison to $ALDH_2$ (pI = 4.9) (77, 88).

The two "high-K_m" (millimolar range for acetaldehyde) isozymes, $ALDH_3$ and $ALDH_4$, are found in the cytosol and the mitochondria, respectively (77). They have limited tissue distribution; $ALDH_3$ is found at the highest level in stomach and lung, while $ALDH_4$ is found only in liver and kidney (74). $ALDH_3$ has been partially purified from stomach (89) and liver (79). Both enzymes can use NAD^+ or $NADP^+$ as cofactor, although both prefer the former. Benzaldehyde and heptaldehyde are optimal substrates. $ALDH_3$ has also been purified from stomach, and a tumor-associated ALDH was partially purified from human hepatocellular carcinoma (90). The kinetic, electrophoretic, and immunological properties of these two preparations were indistinguishable. Liver $ALDH_4$ has broad substrate specificity and oxidizes short-chain aliphatic aldehydes. $ALDH_4$ is most active for glutamic γ-semialdehyde as substrate, and thus the enzyme is classified as glutamic-γ-semialdehyde dehydrogenase (EC 1.5.1.12) (80).

A unique ALDH (γ-ABDH) was recently purified from human liver (81). The enzyme has a low K_m toward acetaldehyde (40–50 μM at the optimum pH, 9.5), propionaldehyde (8–13.8 μM at the optimum pH, 9.5), and γ-aminobutyraldehyde (γ-AB) (8–14 μM at the optimum pH, 7.5). By contrast, $ALDH_1$ and $ALDH_2$ have much higher K_m values for γ-AB, i.e., 760 μM and 512 μM, respectively. Since the new ALDH is most active for γ-AB at the physiological pH, it is designated γ-aminobutyraldehyde dehydrogenase (γ-ABDH). γ-ABDH cross-reacts with anti-$ALDH_1$ and anti-$ALDH_2$ antibodies, indicating structural similarity with the two major liver ALDH isozymes. Unlike $ALDH_1$ and $ALDH_2$, this new ALDH does not bind to a 5'-

TABLE III
BIOCHEMICAL PROPERTIES OF PURIFIED HUMAN ALDH ISOZYMES[a]

Isozymes	Major Tissues	Subcellular[b] localization	pI[c]	K_m (μM) Acetaldehyde (pH)	Propionaldehyde (pH)	Specific[d] aldehyde (pH)	Disulfiram sensitivity (20 μM)	Subunit molecular weight	Subunit/ native molecule
ALDH₁	Liver	C	5.1	22 (7.5)	11 (9.5)		+	54,000	4
ALDH₂	Liver	M	4.9	3.5 (7.5)	1.2 (9.5)		±	54,000	4
γ-ABDH	Liver	5.3 (Major) 5.45 (Minor)	N	50.4 (7.4) 40.3 (7.4)	9 (9.0) 12.6 (9.0)	13.8 (7.4) 8.0 (7.4)	—	54,000	4
ALDH₃	Liver, stomach	C	5.9–6.4	83,000 (8.5)	28,000 (8.5)	11 (8.5)	—	54,000	2
ALDH₄	Liver	M	6.77 6.89	5000 (7.0)	9400	100 (7.0)	—	70,600	2
ALDHₓ	Liver, testis	M	N	N	N	N	N	54,000	N
ALDH₂ₐ	Brain	M	4.9	1 (9.0)	1 (9.0)	1 (9.0)	+	54,000	4
ALDH₂ᵦ	Brain	M	5.0	1 (9.0)	1 (9.0)	0.5 (9.0)	—	54,000	4
Saliva ALDH	Saliva	C	6.5–7.0	106 (8.0)	N	N	N	48,000	N

[a]Data for ALDH₁ and ALDH₂ were obtained from 78, 103, and 156; for γ-ABDH from 81; for ALDH₃ from 79; for ALDH₄ from 80; for ALDH₂ₐ and ALDH₂ᵦ from 82 and 83; and for saliva ALDH from 84. N, Not known.

[b]C, Cytosol; M, mitochondrial; N, not known.

[c]pI (isoelectric point) values determined by different laboratories showed ±0.2 differences.

[d]Specific aldehydes are: γ-aminobutyraldehyde for γ-ABDH, heptaldehyde for ALDH₃, glutamic γ-semialdehyde for ALDH₄, and dopaldehyde for ALDH₂ₐ and ALDH₂ᵦ.

AMP–Sepharose affinity column, and shows a lower K_m value for NAD^+ compared to those of $ALDH_1$ and $ALDH_2$. The subcellular and tissue distributions of this enzyme have not been elucidated.

Human brain ALDH isozymes have attracted attention because of their role in the metabolism of neurotransmitters (91), besides the acetaldehyde oxidation. Three major enzyme groups, each consisting of multiple activity bands on the isoelectric focusing gel stained by acetaldehyde or propionaldehyde, have been purified and characterized (82, 83). The first group was identified as a specific ALDH, i.e., NAD^+-linked succinic semialdehyde dehydrogenase (EC 1.2.1.24), and the second group was classified as glyceraldehyde-3-phosphate dehydrogenase (EC 1.2.1.12). The former belonged to the "high-K_m" ALDH group and did not react with anti-liver $ALDH_1$ and anti-liver $ALDH_2$ antibodies. The latter enzyme catalyzes a reversible oxidative phosphorylation of acetaldehyde and glyceraldehyde 3-phosphate, producing phosphorylated products. The third group contained cytosol $ALDH_1$ (pI = 5.3) and mitochondrial $ALDH_{2a}$ (pI = 4.9) and $ALDH_{2b}$ (pI = 5.0). Brain cytosolic $ALDH_1$ is identical to the liver cytosolic $ALDH_1$. However, judging from the catalytic properties and sensitivity toward disulfiram inhibition, brain $ALDH_{2a}$ and $ALDH_{2b}$ may be brain-specific enzymes that oxidize 3,4-dihydroxyphenyl acetaldehyde (DOPAL). Cerebellum, corpus striatum, and pons show a high ALDH activity with DOPAL (92).

Human saliva ALDH has been purified and characterized (84). Its K_m for acetaldehyde was reported to be 106 μM. This isozyme also exists in liver and kidney. The limited biochemical and immunological data suggest that the saliva ALDH is a unique ALDH isozyme. Further studies are necessary to clarify this point.

A new ALDH isozyme (tentatively designated $ALDH_x$) was recently identified in our laboratory by screening a human testis cDNA library and genomic libraries with an oligonucleotide probe matched to the $ALDH_2$ sequence (unpublished observation). The deduced amino-acid sequence clearly indicated that the gene codes for a unique ALDH isozyme. When $ALDH_x$ mRNA was expressed in the CHO-20 cells, the enzyme produced was capable of oxidizing propionaldehyde, but not benzaldehyde or γ-aminobutyraldehyde. Since the liver and the testis contained the corresponding mRNA, the $ALDH_x$ is expressed in these tissues. Its enzymatic properties and tissue distribution require further investigation. The structure of the $ALDH_x$ gene is discussed in Section I,B,1.

2. STRUCTURE OF THE HUMAN ALDH ISOZYMES

The characteristics of the nine different human ALDH isozymes discussed above are summarized in Table III. The oligomeric forms of saliva ALDH and $ALDH_x$ isozyme are unknown, while $ALDH_3$ and $ALDH_4$ are dimeric and the rest of the isozymes are tetrameric. The subunit molecular weight of ALDH$_4$ is 70,600, that of saliva ALDH is 48,000, and those of the rest of the isozymes are approximately 54,000.

The best-studied isozymes are liver ALDH$_1$ and ALDH$_2$. Their primary structures have been determined at both the protein (93, 94) and cDNA levels (95). Together with the deduced amino-acid sequence of the ALDH$_x$ isozyme, some structure/function correlation can be evaluated. Figure 4

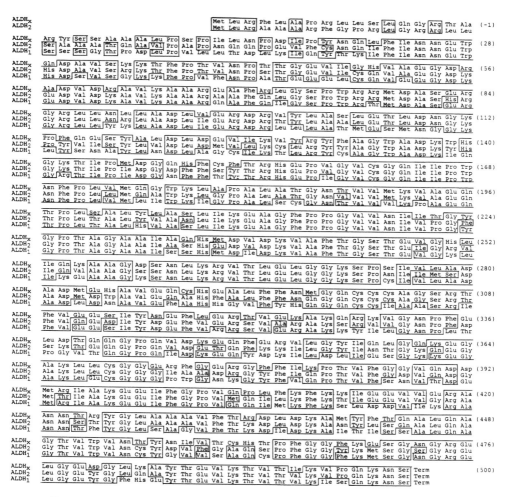

FIG. 4. Comparison of the amino-acid sequences of three human ALDHs. The amino-acid sequence of the ALDH$_x$ derived from the cDNA sequence, and those of the human ALDH$_1$ and ALDH$_2$ proteins (determined by direct protein sequencing) are aligned for maximum identity. Identical portions are boxed. Amino-acid residues are numbered, starting from the NH$_2$-terminal residue of the mature ALDH, consisting of 500 amino-acid residues.

illustrates the position alignment of the sequences of the three human iso-zymes. Mature $ALDH_1$ and $ALDH_2$ subunits are composed of 500 residues, although a minor size heterogeneity was observed in the mature $ALDH_2$ subunit (94). $ALDH_1$ was synthesized as a 501-residue precursor with meth-ionine at the amino terminus, and $ALDH_2$ was synthesized as a 517-residue precursor with a 17-residue signal peptide that was processed during the translocation from the cytoplasm into the mitochondria (96, 97). The cDNA for $ALDH_x$ can encode a peptide with 517 residues. By analogy with $ALDH_2$, it is assumed that the mature $ALDH_x$ isozyme is also 500 residues in length. Comparison of the three 500-residue polypeptides indicates that the degree of resemblance between $ALDH_1$ and $ALDH_2$ is 67.8%, that between $ALDH_1$ and $ALDH_x$ is 64.6%, and that between $ALDH_2$ and AL-DH_x is 73.8% at the protein level.

Based on the fact that no heterotetrameric hybrid ALDH isozymes exist in the liver, possible subunit interaction regions are positions 249–255, 335–340, and 390–394, where the hydropathic properties are expected to be grossly different between $ALDH_1$ and $ALDH_2$. The $ALDH_x$ isozyme also showed different hydropathic properties from that of either $ALDH_1$ or $ALDH_2$ at these regions. Cys-302 has been implicated in the active site by selective modification with iodoacetamide (98, 99), with an affinity-labeling coenzyme analog (100), and by interaction with disulfiram (89, 99). The catalytic role of Cys-49 and Cys-162 has been supported by their reactivity toward N-ethylmaleimide (101). The study of affinity labeling with bro-moacetophenone suggested that Glu-268 is also located at the active site (102). Glu-487 may also be important for the ALDH activity, since the sub-stitution of this Glu by Lys resulted in an inactive mutant $ALDH_2$ (95, 103). Furthermore, the characteristic Gly distribution at positions 223, 225, 229, 245, and 250 has been implicated in the NAD-binding domain (93). All residues mentioned above, except Cys-49, are conserved in the $ALDH_x$ isozyme. The longest stretch (15 amino acids) of the homologous sequence in these three isozymes is positions 260–274, which includes Glu-268 close to the middle.

3. COMPARISON OF HUMAN AND OTHER MAMMALIAN ALDH ISOZYMES

Multiple molecular forms of liver ALDH have also been observed in many mammals other than humans. In several species, including the sheep (104), horse (73, 105), dog (106), cattle (107), pig (107), and baboon (108), two ALDH isozymes, equivalent to the human cytosolic $ALDH_1$ and mitochon-drial $ALDH_2$, on the basis of their kinetic properties, subcellular and tissue distributions, and/or molecular structures, have been identified, and some of these enzymes have been purified (104–107). For some rat strains, liver ALDH activity was found almost exclusively in the mitochondrial and microsomal fractions (108a). A low-K_m mitochondrial ALDH$_2$ and four high-K_m mitochondrial and microsomal ALDHs were purified and characterized (108b, 109). The liver cytosolic ALDH isozymes can only be found during the promotion phase of hepatocarcinogenesis and in the hepatocellular carcinoma cells, as well as after induction by such xenobiotics as phenobarbital (PB) and 2,3,7,8-tetrachlorodibenzo-p-dioxin (TCDD) (109a). The tumor-associated ALDHs appeared to be identical to TCDD-induced ALDH, in that they preferentially use aromatic aldehydes as substrates and NADP$^+$ as the coenzyme; PB-induced ALDHs seemed identical to promotion-associated ALDH, in that they are strictly NAD$^+$-dependent and preferentially oxidize aliphatic aldehydes.

However, Purdue/Wistar rat liver contains cytosolic ALDHs even without induction and these have been isolated and characterized (110). In mouse liver, major liver cytosolic and mitochondrial ALDHs (AHD-2 and AHD-5, respectively, in the mouse nomenclature system) have been characterized. These mouse isozymes, unlike the tetrameric ALDHs from other species, are dimeric. However, the testis-specific ALDHs (AHD-6) have a tetrameric structure (111, 112).

ALDH$_1$ and ALDH$_2$ isolated from different species show greater similarities in their kinetic properties and subcellular distribution with each other than these two isozymes isolated from the same species. The primary sequences of horse cytosolic ALDH$_1$ and mitochondrial ALDH$_2$ have been determined and those of rat PB-induced cytosolic ALDH and cattle and rat ALDH$_2$ have also been deduced from their respective cDNA clones (113–116). The mature horse ALDH$_1$ and ALDH$_2$ consist of 500 amino-acid residues. The rat cDNA for ALDH$_2$ contains an open reading frame for 519 residues, in which 19 were proposed to be the amino-terminal signal peptide, whereas the bovine cDNA for ALDH$_2$ encodes a 520-amino-acid chain, in which 21 were considered to be the signal peptide. The remaining 499 residues of the bovine ALDH$_2$ required an insert at position 4 to obtain the maximal alignment with the 500-residue mature ALDH$_2$ of other mammalian species. The proposed three signal peptides for human, rat, and bovine mitochondrial ALDH$_2$, which have 17, 19, and 21 amino-acid residues, respectively, show high sequence homology and all have characteristics typical of mitochondrial signal peptides (117). The cleavage of the rat ALDH$_2$ signal peptide has been demonstrated in an *in vitro* expression and in *in vitro* import studies (118).

The rat cDNA for PB-induced cytosolic ALDH had an open reading frame for 501 residues. The deduced sequence shows a maximum positional identity of 83% and 81% with human and horse ALDH$_1$, respectively, and 65% with human, horse, and rat ALDH$_2$, respectively.

The 5'- and 3'-non-coding sequences of PB-induced ALDH cDNA show a strong similarity with that of human $ALDH_1$ cDNA. It is even more interesting to note that the 5'-upstream genomic sequences, which include a regulatory region, of the two genes also show strong conservation.

When all of the known primary sequences of $ALDH_1$ and $ALDH_2$ are compared, it is evident that a higher similarity (>90%) is observed between any two sequences of the mitochondrial $ALDH_2$ from various mammalia than between those of $ALDH_1$ and $ALDH_2$ isozymes isolated from the same species (<70%) (Table IV). Forty-nine positions out of a total of 500 residues have amino-acid exchanges in human, rat, bovine, and horse mitochondrial $ALDH_2$. Most of the exchanges are not expected to alter the hydropathicity.

The cDNA of tumor-associated rat ALDH has been cloned from an HTC rat hepatoma cell line (120); it contains an open reading frame for 452 amino-acid residues. The rat tumor ALDH shows a maximum positional identity of 29.8% with human $ALDH_1$ by placing 11 gaps into the two structures (121). The alignment reported showed a conservation of Cys-302, Glu-268, Gly-245, and Gly-250, which are considered to have functional importance in $ALDH_1$ and $ALDH_2$, as discussed in the previous section. It is interesting to note that part of the homologous sequence existing in $ALDH_1$, $ALDH_2$, and $ALDH_x$ (positions 260–274) is also conserved in rat tumor ALDH. This tumor-associated ALDH appears to be identical not only to TCDD-induced cytosolic ALDH, but also to normal rat ALDH isolated from urinary bladder, cornea, lung, and stomach, as judged by kinetic or immunological properties and/or partial amino-acid sequences (109a, 123–125). Based on the structural and functional criteria, the rat tumor ALDH is highly homologous to human $ALDH_3$.

4. DEVELOPMENTAL EXPRESSION OF HUMAN ALDH ISOZYMES

Previously, it had been thought that the activity of $ALDH_2$, $ALDH_3$, and $ALDH_4$ is very low or absent in various fetal tissues, while $ALDH_1$ is expressed in early developmental stages (89, 126). Reports on the $ALDH_2$ mRNA content of fetal liver disagree. One (127) states that the amount in fetal liver is only about 20% of that in adult liver. Another brief report (128) states that the amount is not reduced, but that the fetal mRNA has a longer (~150 bp) 3'-non-coding region than the adult mRNA, suggesting control of gene expression through a post-transcriptional mechanism. However, there is no further report to confirm this notion. Since the absence of the ALDH activity in fetus might be due to enzyme inactivation during sample storage, the ALDH isozymes of 37 fetal and infant liver samples, which were obtained quickly after abortion or death and carefully preserved, were reexamined (129). In contrast to the previous reports, it was found that $ALDH_1$, $ALDH_2$, and $ALDH_4$ were all expressed in fetal liver. Thus, a fetus is capable of detoxifying acetaldehyde transferred from its mother.

B. Genetics of Human ALDH Isozymes

Among the various human ALDH isozymes, three (ALDH$_1$, ALDH$_2$, and ALDH$_x$) are well-characterized at the gene level. Each of these isozymes is controlled by a single corresponding locus. The ALDH$_3$ isozyme appears to be governed by two non-allelic genes, $ALDH_{3a}$ and $ALDH_{3b}$ (130). The chromosomal localizations of human ALDH isozymes are summarized in Table IV.

1. GENOMIC STRUCTURE OF $ALDH_1$, $ALDH_2$, AND $ALDH_x$ GENES

The cDNAs for ALDH$_1$ and ALDH$_2$ were first cloned in 1985 (95). A partial-length ALDH$_1$ cDNA clone (1.6 kbp) encoded carboxy-terminal 340 amino-acid residues and contained a 0.538-kbp, 3'-non-coding region. Two ALDH$_2$ cDNA clones (comprising a total of 1.6 kbp) encoded carboxy-terminal 399 residues and contained a 0.403-kbp, 3'-non-coding region. The nucleotide sequence of a full-length ALDH$_2$ has been reported (131), but the data contained errors due to the sequencing technique. The degree of resemblance is about 65% in the coding nucleotide sequences of ALDH$_1$ and ALDH$_2$. ALDH$_x$ cDNA (1.728 kbp) has an open reading frame for 517 amino-acid residues. The coding sequence of the ALDH$_x$ cDNA has similarities of ~63% and ~71% with those of ALDH$_1$ and ALDH$_2$, respectively.

Based on the 5'-end sequence of ALDH$_2$, it was predicted that a stable loop formed around the translation initiation codon would affect the translation efficiency (132). The (G+C)-rich sequence was observed at the 5' ends of ALDH$_2$ and ALDH$_x$ mRNA.

The $ALDH_1$ gene was assigned to human chromosome 9, and the $ALDH_2$ gene to chromosome 12 by Southern blot hybridization of DNAs prepared from a panel of human–rodent hybrid cell lines with the corresponding

TABLE IV
COMPARISON OF AMINO-ACID SEQUENCES OF ALDH$_1$ AND ALDH$_2$[a]

	Human	Horse	Bovine	Rat
Human	68% [b]	94%	93.3%	96.2%
Horse		66%	94.3%	94.8%
Bovine			-	93.8%
Rat				-

[a] Figures given are the percentages of identity in ALDH$_2$ from different mammals. Identity between human ALDH$_1$ and horse ALDH$_1$ is 91%.

[b] Figures given in boxes are the percentages of identity between ALDH$_1$ and horse ALDH$_2$ from the same species.

cDNA probes (*133–135*). Regional localizations of ALDH$_1$ to 9q21 and ALDH$_2$ to 12q24 were determined by *in situ* hybridization (*136*). The AL-DH$_x$ gene was assigned to chromosome 9 by Southern blot hybridization (unpublished observation).

The genes for *ALDH$_1$* and *ALDH$_2$* were cloned, and the nucleotide sequences of coding exons and intron–exon junctions were determined (96, 97) (Fig. 5). The *ALDH$_1$* gene spans about 53 kbp and contains 13 exons, which encode 501 amino-acid residues together with 53 bp at the 5′-non-coding region and 538 bp at the 3′-non-coding region. The promoter region has an ATA box and a CCAAT box, which are located 85 and 127 bp up-stream, respectively, from the translation initiation site. The *ALDH$_2$* gene spans about 44 kbp and contains 13 exons for the coding region of 517 amino-acid residues. Based on the primer extension and S$_1$ nuclease mapping studies, a part of the 5′-non-coding region (94 of 128 nucleotides) is likely encoded by another upstream exon. Several SpI binding sites are observed upstream from the first coding exon. A TATA box and a CAAT-like sequence are putatively placed 473 and 515 bp upstream from the translation initiation site, respectively. The intron–exon organizations in the two genes are very similar, as shown in Fig. 5. Both enzymes are encoded by 13 exons; nine of the 12 introns interrupt the coding sequences at homologous positions, and one intron (intron 9) is only one nucleotide from the other.

By contrast to the *ALDH$_1$* and *ALDH$_2$* genes, the *ALDH$_x$* gene contains no intron in its coding region. However, an intron of ~3.0 kbp interrupts the 5′-non-coding cDNA region. The sequences of two intron–exon junctions are homologous to the consensus sequences for the splicing signals. North-

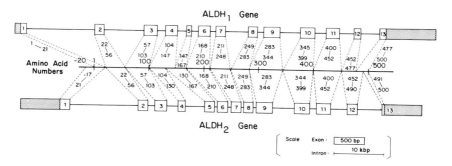

FIG. 5. Comparison of the structural organization of the *ALDH$_1$* and *ALDH$_2$* genes. Cod-ing regions of the 13 exons are represented by open boxes. The hatched boxes in exons 1 and 13 correspond to the 5′- and 3′-untranslated sequence found in the cDNA. The relative positions of introns in the *ALDH$_1$* and *ALDH$_2$* coding regions are indicated by dashed lines. Amino-acid residues are numbered, beginning with the NH$_2$-terminal residue of the mature ALDH, con-sisting of 500 residues. The amino-acid numbers coded by each exon of the *ALDH$_1$* and *ALDH$_2$* genes are shown below and above the gene, respectively. (From 96.)

ern blot hybridization of liver and testis poly(A)$^+$ RNA with an ALDH$_x$ cDNA probe identified two positive signal bands, a major 3.0-kbp band and a minor 2.1-kbp band. The 2.1-kbp band may be the result of the cross-hybridization of ALDH$_2$ mRNA with the probe. The nucleotide sequence of noncoding regions of the 3-kbp mRNA, including the promoter region, remains to be determined. The significance of this gene in evolution and the biological importance of its expression can then be assessed.

2. GENETIC VARIATIONS AND POLYMORPHISMS OF $ALDN_1$, $ALDH_2$, $ALDH_3$, AND $ALDH_x$ LOCI

Racial differences in ALDH$_2$ and in alcohol sensitivity have been found between Orientals and Caucasians (60, 70). Approximately 50% of Orientals lack ALDH$_2$ activity in their livers, but virtually none of the Caucasians exhibited ALDH$_2$ deficiency. It has been proposed that Orientals who lack ALDH$_2$ isozyme activity might exhibit the alcohol-flushing character due to the accumulation of toxic acetaldehyde (70, 137). An enzymatically inactive but immunologically cross-reactive material (CRM) corresponding to ALDH$_2$ was found in an ALDH$_2$-deficient Japanese liver (138). Thus, the ALDH$_2$ deficiency in Orientals should be due to a structural mutation in the $ALDH_2$ gene, not to deletion of the gene. This variant gene ($ALDH_2^2$) product, CRM, was purified and characterized, and a single amino-acid substitution (Gln → Lys) at the 14th position from the COOH terminal was proposed (103). However, this Gln residue in $ALDH_2^1$ was determined as Glu on the basis of the cDNA sequence and direct protein sequencing (94, 95). Hence, the $ALDH_2^2$ variant is associated with a point mutation G·C → A·T in exon 12, which results in the Glu → Lys substitution.

In contrast to the high frequency of the $ALDH_2^2$ variant observed in Orientals, the ALDH$_1$ variant isozyme is less common in this ethnic group. A variant with severely diminished catalytic activity but strong immunological cross-reactivity was found in one of 10 Japanese livers (139). Apparently, the same variant was also found in two of 60 Japanese livers (140). Another ALDH$_1$ variant with different electrophoretic mobility was found in two Oriental subjects (141).

Recently, two ALDH$_1$ kinetic variants, ALDH$_1$-Columbo and ALDH$_1$-Harrow, were found in Caucasian alcohol-flushers (142). The former had 60% of the normal activity and a lower rate of utilization of deamino-NAD and ethanoamide-NAD, while the latter had only 20% of the normal activity. Both variants exhibited altered electrophoretic mobility. Since none of the Caucasians thus far reported have the Oriental-type $ALDH_2^2$ variant, these ALDH$_1$ variants may be directly responsible for the alcohol-flushing found in 5–10% of Caucasians. The mutation sites of these ALDH$_1$ variants can be elucidated by analyzing variant genomic DNA samples after PCR.

Based on the observed multiplicity of ALDH$_3$ bands in stomach samples, a polymorphism at the $ALDH_3$ locus was proposed (143). It was argued that the variation could be due to secondary modification, not to genetic polymorphism (144). However, later studies supported the existence of genetic polymorphism (77, 126). It was proposed that the two common alleles, $ALDH_{3b}^1$ and $ALDH_{3b}^2$, exist in the $ALDH_{3b}$ locus, based on the variations in isoelectric focusing patterns of $ALDH_3$ isozymes in Chinese stomach samples (130). In the model proposed, the $ALDH_{3a}$ locus is expressed in the liver as well as in the stomach and the lungs, while the $ALDH_{3b}$ locus is not expressed in the liver. The frequencies of $ALDH_{3b}^1$ and $ALDH_{3b}^2$ are estimated to be 0.14 and 0.86, respectively, in Chinese (130).

The nucleotide sequences determined from the genomic DNA clone (G) and testis cDNA clone (C) of $ALDH_x$ revealed discrepancies at three positions, resulting in two amino-acid exchanges, Val $\leftrightarrow$ Ala at position 69 and Arg $\leftrightarrow$ Leu at position 90 (unpublished observation). When the genomic DNA samples from unrelated individuals were subjected to PCR of the targeted region following by nucleotide sequence analysis, seven were found to be of the (C) type, while only one was of the (G) type, and two were of the recombinant type with other nucleotide changes. Therefore, the $ALDH_x$ gene is polymorphic in this region. Differences in enzyme activity and electrophoretic mobility were observed when the (G) and (C) types of DNA were expressed in the CHO-20 cells (unpublished observation).

In the study of RFLPs, the TaqI haplotype of the $ALDH_1$ locus was found to be polymorphic in Orientals, but not in Caucasians (145). The MspI haplotype of the $ALDH_1$ locus is polymorphic in both populations, but the frequencies differ. In the $ALDH_2$ locus, the MspI haplotype is polymorphic in both populations, and the frequencies are the same (145). Thus far, no polymorphism was found in the EcoRI and PstI haplotypes.

3. Genetic Polymorphisms and Alcohol-Related Problems

The usual $ALDH_2^1$ and the atypical $ALDH_2^2$ can be distinguished by direct in-gel hybridization of DNA restriction fragments, or by hybridization of amplified targeted DNA fragments with the allele-specific oligonucleotide probes (146, 147).

Genotypes of the $ALDH_2$ loci in Caucasians and Japanese with and without the alcohol-flushing character, and with and without alcoholic liver disease, were determined by the in-gel hybridization method (63, 148) (Table II). The data indicate that the frequencies of $ALDH_2^1$ and $ALDH_2^2$ genes are 0.65 and 0.35, respectively, in the control Japanese, and imply that the heterozygous atypical 1/2 subjects as well as the homozygous atypical 2/2 subjects lack liver $ALDH_2$ activity, i.e., the atypical $ALDH_2^2$ gene is dominant in expression of enzyme activity. The notion is supported by genotyping and phenotyping (147).

TABLE V
HUMAN ALDH LOCI

Isozyme	Locus	Chromosome	Polymorphism	Reference
$ALDH_1$	$ALDH_1$	9q21		133, 136
$ALDH_2$	$ALDH_2$	12q24	Polymorphic in Orientals	133, 136
$ALDH_3$	$ALDH_{3a}$, $ALDH_{3b}$	17	Polymorphic in Chinese	89
$ALDH_x$	$ALDH_x$	9	Polymorphic	Unpublished data

The severe $ALDH_2$ deficiency in the heterozygous $1/2$ status (i.e., dominant expression of the variant $ALDH_2^2$) is not readily compatible with the commonly accepted assumption (and observations of other loci) that both usual and variant genes would be expressed in heterozygous status and hybrid oligomeric enzymes would exhibit catalytic activity. Regarding this problem, the following points should be considered. The direct genotyping method examines only the targeted nucleotide region, which includes the $ALDH_2^2$ mutation site. Therefore, the possibility of the existence of other variant alleles is not excluded.

Another common variant allele, $ALDH_2^3$, which produces a defective subunit, could exist in Japanese. Assuming that: (1) the frequencies of $ALDH_2^1 = 0.3$, $ALDH_2^2 = 0.35$, and $ALDH_2^3 = 0.35$; (2) subjects with $ALDH_2^1/ALDH_2^1$, $ALDH_2^1/ALDH_2^2$ and $ALDH_2^1$ exhibit the enzyme activity; and (3) subjects with $ALDH_2^2/ALDH_2^2$, $ALDH_2^2/ALDH_2^3$, and $ALDH_2^3/ALDH_2^3$ lack the activity, the observed frequency of $ALDH_2$ deficiency (about 50%) can be explained by the three-allele model. This model predicts that approximately 40% of Japanese with the enzyme activity are heterozygous $1/2$. However, none of the Japanese livers with $ALDH_2$ activity thus far examined had the atypical $ALDH_2^2$ gene; thus, the three-allele models must be rejected.

The genotype analysis indicates that all Japanese alcohol-flushers are either heterozygous $ALDH_2^1/ALDH_2^2$ or homozygous $ALDH_2^2/ALDH_2^2$, and that virtually all Japanese with alcoholic liver diseases are homozygous $ALDH_2^1/ALDH_2^1$ (Table II). One can conclude that Orientals with genotypes $ALDH_2^1/ALDH_2^2$ and $ALDH_2^2/ALDH_2^2$ are alcohol sensitive; thus, they are at low risk for developing alcoholic liver disease and presumably other alcohol-related diseases.

Frequencies of the atypical $ALDH_2^2$ gene in other Oriental populations (0.15 in South Koreans and 0.20 in Chinese) have been reported (149).

The ALDH genotyping of American Indians has been a subject of interest. Both American Indians and Orientals are of Mongoloid origin. A high frequency (50–70%) of alcohol-flush has been observed in a North American Indian tribe (*150*). However, unlike Orientals, American Indians have higher frequencies of alcohol-related problems. The ALDH deficiencies in North and South American Indians have been studied (*151–154*). In general, North American Indians (Sioux, Navajo, Pueblo, and Oklahoma) show a low (or no) frequency of $ALDH_2$ deficiency, while approximately 40% of South American Indians (Atacameños, Mapuche, and Shuara) lack $ALDH_2$ activity. Recently, the $ALDH_2$ genotypes of 28 South American (Mapuche) Indians were determined; none of them had the atypical $ALDH_2^2$ gene (i.e., the frequency of $ALDH_2^2$ was less than 2%) (*155*).

Should about 40% of the Mapuche Indians lack $ALDH_2$ activity, another defective mutant $ALDH_2$ gene, which differs from the atypical Oriental-type $ALDH_2^2$ gene, might exist at a high frequency in this population. Further confirmation on the $ALDH_2$ deficiency in South American Indians is necessary, since the previous phenotyping was performed using hair root extracts, and this method has some practical and fundamental problems. Systematic reliable $ALDH_2$ phenotyping and genotyping, together with characterization of alcohol-flushing characters and other alcohol-related problems, may elucidate the relationship between the $ALDH_2$ types and physiological manifestations in American Indians.

III. Concluding Remarks

Our knowledge of the human ADHs and ALDHs, at the enzyme–protein level and at the gene level, has been greatly advanced in recent years, yet it is still rather limited. Five types of subunits (α, β, γ, π, and χ) have been characterized, and four genes (for α, β, γ, and π) have been elucidated to a certain extent. The nature of stomach ADH, which was implicated in susceptibility to alcohol liver injury, and a testes-specific human ADH is not clear.

In the case of the ALDHs, only two isozymes, i.e., the liver-cytosolic $ALDH_1$ and the liver-mitochondrial $ALDH_2$, have been elucidated at the protein level and at the gene level. The protein structure and genomic structure of other ALDHs of other tissues are totally obscure. Our knowledge of the regulatory mechanism for tissue-specific and development-dependent expression of ADHs and ALDHs is very limited.

The recent development of molecular genetics allows us to identify and characterize hitherto-unknown isozymes through direct study of DNA. Since a high degree of resemblance should exist among a group of isozymes at the gene level, new isozyme genes can be cloned by screening human genomic libraries with the appropriate region(s) of a known isozyme gene as a hybridization probe. As described in this review, a new *ADH* gene (*ADH*$_6$)

and corresponding cDNA and a new *ALDH* gene ($ALDH_x$) and corresponding cDNA have been cloned this way. The enzymatic properties of the protein(s) produced by these genes can be examined by expressing the genes in an appropriate system.

A high degree of positive correlation between the Oriental atypical $ALDH_2^2$ gene with alcohol sensitivity and the negative correlation with development of alcoholic liver disease have been proven. Caucasians with the variant $ALDH_1$ genes, presumably even at heterozygous status, are also alcohol-sensitive; hence, they are at low risk for developing alcoholism. Genetic variations of other ADH and ALDH isozymes would also be related to individual and racial differences in alcohol sensitivity, alcohol-seeking behavior, susceptibility to alcoholic tissue injury, and the development of alcohol-related problems.

ACKNOWLEDGMENT

This study was supported by US Public Health Service Grant AA05763.

REFERENCES

1. M. Smith, D. A. Hopkinson and H. Harris, *Ann. Hum. Genet.* **34**, 251 (1971).
2. M. Smith, D. A. Hopkinson and H. Harris, *Ann. Hum. Genet.* **35**, 243 (1972).
3. M. Smith, D. A. Hopkinson and H. Harris, *Ann. Hum. Genet.* **36**, 401 (1973).
4. W. F. Bosron, T.-K. Li, and B. L. Vallee, *PNAS* **77**, 5784 (1980).
5. D. J. Strydom and B. L. Vallee, *Anal. Biochem.* **123**, 422 (1982).
6. T.-K. Li, W. F. Bosron, W. P. Defeldecker, L. G. Lange and B. L. Vallee, *PNAS* **74**, 4378 (1977).
7. A. Adinolfi, M. Adinolfi and D. A. Hopkinson, *Ann. Hum. Genet.* **48**, 1 (1984).
8. T. B. Beisswenger, B. Holmquist and B. L. Vallee, *PNAS* **82**, 8369 (1985).
9. W. P. Defeldecker and B. L. Vallee, *BBRC* **134**, 1056 (1986).
10. M. Frezza, C. di Padova, G. Possato, M. Terpin, E. Baraona and C. S. Lieber, *N. Engl. J. Med.* **322**, 95 (1990).
11. G. Mårdh and B. L. Vallee, *Bchem* **25**, 7279 (1986).
12. G. Mårdh, A. L. Dingley, D. S. Auld and B. L. Vallee, *PNAS* **83**, 8908 (1986).
13. V. Consalvi, G. Mårdh and B. L. Vallee, *BBRC* **139**, 1009 (1986).
14. A. J. McEvily, B. Holmquist, D. S. Auld and B. L. Vallee, *Bchem* **27**, 4284 (1988).
15. G. Mårdh, K. H. Falchuck, D. S. Auld and B. L. Vallee, *PNAS* **83**, 2836 (1986).
16. F. W. Wagner, A. R. Burger and B. L. Vallee, *Bchem* **22**, 1857 (1983).
17. W. B. Rizzo, A. L. Dammann and D. A. Craft, *J. Clin. Invest.* **81**, 738 (1988).
18. H. Esterbauer, H. Zollner and J. Lang, *BJ* **228**, 363 (1985).
19. M. Koivusalo, M. Baumann and L. Uotila, *FEBS Lett.* **257**, 105 (1989).
20. P. Julià, J. Farrés and X. Parés, *EJB* **162**, 179 (1987).
21. W.-M. Keung, *BBRC* **156**, 38 (1988).
22. T. Ikuta, T. Fujiyoshi, K. Kurachi and A. Yoshida, *PNAS* **82**, 2703 (1985).
23. T. Ikuta, S. Szeto and A. Yoshida, *PNAS* **83**, 634 (1986).
24. H. von Bahr-Lindstöm, J.-O. Höög, L.-O. Hedén, R. Kaiser, L. Fleetwood, K. Larsson, M. Lake, B. Holmquist, A. Holmgren, J. Hempel, B. L. Vallee and H. Jörnvall, *Bchem* **25**, 2465 (1986).

25. J.-O. Höög, L.-O. Hedén, K. Larsson, H. Jörnvall and H. von Bahr-Lindström, *EJB* **159**, 215 (1986).
26. J.-O. Höög, H. von Bahr-Lindström, L.-O. Hedén, B. Holmquist, K. Larsson, J. Hempel, B. L. Vallee and H. Jörnvall, *Bchem* **26**, 1926 (1987).
27. R. Kaiser, B. Holmquist, J. Hempel, B. L. Vallee and H. Jörnvall, *Bchem* **27**, 1132 (1988).
28. C. P. Sharma, E. A. Fox, B. Holmquist, H. Jörnvall and B. L. Vallee, *BBRC* **164**, 631 (1989).
29. P. R. Giri, J. F. Krug, C. Kozak, T. Moretti, S. J. O'Brien, H. N. Seuanez and D. Goldman, *BBRC* **164**, 453 (1989).
30. H. Eklund, *Biochem. Soc. Trans.* **17**, 293 (1989).
31. V. Bilanchone, G. Duester, Y. Edwards and M. Smith, *NARes* **14**, 3911 (1986).
32. T. Ikuta and A. Yoshida, *BBRC* **140**, 1020 (1986).
33. M. Yasunami, I. Kikuchi, D. Sarapata and A. Yoshida, *Genomics* **7**, 152 (1990).
34. L.-O. Hedén, J.-O. Höög, K. Larsson, M. Lake, E. Lagerholm, A. Holmgren, B. L. Vallee, H. Jörnvall and H. von Bahr-Lindström, *FEBS Lett.* **194**, 327 (1986).
35. S. Ohno, C. Stenius, L. Christian, C. Harris and C. Ivey, *Biochem. Genet.* **4**, 565 (1970).
36. C. E. Wolfla, R. A. Ross and D. W. Crabb, *ABB* **263**, 69 (1988).
37. Y. Dong, L. Poellinger, S. Okret, J.-O. Höög, H. von Bahr-Lindström, H. Jörnvall and J.-Å. Gustafsson, *PNAS* **85**, 767 (1988).
38. G. Duester, M. Smith, V. Bilanchone and G. W. Hatfield, *JBC* **261**, 2027 (1986).
39. K. Zhang, W. F. Bosron and H. J. Edenberg, *Gene* **57**, 27 (1987).
40. D. W. Crabb, P. M. Stein, K. M. Dipple, J. B. Hittle, R. Sidhu, M. Qualali, K. Zhang and H. J. Edenberg, *Genomics* **5**, 906 (1989).
41. Y. Matsuo and S. Yokoyama, *FEBS Lett.* **243**, 57 (1989).
42. Y. Matsuo, R. Yokoyama and S. Yokoyama, *EJB* **183**, 317 (1989).
43. L. G. Carr, Y. Xu, W.-H. Ho and H. J. Edenberg, *Alcoholism* **13**, 594 (1989).
44. Y. Matsuo and S. Yokoyama, *Am. J. Hum. Genet.* **46**, 85 (1990).
45. L. G. Carr, K. Zhang and H. J. Edenberg, *Gene* **78**, 277 (1989).
46. L. G. Carr and H. J. Edenberg, *JBC* **265**, 1658 (1990).
47. M. Tsukahara and A. Yoshida, *Genomics* **4**, 218 (1989).
48. J. D. McPherson, M. Smith, C. Wagner, J. Wasmuth and J.-O. Höög, *Cytogenet. Cell Genet.* **51**, 1043 (1989).
49. L. Carlock, S. Hiroshige, J. Wasmuth and M. Smith, *Cytogenet. Cell Genet.* **40**, 598 (1985).
50. H. Jörnvall, J. Hempel, B. L. Vallee, W. F. Bosron and T.-K. Li, *PNAS* **81**, 3024 (1984).
51. T. Ehring, J.-P. von Wartburg, and B. Wermuth, *FEBS Lett.* **234**, 53 (1988).
52. A. Yoshida, C. C. Impraim and I.-Y. Huang, *JBC* **256**, 12430 (1981).
53. J. C. Burnell, L. G. Carr, F. E. Dwulet, H. J. Edenberg, T.-K. Li and W. F. Bosron, *BBRC* **146**, 1227 (1987).
54. J. Hempel, R. Buhler, R. Kaiser, B. Holmquist, C. de Zalenski, J.-P. von Wartburg, B. Vallee and H. Jörnvall, *EJB* **145**, 447 (1984).
55. T. Shah, A. J. S. MacPherson, R. J. Ward, T. J. Peters and A. Yoshida, *NARes* **17**, 7549 (1989).
56. K. K. Kidd, A. M. Bowcock, J. Schmidtke, R. K. Track, F. Riciuti, G. Hutchings, A. Bale, P. Pearson and H. F. Willard, *Cytogenet. Cell Genet.* **51**, 622 (1989).
57. D. R. Cox, J. C. Murray and K. H. Buetow, *Cytogenet. Cell Genet.* **51**, 121 (1989).
58. T. Ikuta, A. Shibuya and A. Yoshida, *Biochem. Genet.* **26**, 519 (1988).
59. M. Dean, C. Stewart, P. R. Giri, J. Krug, T. Moretti, H. Seuanez, S. J. O'Brien and D. Goldman, *Cytogenet. Cell Genet.* **51**, 985 (1989).
60. P. H. Wolff, *Science* **175**, 449 (1972).

61. G. Stamatoyannopoulos, S.-H. Chen and M. Fukui, *Am. J. Hum. Genet.* **27**, 789 (1975).
62. A. Shibuya and A. Yoshida, *Am. J. Hum. Genet.* **43**, 741 (1988).
63. A. Shibuya, M. Yasunami and A. Yoshida, *Hum. Genet.* **82**, 14 (1989).
64. K. Gennari, B. Wermuth, D. Muellener, T. Ehring and J.-P. von Wartburg, *FEBS Lett.* **228**, 305 (1988).
65. H. Eklund, E. Horjales, H. Jörnvall, C.-I. Brändén and J. Jeffery, *Bchem* **24**, 8005 (1985).
66. A. E. O. Trezise, E. A. Godfrey, R. S. Holmes and I. R. Beacham, *PNAS* **86**, 5454 (1989).
67. R. A. Dietrich, *Biochem. Pharmacol.* **15**, 1911 (1966).
68. E. Racker, *JBC* **177**, 883 (1949).
69. M. C. Harrington, G. T. M. Henehan and K. F. Tipton, *Prog. Clin. Biol. Res.* **232**, 111 (1987).
70. H. W. Goedde, S. Harada and D. P. Agarwal, *Hum. Genet.* **51**, 331 (1979).
71. S. Harada, D. P. Agarwal, H. W. Goedde and B. Ishikawa, *Pharmacol. Biochem. Behav.* **18** (Suppl. 1), 151 (1983).
72. W. F. Bosron and T. K. Li, *Hepatology* **6**, 502 (1986).
73. J. Eckfeldt, L. Mope, K. Takio and T. Yonetani, *JBC* **251**, 236 (1976).
74. S. Harada, D. P. Agarwal and H. W. Goedde, *Life Sci.* **26**, 1773 (1980).
75. R. Pietruszko, *Isozymes: Curr. Top. Biol. Med. Res.* **8**, 195 (1983).
76. *Prog. Clin. Biol. Res.* **290**, xix (1989).
77. J. A. Duley, O. Harris and R. S. Holmes, *Alcohol.: Clin. Exp. Res.* **9**, 263 (1985).
78. N. J. Greenfield and R. Pietruszko, *BBA* **483**, 35 (1977).
79. S.-J. Yin, C.-S. Liao, S.-L. Wang, Y.-J. Chen and C.-W. Wu, *Biochem. Genet.* **27**, 321 (1989).
80. C. M. Forte-McRobbie and R. Pietruszko, *JBC* **261**, 2154 (1986).
81. G. Kurys, W. Ambroziak and R. Pietruszko, *JBC* **264**, 4715 (1989).
82. M. T. Ryzlak and R. Pietruszko, *Alcohol.: Clin. Exp. Res.* **13**, 755 (1989).
83. M. T. Ryzlak and R. Pietruszko, *ABB* **255**, 409 (1987).
84. S. Harada, T. Muramatsu, D. P. Agarwal and H. W. Goedde, *Prog. Clin. Biol. Res.* **290**, 133 (1989).
85. K. Inoue, H. Nishimukai and K. Yamasawa, *BBA* **569**, 117 (1979).
86. A. Helander and O. Tottmar, *Alcohol.: Clin. Exp. Res.* **10**, 71 (1986).
87. J. W. Rawles, D. L. Rhodes, J. J. Potter and E. Mezey, *Biochem. Pharmacol.* **36**, 3715 (1987).
88. R. C. Vallari and R. Pietruszko, *Science* **216**, 637 (1982).
89. I. Santisteban, S. Povey, L. F. West, J. M. Parrington and D. A. Hopkinson, *Ann. Hum. Genet.* **49**, 87 (1985).
90. D. P. Agarwal, R. Eckey, A.-C. Rudnay, T. Volkens and H. W. Goedde, *Prog. Clin. Biol. Res.* **290**, 119 (1989).
91. K. F. Tipton, M. D. Houslay and A. J. Turner, *Essays Neurochem. Pharmacol.* **1**, 103 (1977).
92. G. Hafer, D. P. Agarwal and H. W. Goedde, *Alcohol* **4**, 413 (1987).
93. J. Hempel, H. von Bahr-Lindström and H. Jörnvall, *EJB* **141**, 21 (1984).
94. J. Hempel, R. Kaiser and H. Jörnvall, *EJB* **153**, 13 (1985).
95. L. C. Hsu, K. Tani, T. Fujiyoshi, K. Kurachi and A. Yoshida, *PNAS* **82**, 3771 (1985).
96. L. C. Hsu, W.-C. Chang and A. Yoshida, *Genomics* **5**, 857 (1989).
97. L. C. Hsu, R. E. Bendel and A. Yoshida, *Genomics* **2**, 57 (1988).
98. J. Hempel and R. Pietruszko, *JBC* **256**, 10889 (1981).
99. J. Hempel, R. Pietruszko, P. Fietzek and H. Jörnvall, *Biochem.* **21**, 6834 (1982).
100. H. von Bahr-Lindström, R. Jeck, C. Woenckhaus, S. Sohn, J. Hempel and H. Jörnvall, *Bchem* **24**, 5847 (1985).

101. G.-C. Tu and H. Weiner, *JBC* **263**, 1212 (1988).

102. D. P. Abriola, R. Fields, S. Stein, A. D. MacKerell, Jr., and R. Pietruszko, *Bchem* **26**, 5679 (1987).

103. A. Yoshida, I.-Y. Huang and M. Ikawa, *PNAS* **81**, 258 (1984).

104. K. E. Crow, T. M. Kitson, A. K. H. MacGibbon and R. D. Batt, *BBA* **350**, 121 (1974).

105. R. I. Feldman and H. Weiner, *JBC* **247**, 260 (1972).

106. C. G. Sanny, *Alcohol.: Clin. Exp. Res.* **9**, 255 (1985).

107. K. L. Guan, Y. K. Pak, G. C. Tu, Q. N. Cao and H. Weiner, *Alcohol.: Clin Exp. Res.* **12**, 713 (1988).

108. R. S. Holmes and J. L. Vandeberg, *Alcohol* **3**, 205 (1986).

108a. R. Lindahl and S. Evces, *Biochem. Pharmacol.* **33**, 3383 (1984).

108b. C. Siew, R. A. Dietrich and V. G. Erwin, *ABB* **176**, 638 (1976).

109. R. Lindahl and S. Evces, *JBC* **259**, 11986 (1984).

109a. R. Lindahl and S. Evces, *JBC* **259**, 11991 (1984).

110. Q. N. Cao, G. C. Tu and H. Weiner, *Biochem. Pharmacol.* **38**, 77 (1989).

111. R. S. Holms, *Genet. Alcohol.* p. 141 (1987).

112. U. K. Rout and R. S. Holms, *Prog. Clin. Biol. Res.* **290**, 105 (1989).

113. H. von Bahr-Lindström, J. Hempel and H. Jörnvall, *EJB* **141**, 37 (1984).

114. J. Johansson, H. von Bahr-Lindström, R. Jeck, C. Woenckhaus and H. Jörnvall, *EJB* **172**, 527 (1988).

114a. T. J. Dunn, A. I. Koleske, R. Lindahl and H. C. Pitot, *JBC* **264**, 13057 (1989).

115. J. Farrés, K. Guan and H. Weiner, *EJB* **180**, 67 (1989).

116. K. Guan and H. Weiner, *ABB* **277**, 351 (1990).

117. E. C. Hurt and G. Schatz, *Nature* **325**, 499 (1987).

118. T. T. Y. Wang, J. Farrés and H. Weiner, *ABB* **272**, 440 (1989).

120. D. E. Jones, Jr., M. D. Brennan, J. Hempel and R. Lindahl, *PNAS* **85**, 1782 (1988).

121. J. Hempel, K. Harper and R. Lindahl, *Bchem* **28**, 1160 (1989).

123. R. Lindahl, *Cancer Res.* **46**, 2502 (1986).

124. S. Evces and R. Lindahl, *ABB* **274**, 518 (1989).

125. M. Koivusalo, M. Aarnio, M. Baumann and P. Rautoma, *Prog. Clin. Exp. Res.* **290**, 19 (1989).

126. D. A. Hopkinson, I. Santisteban, S. Povey and M. Smith, *Alcohol* **2**, 73 (1985).

127. T. Braun, E. Bober, J. Schaper, D. P. Agarwal, S. Singh and H. W. Goedde, *Alcohol Alcohol., Suppl.* **1**, 161 (1987).

128. R. Bauman, D. Tower and M. Smith, *Am. J. Hum. Genet.* **41A**, 206 (1987) (abstr.).

129. A. Yoshida, A. Shibuya, V. Davé, M. Nakayama and A. Hayashi, *Experientia* in press.

130. S.-J. Yin, T.-C. Cheng, C.-P. Chang, Y.-J. Chen, Y.-C. Chao, H.-S. Tang, T.-M. Chang and C.-W. Wu, *Biochem. Genet.* **26**, 343 (1988).

131. T. Braun, E. Bober, S. Singh, D. P. Agarwal and H. W. Goedde, *FEBS Lett.* **215**, 233 (1987).

132. K. Guan and H. Weiner, *JBC* **264**, 17764 (1989).

133. L. C. Hsu, A. Yoshida and T. Mohandas, *Am. J. Hum. Genet.* **38**, 641 (1986).

134. T. Braun, K. H. Grzeschik, E. Bober, S. Singh, D. P. Agarwal and H. W. Goedde, *Hum. Genet.* **73**, 365 (1986).

135. M. Smith, S. Hiroshige, P. Saxon and J. Wasmuth, *Cytogenet. Cell Genet.* **40**, 748 (1985).

136. L. Raghunatan, L. C. Hsu, I. Klisak, R. S. Sparkes, A. Yoshida and T. Mohandas, *Genomics* **2**, 267 (1988).

137. Y. Mizoi, I. Ijiri, Y. Tatsuno, T. Kijima, S. Fujiwara and J. Adachi, *Pharmacol. Biochem. Behav.* **10**, 303 (1979).

138. C. Impraim, G. Wang and A. Yoshida, *Am. J. Hum. Genet.* **34**, 837 (1982).

139. A. Yoshida, *Am. J. Hum. Genet.* **35**, 1115 (1983).
140. R. Kanayama, Y. Matsuda, S. Takase and A. Takada, *Alcohol Metab. Liver* **2**, 223 (1984) (in Japanese).
141. R. Eckey, D. P. Agarwal, N. Saha and H. W. Goedde, *Hum. Genet.* **72**, 95 (1986).
142. A. Yoshida, V. Davé, R. J. Ward and T. J. Peters, *Ann. Hum. Genet.* **53**, 1 (1989).
143. Y.-S. Teng, *Hum. Genet.* **31**, 74 (1981).
144. D. Meier-Tackmann, D. P. Agarwal, N. Saha and H. W. Goedde, *Enzyme* **32**, 170 (1984).
145. A. Yoshida and S.-H. Chen, *Hum. Genet.* **83**, 204 (1989).
146. L. C. Hsu, R. E. Bendel and A. Yoshida, *Am. J. Hum. Genet.* **41**, 996 (1987).
147. D. W. Crabb, H. J. Edenberg, W. F. Bosron and T.-K. Li, *J. Clin. Invest.* **83**, 314 (1989).
148. A. Shibuya and A. Yoshida, *Am. J. Hum. Genet.* **43**, 744 (1988).
149. H. W. Goedde, S. Singh, D. P. Agarwal, G. Fritze, K. Stapel and Y. K. Paik, *Hum. Genet.* **81**, 305 (1989).
150. P. H. Wolff, *Am. J. Hum. Genet.* **25**, 193 (1973).
151. H. W. Goedde, D. P. Agarwal, S. Harada, F. Rothhammer, J. O. Whittaker and R. Liskar, *Am. J. Hum. Genet.* **38**, 395 (1986).
152. A. R. Zeiner, J. M. Girardot, N. Nichols and D. Jones-Saumty, *Alcohol.: Clin. Exp. Res.* **8**, 129 (1984).
153. D. Rex, W. F. Bosron, J. E. Smialek and T.-K. Li, *Alcohol.: Clin. Exp. Res.* **9**, 147 (1985).
154. W. F. Bosron, D. K. Rex, C. A. Harden and T.-K. Li, *Alcohol.: Clin. Exp. Res.* **12**, 454 (1988).
155. B. F. O'Dowd, F. Rothhammer and Y. Israel, *Alcohol: Clin. Exp. Res.*, in press.
156. M. Ikawa, C. C. Impraim, G. Wang and A. Yoshida, *JBC* **258**, 6282 (1983).

DNA Helicases of
Escherichia coli[1]

STEVEN W. MATSON

Department of Biology and Curriculum
  in Genetics
University of North Carolina
Chapel Hill, North Carolina 27599

That DNA helicases play a critical role in all aspects of nucleic acid metabolism is now being fully appreciated. These enzymes, which disrupt the hydrogen bonds between the two strands of duplex DNA, have fundamental roles in DNA replication, DNA repair, recombination, and conjugation. In addition, roles have been suggested for helicases that unwind DNA·RNA hybrids and/or duplex RNA in transcription, translation, and RNA splicing (for reviews, see 1 and 2). Consistent with myriad roles in DNA and RNA metabolism, numerous helicases have been described; *Escherichia coli* has at least 10 different enzymes with helicase activity (3). Helicases have also been isolated from a number of eukaryotic sources (4–8), including three apparently different helicases from yeast (9–12). A recent report suggests that there may be five additional RNA helicases in yeast (13). Thus, unwinding enzymes are ubiquitous in nature, and it seems likely that indi-

---

[1] Abbreviations used: NTPase, nucleoside 5′-triphosphatase; ssDNA, single-stranded DNA; dsDNA, double-stranded DNA; NTP, nucleoside 5′-triphosphate; SSB, *E. coli* single-stranded-DNA binding protein; ssRNA, single-stranded RNA; PAS, primosome assembly site.

Progress in Nucleic Acid Research
and Molecular Biology, Vol. 40

vidual cells contain a collection of helicases that participate in many, if not all, facets of DNA and RNA metabolism.

Helicases catalyze two interrelated reactions: (1) the DNA (RNA)-dependent hydrolysis of nucleoside 5'-triphosphates (NTPs) and (2) the unwinding of duplex nucleic acids. The latter reaction is characterized by the disruption of the hydrogen bonds between complementary base-pairs. There is no breakage of covalent bonds in the backbone of the DNA molecule; thus, helicases are distinct from topoisomerases. These two classes of proteins differ both in enzymology and in their known roles in the cell. The energy released as a consequence of NTP hydrolysis is presumably utilized in the unwinding reaction. Exactly how the energy is utilized and how much energy is required are questions that remain to be fully answered. Within this framework, it is important to recognize that unwinding reactions exhibit a specific polarity, which is expressed with respect to the strand of DNA on which the helicase is presumed to be bound. Helicases with 3'-to-5' polarity and those with 5'-to-3' polarity are abundant. Presumably, the helicase tracks unidirectionally along one DNA strand, causing the hydrogen bonds between base-pairs to be melted. This unidirectional migration may be one of the energy-requiring components of the unwinding reaction.

Although first recognized as duplex-DNA unwinding enzymes, it is now clear that the term "helicase" should be applied to enzymes that unwind DNA·RNA hybrids and/or duplex RNA (14–21). The discovery of these additional unwinding reactions, and the enzymes that catalyze them, has resulted in speculation regarding potential roles for helicases in both transcription and translation (2). As yet, there are few data to support these speculations. However, E. coli Rho protein, which has been demonstrated to unwind RNA·DNA hybrids (18, 19), has a well-documented role in the termination of transcription (22). In this case, termination may be achieved by virtue of the RNA·DNA unwinding reaction catalyzed by Rho protein.

This review focuses on the helicases of E. coli, as this represents the organism about which most is known. A review of prokaryotic and eukaryotic helicases appeared recently (2) and the reader is referred to this review for specific information regarding eukaryotic helicases. The current list of E. coli helicases stands at 10 (Table I); each of these enzymes is discussed separately. I have chosen to group these proteins into four classes based on physiological roles. These groups are (1) the replicative helicases, including Rep protein, PriA protein, and DnaB protein; (2) the repair helicases, including helicase II and the UvrAB complex; (3) a recombination helicase, the RecBCD enzyme; and (4) other helicases, including helicases I, III, and IV, and Rho Protein. I focus primarily on the biochemistry of these proteins and genetics as it relates to physiological function.

TABLE I
E. coli HELICASES

Enzyme	Gene	Map position (min)	M_r^a	Native structure	Cellular concentration[b]
Helicase I	F plasmid (traI)	—	192,068	?	500–700
Helicase II	uvrD	84	82,116	Monomer	3000–8000
Helicase III	?	?	20,000[c]	Dimer	?
Helicase IV	helD	22	78,033	Monomer	10
Rep protein	rep	84	72,802	Monomer	50
DnaB protein	dnaB	92	52,265	Hexamer	20
PriA protein	priA	88	81,700	Monomer	70
RecBCD enzyme	recB	60	133,973	Complex	10
	recC	60	129,000		
	recD	60	66,973		
Rho protein	rho	85	46,094	Hexamer	6000
UvrAB complex	uvrA	92	103,874	Complex	10
	uvrB	18	76,118		

[a]Calculated molecular mass based on the amino-acid sequence deduced from the published DNA sequence.
[b]Estimated number of molecules per cell.
[c]Relative molecular mass determined by dodecyl/polyacrylamide gel electrophoresis.

I. Unwinding Reaction

A. Helicase Assays

During the past 15 years, several different biochemical assays for helicase activity have been employed. The assay developed by Hoffmann-Berling and colleagues (23, 24) was a coupled assay that measured the conversion of S1-nuclease-resistant duplex DNA to S1-nuclease-sensitive, single-stranded DNA (ssDNA). This assay was modified slightly by Gefter and colleagues (25) to include an ssDNA binding protein (*E. coli* SSB) to prevent strand reannealing. Sucrose gradients and nitrocellulose filter-binding assays complemented the S1 assay in early analyses of the unwinding reactions catalyzed by helicase enzymes (24).

During the last 8 years, a more direct assay for helicase activity has been developed (26, 27). This assay utilizes partial-duplex-DNA molecules containing a region of ssDNA to which the enzyme binds initially and a region of duplex DNA to be unwound. The products of the reaction are resolved from the substrate on a polyacrylamide or agarose gel to permit direct visualization of one of the products and quantitation of the results (Fig. 1). An advantage of this assay is that it does not require a second incubation at low pH with S1 nuclease to quantitate product formation. In addition, the par-

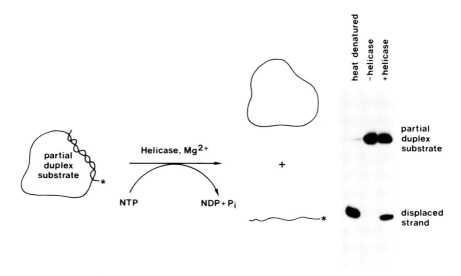

FIG. 1. Assay for measuring helicase activity *in vitro*. Details for the construction of partial-duplex substrates are provided in 32. The asterisk denotes the position of the radioactive label on the 3' terminus of the DNA fragment. (Reproduced with permission from 2.)

tial-duplex-DNA molecule can be altered in predictable ways to provide a variety of different DNA substrates. For instance, the length of the duplex region can be varied, non-homologous (and therefore single-stranded) sequences can be added onto either end of the DNA fragment to be displaced, providing a denatured entry site for the enzyme, or the substrate can be converted into a linear molecule by cleavage with a restriction enzyme within the double-stranded DNA (dsDNA). Duplex regions as short as 17 base-pairs (bp) and as long as 2500 bp have been used successfully. An RNA transcript can be substituted for the DNA fragment to yield a substrate for measuring DNA·RNA helicase activity (17). Alternatively, the entire duplex substrate can be constructed from two RNA transcripts to measure RNA· RNA unwinding (16). However, only complete unwinding events are observed using this assay, and the substrate is artificial in terms of the DNA structure likely to be encountered *in vivo*. Nevertheless, these substrates have been extremely useful in characterizing the reactions catalyzed by various helicases.

A variation of this partial-duplex substrate (28) has been used to determine the polarity of an unwinding reaction (Fig. 2). In this case, the circular partial-duplex molecule has been cleaved with a restriction enzyme to produce a linear molecule with duplex regions of different lengths at either end. There is a large, internal region of ssDNA for initial binding by the enzyme. Unwinding in one direction results in displacement of a fragment of a specific length. Using this assay, the polarity of unwinding has been determined for each helicase found in *E. coli* (Table II); none of the enzymes catalyzes unwinding in both directions.

Recently, a new unwinding assay has been developed using the RecBCD enzyme (29). This assay takes advantage of the quenching of intrinsic protein fluorescence caused by the binding of *E. coli* SSB to ssDNA, and the fact that RecBCD initiates an unwinding reaction from a blunt duplex end. As the RecBCD unwinding reaction proceeds, the ssDNA generated is bound by the free SSB present in the reaction mixture. This has two effects: (1) reannealing of the unwound DNA is prevented, and (2) the intrinsic fluorescence emission of SSB is quenched by the binding of SSB to ssDNA. The latter property is exploited to provide a measure of the amount of duplex DNA that has been unwound. The use of this assay has provided a great deal of insight into the reaction catalyzed by the RecBCD protein (29). However, this assay has limited utility at this time, as most other helicases require a region of ssDNA to initiate an unwinding reaction *in vitro*. This ssDNA would be masked by the SSB included in the reaction mixture, making it impossible to initiate an unwinding reaction. As fully duplex DNA substrates are developed for the other helicases, this assay is likely to find wider application in the field.

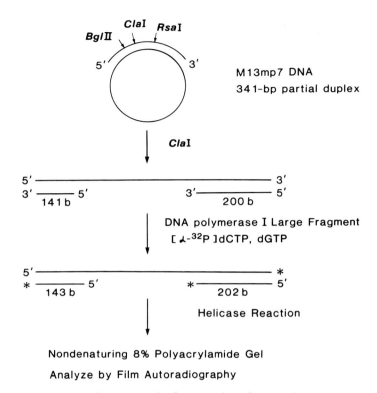

FIG. 2. Scheme for determining the direction of translocation of a helicase. Details for the construction of this substrate are presented in 28. The asterisks denote the position of the radioactive label on all available 3' termini. (Reproduced with permission from 29.)

B. Reaction Mechanisms

Helicases catalyze two interrelated biochemical reactions, (1) DNA-dependent NTP hydrolysis, and (2) the unwinding of duplex substrates. In addition, these enzymes bind ssDNA. The interaction between the enzyme and ssDNA can be described as being either distributive or processive. A distributive enzyme binds and dissociates frequently from the substrate; a processive enzyme binds and remains bound, dissociating infrequently.

A kinetic method for determining whether the enzyme–DNA interaction is distributive or processive, using DNA-dependent NTPase activity as a measure of the interaction, has been described (30–33). The rate of the NTPase reaction, as a function of DNA concentration, is determined for

TABLE II
BIOCHEMICAL PROPERTIES OF THE *E. coli* HELICASES[a]

Enzyme	Polarity	Requirement for non-homologous tail	Stimulation by SSB
Helicase I	5′ to 3′	−	+
Helicase II	3′ to 5′	−	+
Helicase III	5′ to 3′	ND	+
Helicase IV	3′ to 5′	−	+
Rep protein	3′ to 5′	−	±[b]
DnaB protein	5′ to 3′	+	+
PriA protein	3′ to 5′	−	+
RecBCD enzyme	c	−	+
UnrAB complex	5′ to 3′	−	−
Rho protein	5′ to 3′	d	d

[a]ND, not determined.
[b]Rep protein is stimulated by the addition of SSB under some conditions.
[c]No polarity, as defined by the convention used.
[d]Property does not apply to this enzyme.

several ssDNAs that vary in length. If the DNA concentration required to achieve one-half maximal NTP hydrolysis reaction velocity is independent of the length of the DNA, the interaction is classified as distributive. This interpretation derives from the notion that the enzyme binds ssDNA and then dissociates, presumably due to NTP hydrolysis, and then binds ssDNA again. In this case, the length of the DNA molecule should have no effect on the amount of DNA required to saturate the reaction. If, on the other hand, the DNA concentration required for half-maximal reaction velocity depends on the length of the DNA, then the interaction is processive. In this case, the enzyme is presumably translocating along the ssDNA, using ATP hydrolysis to fuel its movement. The enzyme is forced to dissociate from longer DNA molecules less frequently; thus, less DNA is required to achieve saturation. Although useful in terms of thinking about how these enzymes interact with DNA, these reaction mechanisms have not been formally proven.

The unwinding reaction catalyzed by each of the *E. coli* helicases can be classified as catalytic or protein-concentration-dependent, depending on the amount of protein required to unwind duplex-DNA molecules of increasing length (Table III). Examples of catalytic helicases include helicase I, DnaB protein, PriA protein, RecBCD enzyme, Rho protein, and Rep protein under some conditions (see Section II,A). Helicase II catalyzes a protein-concentration-dependent unwinding reaction (32, 36), as does the dda protein from bacteriophage T4 (34–36). A third, somewhat unusual, unwinding reac-

TABLE III
UNWINDING PROPERTIES[a]

Enzyme	Unwinding activity			Unwinding reaction
	Duplex DNA	DNA·RNA	Duplex RNA	
Helicase I	+	±	ND	Catalytic
Helicase II	+	+	−	Stoichiometric
Helicase III	+	ND	ND	ND
Helicase IV	+	±	−	Limited
Rep protein	+	±	−	Catalytic/limited
DnaB protein	+	ND	ND	Catalytic
PriA protein	+	ND	ND	Catalytic
RecBCD enzyme	+	ND	ND	Catalytic
Rho protein	−	+	+	ND
UvrAB complex	+	ND	ND	Limited

[a] ±, Unwinds short hybrid molecules, but fails to unwind long hybrid molecules; ND, not determined.

tion mechanism has been proposed for helicase IV, and for Rep protein in the absence of the phage cistron A (CisA) protein. In this case, the enzyme unwinds short duplex regions efficiently, but unwinds longer duplex regions very poorly (3, 33). Thus, the unwinding reaction is "limited" in terms of the length of the duplex region that is unwound. The reason for this observation is not clear at present.

II. Replicative Helicases

A. Rep Protein

Rep protein was the first helicase in *E. coli* identified by genetic criteria (37). Cells containing mutations (or a deletion) at the *rep* locus are viable (38), but fail to replicate a number of ssDNA phages, including φX174, fd, M13, and P2. The development of an *in vitro* replication system for RFI DNA of phage φX174 provided a complementation assay that was used in the initial purifications of Rep protein (39–41). The purified enzyme (M_r = 68,000) was subsequently shown to catalyze ATP hydrolysis and to cause unwinding of φX174 RF DNA that had been nicked by the phage-encoded CisA protein (40, 42).

Subsequent experiments demonstrated the helicase activity of Rep protein, in the absence of CisA protein, using partial-duplex-DNA substrates and the S1 nuclease assay (25, 43). Unwinding was dependent on the presence of *E. coli* SSB and unidirectional in the 3'-to-5' direction. This polarity is consistent with a role for Rep protein as a helicase in φX174-RF replication, assuming the enzyme is bound to the template strand moving ahead of the advancing DNA polymerase-III holoenzyme. Helicase II, which also catalyzes a 3'-to-5' unwinding reaction (28) and has considerable amino-acid homology with Rep protein (44), does not substitute for Rep protein in this reaction. On the basis of these results, Rep protein is classified as a replicative helicase; the enzyme has no *known* role in replication of the *E. coli* chromosome. Recently, the *rep* gene has been cloned and sequenced (44–46), and an over-producing strain has been constructed (38). This has facilitated the large-scale purification of Rep protein and a description of its solubility properties (47).

The DNA-dependent ATPase reaction catalyzed by Rep protein has been studied by a number of investigators (25, 41, 43, 48–50). The enzyme hydrolyzes dATP as well as ATP, but GTP and dGTP only about one-third as rapidly; CTP, dCTP, UTP, and TTP are poor substrates in the hydrolysis reaction. Essentially, no hydrolysis of ATP is observed in the absence of DNA, while ssDNAs are the best effectors of the ATPase reaction (48). Some hydrolysis of ATP is observed in the presence of duplex DNA, although this may be due to the presence of regions of ssDNA in these duplex molecules. The concentration of DNA required to achieve one-half the maximal rate of ATP hydrolysis is independent of the length of the polynucleotide (longer than dT_8) (48, 33), suggesting a distributive interaction between Rep protein and ssDNA.

The binding of Rep protein to ssDNA has been demonstrated (49) and is stimulated by the addition of non-hydrolyzable ATP analogs. In addition, Rep protein binds ATP with an apparent K_d of 1.8×10^{-7} M. Thus, a ternary Rep-protein·ATP·ssDNA complex can be formed, and is presumably the complex competent for ATP hydrolysis (49). Rep protein is apparently released from the DNA upon ATP hydrolysis, consistent with kinetic results derived from ATPase assays (33), and suggestive of a distributive interaction with ssDNA. This is to be contrasted with a processive interaction with a replication-fork DNA substrate (see below). The K_m for ATP (dATP) in the hydrolysis reaction is influenced by the structure of the DNA effector (48). When dT_{3000} was used, a K_m of 167 μM was measured. In the presence of φX174 ssDNA, an Eadie–Hofstee plot suggests two slopes, one a high K_m (330 μM) and the other a low K_m (21 μM).

The CisA-protein φX-RFII complex is also active as an effector of the Rep protein ATPase. This probably reflects an interaction between Rep protein and CisA protein (25, 48–50). Several interesting differences in the ATPase reaction catalyzed by Rep protein have been observed when the CisA-protein/φX-RFII complex is compared with ssDNA as an ATPase effector (48). In this analysis, the CisA-protein/φX-RFII complex is assumed to be an analog of a replicating fork. As such, it may reveal properties of Rep protein that are more physiologically relevant than those observed using ssDNA as an ATPase effector. First, the K_m for ATP is high in the presence of ssDNA and low in the presence of the replicating-fork DNA. Using the CisA-protein/φX-RFII complex, a K_m of 26 μM was measured, although the plots at low ATP concentration become complicated. The latter fact has been interpreted as an indication of multiple interactions of Rep protein with ATP (48). Second, rNTPs (dNTPs) other than ATP are hydrolyzed in the presence of ssDNA, but not when the replication fork is used as the effector. Moreover, ATP and dATP are apparently not distinguished by Rep protein, leading to the inference that they are used equally well during the course of strand separation. Third, a number of ATP analogs are strong inhibitors of the ssDNA-dependent ATPase reaction, but poor inhibitors in the presence of the replicating fork. Last, SSB inhibits the ssDNA-dependent ATPase reaction, but stimulates the replication-fork-dependent ATPase reaction.

Rep protein is active as a helicase (and an ATPase) in the presence of φX174-RFI DNA only when CisA protein and SSB are added (25, 42, 43, 48–50). When coupled to DNA replication, a complex of CisA protein, Rep protein, DNA polymerase-III holoenzyme, and DNA can be isolated (50). Even in the absence of DNA replication, a complex of CisA protein, Rep protein, and DNA can be observed. Rep protein is present in this complex at about one molecule per molecule of DNA, suggesting a processive mode of helicase action. The binding of Rep protein in a 1:1 ratio with CisA protein suggests an interaction between the two proteins, which may promote a processive unwinding reaction. When the unwinding of duplex DNA by this complex was monitored by the binding of SSB, the K_m for ATP was about 8 μM, and two molecules of ATP were hydrolyzed per base-pair unwound. These values are in close agreement with those determined measuring DNA replication using the same complex and holoenzyme (48). Thus, one molecule of Rep protein is apparently sufficient to catalyze the complete unwinding of φX174-RF DNA in the presence of enough SSB to coat the ssDNA.

The unwinding of a partial-duplex DNA, in the absence of CisA protein (43), proved that Rep protein has an intrinsic helicase activity not dependent on CisA protein. This reaction requires a region of ssDNA adjacent to the duplex, for the initial binding of Rep protein, and the addition of SSB. The polarity of the initiator region is consistent with a 3'-to-5' unwinding reaction. These studies have recently been extended using partial-duplex-DNA substrates and the helicase assay described in Section I,A (3, 51). Rep protein, in the absence of either CisA protein or SSB, catalyzes a limited unwinding of duplex DNA. Although a 71-bp partial-duplex molecule is efficiently unwound, a 343-bp partial-duplex substrate is very poorly unwound by Rep protein. The latter reaction is not stimulated by the addition of SSB, presumably because SSB prevents the association of Rep protein with the extensive ssDNA present in the substrate. It has been suggested (*48, 50*) that the processive character of the Rep protein unwinding reaction in φX174 DNA replication is due to the association of Rep protein with CisA protein. This is consistent with the observation of a limited unwinding reaction in the absence of CisA protein.

A protein factor from *E. coli* cell extracts that stimulates the Rep helicase reaction has been isolated (*51*). This factor interacts with the DNA substrate to stimulate unwinding of the 343-bp partial-duplex substrate 20- to 40-fold. This factor has tentatively been identified as large-ribosomal-subunit protein L14 (J. E. Yancey and S. W. Matson, unpublished). The factor binds to ssDNA and duplex DNA with apparently equal affinity; its affinity for rRNA is somewhat higher. Interestingly, this factor also stimulates the unwinding reaction catalyzed by helicase II (*3, 51*). A potential role (if any) with Rep protein in the cell is currently being investigated.

The physiological role of Rep protein remains unknown. Cells harboring mutations at the *rep* locus appear to propagate replication forks more slowly than wild-type cells (*52*), hinting at a role in DNA replication. In addition, it has been reported that *rep–uvrD* double mutants show decreased viability (*53*). However, cells lacking the gene encoding Rep protein are viable (*38*). The observation that Rep protein catalyzes a limited unwinding reaction in the absence of CisA protein, coupled with the viability of a *rep* deletion strain and the demonstration of helicase activities associated with both DnaB and PriA proteins, suggests that Rep protein is not directly involved in propagation of the replication fork. It is interesting to note that *rep–rho* double mutants are not viable (*54*). We have recently found that Rep protein can unwind short DNA·RNA hybrids (R. J. Sheaff, J. E. Yancey and S. W. Matson, unpublished) in a reaction similar to the unwinding of RNA·DNA hybrids reported for Rho protein (*18*). The unwinding of DNA·RNA hybrids by Rep protein is limited to short regions of duplex hybrid, in contrast to the long hybrid regions unwound by helicase II (*17*). Rep protein and helicase II share considerable amino-acid sequence homology (*44*), and they may substitute for one another in the cell in some capacity. This could provide an explanation for the lack of viability in *rep–uvrD* double mutants.

B. PriA Protein

The most recent addition to the growing list of *E. coli* enzymes with helicase activity is replication factor Y (*55*), also called the n′ protein (*56*) and more recently named PriA protein (*57*). Replication factor Y (*58*) and protein n′ (*59*) were discovered independently as an *E. coli* protein required to reconstitute the replication of the ssDNA of phage φX174 *in vitro*. Both designations are currently used in the literature; I refer to this helicase as PriA protein, in keeping with the most recent designation. I do not review the PriA protein literature extensively, but consider those aspects of the protein's activity important for its helicase function (for a more thorough review, see 60).

PriA protein (M_r = 78,000) has been purified to homogeneity from *E. coli* cell extracts. The enzyme appears to be a single polypeptide chain, as determined by glycerol gradient sedimentation, gel filtration, and poly-acrylamide gel electrophoresis in dodecyl sulfate, and is estimated to be present in about 70 copies per cell (*61*). PriA protein is a component of the *E. coli* "primosome," a multiprotein complex thought to be responsible for the synthesis of primers on the lagging strand at the replication fork (*57, 62, 63*). The primosome was originally identified based on its participation in the priming of replication on the complementary strand of phage φX174 DNA (*64, 65*). The multiprotein complex, which contains one molecule of PriA protein, migrates processively along ssDNA in the 5'-to-3' direction, syn-thesizing short RNA primers at multiple locations on the φX174 chromo-some through the action of DnaG protein (*66*). The primosome assembles at a specific site on ssDNA, termed the primosome assembly site (PAS), pre-sumably directed by the binding of PriA protein (*60, 67, 68*).

As is true of all other helicase enzymes, PriA protein is an ssDNA-dependent ATPase. The PriA protein catalyzes the hydrolysis of both ATP and dATP with approximately equal efficiency, while the other six predomi-nant NTPs are not hydrolyzed to an appreciable extent (*61*). However, unlike other helicases, the ATPase activity of PriA protein depends on the presence of a specific DNA structure called a PAS, first identified on the φX174 chromosome (*67, 68*). PASs are also present on a number of plasmids and in the *E. coli* chromosome (*60, 69–72*). Interestingly, PASs share little se-quence homology, although they can form apparently similar higher-order structures. The PAS on the φX174 chromosome is located in a 55-nucleotide (nt) fragment between the phage F and G genes (*68*). This DNA sequence forms a stable hairpin resistant to digestion by exonuclease VII. An isolated restriction fragment carrying this sequence is as active in promoting PriA-protein-catalyzed ATP hydrolysis as the entire φX174 chromosome. DNAs lacking a PAS (i.e., M13 or G4 ssDNA) are less active than φX174 DNA as effectors of the PriA protein ATP hydrolysis reaction; homopolymeric DNAs [e.g., poly(dT) or poly(rU)] are inactive (*67*). In addition, φX174 ssDNA coated with *E. coli* SSB retains its ability to activate the ATPase activity of PriA protein. Presumably, the stable hairpin formed by the PAS is resistant to coating by SSB, and is therefore available for interaction with PriA pro-tein. Also, the binding of PriA protein to φX174 ssDNA coated with SSB results in the displacement of about one-third of the bound SSB in an in-teraction that is at least partially ATP (dATP)-dependent (*67*).

The helicase activity of PriA protein has been demonstrated using partial-duplex-DNA substrates (55, 56). As expected, in light of the PAS requirement for ATPase (dATPase) activity, the rate of the unwinding reaction is 10- to 15-fold greater when DNA substrates containing a PAS are used, compared to DNA substrates lacking a PAS. The partial-duplex-DNA substrates utilized in these experiments contained a PAS in the single-stranded region of the DNA substrate. A single-stranded tail on the fragment to be displaced is not required (K. J. Marians, personal communication). The helicase reaction is dependent on the presence of ATP or dATP. Poorly hydrolyzed ATP analogs [ATP(γ)S, p(NH)ppA] do not substitute for ATP in the helicase reaction, suggesting a requirement for concomitant ATP hydrolysis. The unwinding reaction catalyzed by PriA protein also depends on the presence of *E. coli* SSB for unwinding duplex regions greater than 40 nt in length (56). The biochemical mechanism of the PriA protein unwinding reaction appears to be processive. The enzyme binds to the substrate, catalyzes unwinding of the duplex region, and fails to recycle to a new substrate molecule (56). PriA protein unwinds duplex DNA in the 3'-to-5' direction (55, 56). Assuming that PriA protein initially binds the PAS, and then moves in a 3'-to-5' direction to the duplex region, a rate of translocation on ssDNA of at least 50 nt/sec has been determined (55).

The gene encoding the PriA protein (*priA*) has recently been cloned, sequenced, and mapped to 88.5 min on the *E. coli* chromosome (73). Unfortunately, no mutants in this gene have been described. Thus, the physiological role of PriA protein remains equivocal. However, compelling biochemical evidence has been obtained suggesting that PriA protein is involved as a helicase (DNA translocase) in the replication of the *E. coli* chromosome (see Section II,C). Nevertheless, certainty of this role for PriA protein in the cell must await the isolation of *priA* mutations.

C. DnaB Protein

DnaB protein, first isolated based on its requirement in the *in vitro* ϕX174 ssDNA replication system (74, 75), is an essential component of the replication machinery utilized by phage λ (76) and *oriC* plasmids (77). This enzyme is also a component of the primosome (62, 63). Purified DnaB protein has an M_r of approximately 50,000, as determined by dodecyl sulfate–polyacrylamide gel electrophoresis. Glycerol gradient sedimentation and gel filtration chromatography suggest a native M_r of approximately 300,000. Cross-linking studies indicate that the native DnaB protein molecule is a hexamer of identical 50-kDa subunits (75, 78). DnaB protein possesses an intrinsic helicase activity (79), which has clarified its role in DNA replication. I focus here on those biochemical properties of DnaB protein relevant to its helicase activity.

DnaB protein catalyzes the DNA-dependent hydrolysis of NTPs with little or no preference as to which NTP is hydrolyzed *in vitro* (*81*, *82*). However, studies carried out using two rNTPs simultaneously demonstrated a two-fold preference for ATP over CTP or UTP (*82*). A K_m value of 100 μM for ATP has been determined in the presence of ϕX174 ssDNA (*81*). The DNA cofactor requirement can be satisfied by ssDNA, oligodeoxythymidylates greater than 4 in length, and some duplex DNAs including duplex ColE1 DNA and poly(dA)·poly(dT) (*81*, *82*). Apparently, the ability of supercoiled ColE1 DNA to effect the ATPase activity of DnaB protein is due to the presence of ssDNA regions. However, this possibility was ruled out for poly(dA)·poly(dT), suggesting that this synthetic duplex DNA is an effector of the ATPase reaction. Polyribonucleotides do not support the DnaB ATPase reaction to an appreciable extent (*81*). *E. coli* SSB inhibits the ATPase reaction catalyzed by DnaB protein in the presence of ssDNAs, but has little or no effect on the ATPase reaction in the presence of poly(dA)·poly(dT). Presumably, SSB coats the ssDNA and prevents the binding of DnaB protein.

The helicase reaction catalyzed by DnaB protein was demonstrated using a partial duplex substrate, similar to that depicted in Fig. 1, with about 1000 bp of duplex DNA and single-stranded sequences on both ends of the fragment to be displaced (*79*). DnaB protein catalyzes the ATP-dependent unwinding of this substrate in a reaction that is stimulated by the addition of either SSB or SSB and DnaG primase. Unidirectional unwinding proceeds in the 5'-to-3' direction and requires the presence of a single-stranded tail on the 3' end of the fragment to be displaced. In this regard, DnaB protein is similar to both the phage T7 gene-4 protein (*27*) and the phage T4 gene-41 protein (*83*). A large molar excess of DnaB protein is required to achieve complete unwinding of the partial-duplex substrate. This most likely reflects a relatively low affinity of DnaB protein for the DNA substrate (*79*). ATP supports the DnaB helicase reaction better than do the other rNTPs; UTP is significantly less active. Although the helicase reaction requires the presence of a hydrolyzable NTP, AMP-PNP enables DnaB protein to bind ssDNA (*81*) and can serve a similar role in the binding of DnaB protein to the helicase substrate (*79*). Thus, the first step in the unwinding reaction appears to be rNTP-dependent binding of DnaB protein to ssDNA.

Structure–function analysis of DnaB protein, using limited trypsin digestion under native conditions (*84*), suggests that DnaB protein promoters have two distinct domains. The carboxy-terminal domain appears to be the site of ATP binding, ssDNA binding, and oligomerization. This domain also retains ATPase activity. No activity could be ascribed to the amino-terminal domain. The two domains, either alone or together, no longer support DNA replication. In addition, evidence has been obtained for a difference in conformation between ATP- and ADP-bound DnaB proteins, based on their different cleavage rates. Helicase activity was not assayed as part of these studies, and the site of helicase activity remains unknown.

Purified DnaB protein has been incorporated into the *in vitro* replication systems developed for phage λ (76) and *oriC* plasmids (77, 85). In each case, DnaB protein acts as a helicase to initiate the unwinding of duplex DNA from the origin of replication. The initiation of replication from the *E. coli* origin, *oriC*, proceeds bidirectionally. Initially, a complex containing DnaA protein, DnaB protein, and DnaC protein assembles at *oriC*, directed through the site-specific binding of DnaA protein (85). DnaB protein is introduced as a DnaB–DnaC complex. Genetic and biochemical studies indicate an interaction between DnaC protein and DnaB protein (86). Similar interactions between DnaB protein and the phage λ P protein, and between DnaB protein and the phage P1 *ban* protein, have also been observed (87). Interestingly, DnaC protein inhibits the ATPase activity of DnaB protein approximately 30% when poly(dT) is the nucleic acid effector (88, 89), and more than 90% when poly(dT)·poly(dA) is the effector. DnaC protein also inhibits the helicase activity of DnaB protein (90) as does the phage λ P protein (76). After release from the DnaC protein, DnaB helicase proceeds to unwind the duplex DNA bidirectionally, providing a template for the action of the DnaG primase and DNA polymerase-III holoenzyme.

In the absence of accompanying DNA synthesis, the unwinding reaction produces "bubbles" coated with SSB (77, 85). This unwinding reaction is constrained by the topology of the supercoiled plasmid to unwinding a small percentage of the plasmid. The addition of DNA gyrase relieves this constraint, and allows significant unwinding of the plasmid in the absence of DNA replication. Under these conditions, the rate of the unwinding reaction appears to be limiting, and proceeds at about 60 bp/sec per fork at 37°C. This rate can be stimulated by the addition of DnaG primase and holoenzyme. A similar sequence of events can be observed in the initiation of phage λ replication. DnaB protein must be liberated from the P protein–DnaB protein complex through the action of DnaJ, DnaK, and GrpE proteins (90a).

Genetic studies indicate DnaB protein to be involved in DNA replication (91–95). In fact, replication ceases abruptly upon a shift to the nonpermissive temperature using some *dnaB*[ts] alleles, suggesting involvement in propagation of the replication fork. Genetic evidence also suggests a role for DnaB protein in the initiation of DNA replication (96), consistent with the biochemical studies cited above. Together, these data suggest that DnaB protein is the long-sought-after replicative DNA helicase in *E. coli*.

However, this picture has been complicated by the finding of a helicase activity, opposite in polarity, associated with the PriA protein (see above). The relative contributions of the two helicase components of the primosome have been examined (97). Using partial-duplex substrates containing a PAS, the directionality of the unwinding reaction catalyzed by the primosome can be modulated by the concentration and identity of the NTP present in the reaction mixture. Under these conditions, the primosome retains all of its properties in terms of protein requirements and assembly at a PAS. Furthermore, unwinding in the 5'-to-3' direction requires a single-stranded tail on the fragment to be displaced, while unwinding in the 3'-to-5' direction does not. Thus, the individual helicases thought to drive unwinding in either direction also retain the biochemical properties ascribed to the purified enzymes. Interestingly, primosomes moving in either direction are capable of synthesizing RNA primers.

Together, the data place the primosome on the lagging strand at the replication fork. Unwinding of the duplex ahead of the advancing replication machinery requires a 5'-to-3' helicase, such as DnaB protein (Fig. 3). It has been demonstrated that DnaB protein alone can provide the helicase activity required to allow replication at a rate of more than 700 bp/sec at 30°C, which is close to the physiological rate (98). What role, then, does the helicase activity of PriA protein play? Lee and Marians (97) have suggested that PriA protein may be a "DNA translocase" capable of pumping DNA through the replisome complex so as to aid in the overall 5'-to-3' migration of the primosome, and to help in the creation of the looped lagging strand suggested by the dimeric polymerase model (Fig. 3). Isolation of mutants at the priA locus will be required to further substantiate this hypothesis.

The recent identification of a protein (Tus) and DNA sequences (termination sites) involved in the termination of DNA replication in E. coli has prompted investigations into the mechanism by which replication forks are halted (99, 100). Results obtained from in vitro experiments suggest that the binding of Tus to termination sites impedes the unwinding reaction catalyzed by DnaB protein. Inhibition of the unwinding reaction exhibits the same polarity, with respect to the interaction of Tus with termination sites, as observed in vivo. Thus, a simple "block" to unwinding provided by the bound protein cannot account for the action of Tus on the helicase activity of DnaB protein. Two additional helicases were utilized in these studies, Rep protein and helicase II. The two groups (99, 100) report conflicting data regarding the ability of Tus bound of termination sites to inhibit the unwinding reaction catalyzed by these two enzymes. Kuempel et al. (100a) have suggested that this may be due to the different termination sites used in the two studies. Whether or not protein–protein interactions are involved in this inhibition of unwinding remains to be determined. However, it is clear that inhibition of the unwinding reaction is a primary mechanism by which replication forks are halted in E. coli.

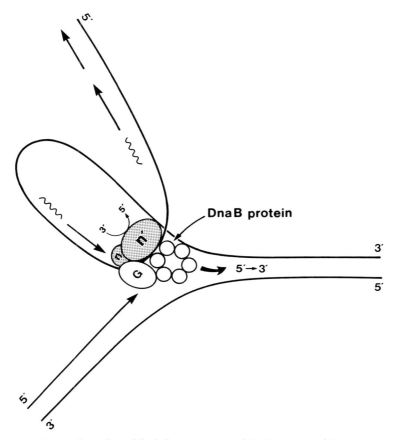

FIG. 3. Proposed coupling of the helicase activities of DnaB protein and PriA protein at the replication fork (see Section II,C and 97 for details). Various components of the primosome, DNA polymerase-III holoenzyme, and *E. coli* SSB have been omitted from this model for clarity. (Reproduced with permission from 2.)

III. Repair Helicases

A. Helicase II

E. coli helicase II was originally purified as a DNA-dependent ATPase called DNA-dependent ATPase I (*101*). An enzyme with similar ATPase properties, called helicase II, was subsequently purified (*102, 103*) and shown to be identical to DNA-dependent ATPase I (*104*). Helicase II is encoded by the *uvrD* gene (*105–112*), which is located at approximately 84 min on the *E. coli* chromosome (*106–108, 113, 114*). More recently, the *uvrD* gene has been cloned and sequenced (*105, 108–112*). At various times in the literature, this gene has also been referred to as *uvrE, recL,* and *mutU.* Helicase II apparently exists as a monomer with an M_r estimated at 73,000–77,000 (*101–104*) based on dodecyl sulfate–polyacrylamide gel electrophoresis; the M_r deduced from the DNA sequence is 82,115 (*115*).

Helicase II hydrolyzes both ATP and dATP; GTP, CTP, and UTP are hydrolyzed poorly or not at all. The K_m for dATP is approximately 70 μM, while that for ATP is 110–150 μM in a reaction that depends on both ssDNA and Mg^{2+} (*32, 101–103*). There is little variability in ATP hydrolysis reaction rates using different natural ssDNA templates, including those that contain pyrimidine dimers. Synthetic polydeoxyribonucleotides can also serve as effectors of the ATP hydrolysis reaction. Filter-binding studies indicate that dsDNA is a poor binding substrate for helicase II (*103*), consistent with its inability to support the ATPase reaction. However, fully duplex DNA can be unwound by helicase II at high enzyme-to-DNA ratios (*116, 117*), suggesting that the enzyme is able to bind this substrate under some conditions. RNA substrates do not support helicase-II-catalyzed NTP hydrolysis, and the enzyme presumably has little or no affinity for RNA (*32, 102, 103*).

ATP hydrolysis is apparently responsible for the unidirectional translocation of helicase II along ssDNA (*32*). While translocation and unwinding are thought to proceed 3' to 5' with respect to the strand on which the enzyme is bound (*28, 116*), some evidence for 5'-to-3' movement has been reported (*23, 36*). It seems likely that the latter results stem from the enzyme's ability to utilize duplex ends and/or nicks under certain conditions. The DNA concentration required to achieve one-half maximal velocity of the ATPase reaction is markedly influenced by the length of the polynucleotide effector (*32*). This has been interpreted as evidence for processive translocation along ssDNA. The different ATP hydrolysis inhibition curves obtained for helicase II in the presence of *E. coli* SSB, which binds DNA non-cooperatively, and T4 gene-32 binding protein, which binds DNA cooperatively, support the notion that translocation is processive (*32*).

The unwinding reaction catalyzed by helicase II was initially demonstrated using the S1 nuclease assay (*103*). At low ratios of helicase II to nucleotide, an ssDNA region is required to initiate an unwinding reaction (*23, 32, 36, 103, 116*). Once the duplex region is invaded, helicase II utilizes a concentration-dependent (stoichiometric) interaction to unwind dsDNA (*32, 36, 103*). The number of base-pairs unwound is directly proportional to the amount of helicase II in the reaction, regardless of the length of the duplex region to be unwound (*32, 36*). This reaction can be stimulated (two- to three-fold) by the addition of *E. coli* SSB at concentrations sufficient to coat approximately one-third of the ssDNA present (32). SSB is thought to act by maintaining the single-stranded conformation of unwound duplex regions and/or artificially increasing the concentration of helicase II at the ssDNA–duplex junction by decreasing the ssDNA available for initial binding.

When the ratio of helicase II to nucleotide is increased approximately five-fold, blunt-ended and nicked duplexes can be unwound (116, 117). Recent electron-microscopic data suggest that initiation is occurring at an end or at a nick (117). This observation may have significance in terms of understanding how helicase II "loads" onto a DNA substrate *in vivo* (116, 117), as helicase-II concentrations are high in the cell (Table I).

In addition to unwinding duplex DNA, helicase II unwinds DNA·RNA partial-duplex molecules (17, 103). DNA·RNA hybrids are unwound at a rate that is 10 times that observed for the unwinding of DNA duplexes (17). Unwinding experiments performed using hybrid substrates of different lengths suggest that the unwinding of DNA·RNA hybrids may be catalytic and processive in contrast to the stoichiometric unwinding of duplex DNA that has been reported (S. W. Matson, unpublished). The possibility exists, therefore, that helicase II may be involved in some aspect of RNA metabolism not previously recognized. RNA duplexes are not substrates for unwinding by helicase II (S. W. Matson, unpublished).

It has been suggested that helicase II, in conjunction with Rep protein, may be directly involved in propagating the replication fork in *E. coli* (53). This notion derives from several observations: (1) Helicase II can stimulate *in vitro* DNA synthesis on an artificially forked and primed λ DNA template in the presence of DNA polymerase-III holoenzyme, SSB, dNTPs, and ATP (118). This stimulation is enhanced by the addition of helicase III or Rep protein, neither of which shows substantial stimulatory effects of its own. (2) Anti-helicase-II antibodies cause a partial inhibition of *E. coli*, ColE1, and phage λ replication in a subcellular *E. coli* replication system (119). (3) *rep–uvrD* double mutants exhibit slow growth (53, 112) and in other cases appear to be inviable (53).

However, *uvrD* mutants show none of the growth deficiencies associated with replication defects (53, 104), and replicate various non-chromosomal DNAs, including ColE1-like plasmids and λ, φX174, and fd DNA. It has been suggested that Rep protein substitutes for helicase II in its role as a replication enzyme within *uvrD* mutants, accounting for the inviability of *uvrD–rep* double mutants (53). Nevertheless, the biochemical and genetic data now available provide compelling support for the notion that DnaB protein, and perhaps PriA protein, are involved in propagation of the replication fork. Helicase II (and Rep protein) may have dispensable functions in replication; they appear not to be primary replicative helicases.

Many of the phenotypes exhibited by *uvrD* mutants implicate helicase II in repair and/or recombination processes. *uvrD* mutants are deficient in host-cell reactivation (*120, 121*), show increased spontaneous mutation frequencies (*114, 121–123*), and exhibit sensitivity to UV-irradiation and other DNA-damaging agents (*106–108, 114, 120, 121, 123*). Using both cell-free extracts (*124*) and purified excision repair enzymes (*125–128*), it has been demonstrated that helicase II and DNA polymerase I are responsible for the turnover of UvrABC excinuclease at *in vivo* rates. The DNA polymerase-I Klenow fragment and T4 DNA polymerase substitute for polymerase I in this reaction; however, helicase II cannot be replaced by Rep protein (*126*), T7 gene-4 protein, or T4 gene-41/gene-61 complex (*128*). As one might expect for an enzyme involved in turnover of the excinuclease complex, deficiencies in both incision and excision of damaged DNA are observed in *uvrD* mutants (*121, 124*). When cells are held in buffer following UV-irradiation, thousands of thymine dimers are removed. However, this liquid holding effect is lost in *uvrD* mutants, presumably because the UvrABC excinuclease is unable to turn over (*129*). Thus, helicase II plays a role in excision repair that may involve direct protein–protein interactions with other excision enzymes. It is important to note that *uvrD–polA1* double mutants are not viable (*122, 123, 130*).

Helicase II has also been shown to be involved in methyl-directed mismatch repair, a system that identifies and repairs mismatched nucleotides that arise during DNA synthesis and recombination in *E. coli* (for a review, see *131*). Extracts from *uvrD⁻* cells repair mismatched, heteroduplex substrates at a rate 10% of that of wild-type cells. Normal levels of repair can be restored by the addition of extracts that contain wild-type helicase II (*132–135*). Mismatch repair has also been reconstituted *in vitro* using purified enzymes, and requires helicase II. *In vivo*, *uvrD* mutants are deficient in the repair of transfected mismatched heteroduplexes (*136*). The precise role played by helicase II in mismatch repair remains to be determined, although presumably the unwinding reaction catalyzed by helicase II is involved.

In addition to the repair phenotypes associated with *uvrD* mutants, high recombination frequencies have also been observed in these cells (*108, 123, 137–141*). Cells deficient in the *Rec*BC recombination pathway have provided insight into the *Rec*F pathway, which may involve helicase II (*142*). While it is not known how helicase II is involved in recombination, it has been suggested that it may function as an antirecombinase (*141*). Precise and nearly precise transposon excision is enhanced in *uvrD* mutants 10- to 100-fold (*143*) and may occur by a copy-choice recombination mechanism (*141*). According to the copy-choice model, slippage of the replication machinery occurs between short, repeated sequences, and replication proceeds, generating a recombinant molecule missing the region between the repeats. Helicase II could destroy the recombination intermediate and restore the pre-slippage configuration by melting the short duplex regions involved in homologous pairing. As part of the methyl-directed mismatch-repair pathway, helicase II has also been implicated in the barrier to recombination between DNAs of different species (*144*). Recombination between *E. coli* and *Salmonella typhimurium*, which are about 80% homologous in their DNA sequences, is increased in cells harboring mutations in *uvrD*.

Some regulation of helicase-II intracellular concentration appears to be essential for the viability of *E. coli* cells. High concentrations of helicase II interfere with normal repair and recombination functions (*53, 107, 108, 141*) and can be lethal (*116*). RecA–LexA regulation and attenuation may provide the mechanisms by which appropriate helicase-II levels are maintained. Within the upstream regulatory region of the *uvrD* gene, there are two promoter sites located on opposite sides of a functional LexA-protein binding site (*115, 145*). Promoter 2 is located downstream from the LexA-protein binding site, presumably beyond the reach of LexA control. This promoter may be responsible for maintaining basal levels of helicase II (*115*), which have been estimated at 3000–8000 molecules per cell (*119, 140*). However, *in vitro* transcription experiments suggest that this promoter may not be used, as no runoff transcripts initiated at this site (*145*). Promoter 1 is positioned upstream from the LexA-protein binding site and is believed to be under LexA control (*145, 146*). This promoter may, therefore, be responsible for the RecA-dependent, 1.5- to 2.5-fold stimulation of helicase-II levels seen following DNA damage with UV-irradiation, mitomycin C, and naladixic acid (*111, 112, 140, 147, 148*).

Approximately one-half of the transcripts initiated *in vitro* from promoter 1 terminate as an oligonucleotide, approximately 60 nt in length, at nucleotide positions -15 to -19 with respect to the AUG start site (*145*). The potential for secondary structures resembling a rho-independent termination site exists within this 60-nt, truncated transcript and, like rho-independent terminators, when ITP substitutes for GTP during transcription, termination no longer occurs (*145*). Furthermore, this region contains a GGAGG site to which the 3′ end of the 16-S rRNA could bind and thus disrupt the secondary structure responsible for attenuation (*145*).

B. UvrAB Complex

A complex composed of the UvrA and UvrB subunits of the UvrABC excinuclease has helicase activity (*149, 150*). Neither protein alone is capable of catalyzing the unwinding of duplex DNA; however, the two proteins together catalyze the unwinding of D-loops (*149*) and short duplex regions (*150*). Since incision of DNA near a damage site, such as a pyrimidine dimer, is thought to proceed through a series of protein–protein and protein–DNA interactions, it is not unreasonable to postulate an interaction between UvrA and UvrB that is independent of the addition of UvrC protein. In fact, current models for excision repair (128) suggest that the damage site is recognized by UvrA protein, perhaps in conjunction with the UvrB protein. This complex is competent for incision upon the addition of UvrC protein. The UvrD protein (helicase II) and/or DNA polymerase I is required for the turnover of UvrC protein (125, 126).

The unwinding reaction catalyzed by the UvrAB complex requires hydrolysis of ATP (dATP); none of the other NTPs will substitute, nor will poorly hydrolyzed analogs of ATP. The UvrA protein has an intrinsic ATPase activity and DNA-binding activity (151). However, the ATPase activity of the UvrA protein is not dependent on the presence of DNA, although it is influenced by UvrB protein. Interestingly, both UvrA and UvrB possess a consensus nucleotide binding site (152). The ATPase activity of UvrB has been suggested to be cryptic (152). Site-directed mutagenesis studies suggest that this site is important in the overall process of excision repair (152). Whether or not this site is involved in the helicase reaction catalyzed by the UvrAB complex has yet to be determined.

The unwinding reaction catalyzed by the UvrAB complex is confined to short duplex regions; a 22-bp partial-duplex substrate is efficiently unwound, while a 346-bp substrate is not unwound (149). The unwinding of a 51-bp partial-duplex substrate is substantially reduced compared to that of a 22-bp substrate. The addition of SSB, UvrC protein, or photolyase does not increase the length of the duplex region this protein complex can unwind (150). Unwinding is unidirectional in the 5'-to-3' direction and does not require the presence of a single-stranded tail on the fragment to be unwound. The reaction does, however, require a short region of ssDNA (a minimum of 10 nt) for binding of the protein complex to initiate an unwinding reaction (150). Competition experiments suggest a distributive mechanism, and UV-induced photoproducts in the DNA substrate inhibit the reaction.

The role this helicase reaction may play in nucleotide excision repair is not clear. It has been reported that a complex composed of UvrA and UvrB can cause the localized melting of supercoiled or damaged duplex DNA in the presence of a non-hydrolyzable ATP analog. This may represent a partial helicase reaction in the absence of protein translocation (153). Perhaps the UvrAB complex alters the conformation of the DNA near the damage site to provide a configuration conducive to the subsequent incisions events carried out by UvrABC excinuclease (150). This will have to be reconciled with the role of helicase II in excision repair (125, 126) and the observation that UvrA protein dissociates prior to the binding of UvrC protein and incision (154).

IV. RecBCD Enzyme

The RecBCD enzyme (exonuclease V, Ec 3.1.11.5) was first identified in *E. coli* cell extracts as an ATP-dependent dsDNA exonuclease (*155–158*). Since then, the enzyme has been shown to possess four additional activities: ATP-dependent ssDNA endonuclease and exonuclease activities, DNA-dependent ATPase activity (*159–163*) and helicase activity (*29, 164–167*). These functions are presumably utilized by the enzyme in homologous recombination and DNA repair. The RecBCD enzyme complex, composed of one copy each of three non-identical subunits, has an M_r of approximately 330,000 (*29, 156*), exists in about 10 copies per cell (*168*), and is a nonessential enzyme (*169*). The RecD subunit was not immediately recognized as a component of the RecBCD enzyme (*170–172*), and thus this enzyme was known as the RecBC enzyme for several years. The RecB ($M_r = 140,000$), RecC ($M_r = 130,000$), and RecD ($M_r = 60,000$) polypeptides are encoded by the *recB*, *recC*, and *recD* genes respectively (*160, 163, 168, 173, 174, 176*), located at approximately 60 min on the *E. coli* chromosome (*171, 175*). Originally, it was thought that these genes might all exist within a single operon (*158*). Recent experiments suggest that this is not the case (*171*; P. T. Emmerson, personal communication).

The DNA-dependent NTPase activity of the RecBCD enzyme is optimal using either ATP or dATP; other NTPs are inefficiently utilized (*156, 159, 160*). The RecB and RecD subunits both contain ATP-binding sequences, and therefore are probably responsible for the ATPase activity of the RecBCD complex (*168, 172, 174*). The RecB subunit, in the absence of the other subunits, can catalyze ATP hydrolysis (*170, 177, 178*). This property is not shared by the isolated RecD subunit (*170*). However, both RecB and RecD bind 8-azido-ATP in an intact RecBCD complex (*179*). The small amount of ATP hydrolysis measured in the absence of DNA substrate is stimulated by either ssDNA or linear dsDNA. Linear dsDNA is the preferred effector of the ATPase reaction (*180*). In fact, in the presence of SSB, the stimulatory effect of ssDNA is completely lost (*180*). RNA·DNA hybrids, duplex DNA with interstrand cross-links, and DNA that has been damaged by UV-irradiation also stimulate RecBCD-catalyzed ATP hydrolysis (*181, 182*). The K_ms for ATP and dsDNA have been estimated to be 85 μM and 0.13 nM, respectively, in the ATPase reaction. The similarity in apparent K_m and K_{cat} values obtained when linear and circular ssDNA substrates are compared indicate that the ssDNA-dependent ATPase activity does not require DNA ends (*180*).

The discovery of conditions that minimized the nucleolytic properties of the RecBCD complex enabled the helicase activity of this enzyme to be observed (*165*). Examination of unwinding intermediates using electron microscopy revealed three interrelated structures referred to as forks, loop-tails, and twin-loops (164–166, 183, 184). All three structures indicate that the RecBCD enzyme possesses unwinding activity that initiates from DNA ends and proceeds more quickly on one strand than on the other, producing a loop (see models proposed in 158 and 180). By labeling either the 3' or the 5' end of the DNA substrate prior to unwinding, and examining the resulting loop-tail structures, a strand specificity has been demonstrated (184). In each case, the RecBCD enzyme formed a loop on the 3' strand with respect to the end used for entry.

The enzyme prefers linear dsDNA with blunt ends as an unwinding substrate. Linear dsDNA molecules with 3' or 5' tails greater than 25 nt in length are not unwound by the enzyme (183). Apparently, the enzyme fails to bind these substrates (183), perhaps because RecBCD must interact with both strands of DNA for optimal binding (29, 180). An interaction with both strands of DNA is also suggested by the absence of translocation polarity. Not only is a single-stranded loading region unnecessary, but, when present, its polarity is unimportant, indicating that both strands must be equally capable of providing a substrate for movement (183). Furthermore, ssDNA is much less efficient than dsDNA at stimulating the ATP hydrolysis reaction, presumed essential for unwinding, suggesting that optimal activity may require interaction with both strands (180).

The helicase reaction catalyzed by the RecBCD enzyme has also been characterized, using the fluorometric helicase assay described in Section I,A. (29). ATP hydrolysis is required for RecBCD-catalyzed unwinding and approximately two or three ATP molecules are hydrolyzed per base-pair unwound (29, 180). The unwinding reaction is processive, unwinding up to 25 kilobases (kb) of dsDNA prior to dissociation in a catalytic reaction (29). Unwinding occurs at a rate of approximately 250 bp/sec per functional RecBCD enzyme at 25°C and 930 bp/sec per enzyme molecule at 37°C. (29). The apparent K_m values for ATP and dsDNA in this reaction are 0.6 nM dsDNA molecules and 130 μM ATP (29).

RecBCD involvement in DNA repair and recombination is suggested by the facts that mutants are sensitive to DNA-damaging agents (175, 181), their viability is poor (185), and they are recombination-deficient (175, 186–189). Recombination deficiencies appear at both early (188, 189) and late times (187) in genetic recombination and appear to be the result of both nuclease and unwinding deficiencies (165). In vitro studies demonstrate reconstitution of homologous pairing which is dependent on the combined activities of purified E. coli RecA, RecBCD, and SSB proteins (167, 190). In this assay, the RecBCD enzyme initiates homologous recombination, utilizing its helicase activity to produce ssDNA, which serves as the substrate for RecA protein-mediated homologous pairing. RecBCD also converts the damage from certain agents, such as naladixic acid, into an active inducer of the SOS response (*158, 191*). Both foreign and damaged DNAs are thought to be removed from the cell by RecBCD as well (*186, 192*).

V. Other Helicases

A. Helicase I

Helicase I was the first helicase identified solely on the basis of its DNA-dependent ATPase and helicase activities (*24, 193*). The purified enzyme has an M_r of 180,000, as determined on dodecyl sulfate–polyacrylamide gels, and sedimentation studies indicate that helicase I is an anisometric molecule. These early studies also suggested that helicase I forms large aggregates in solutions of low ionic strength, which led to the conclusion that helicase I might be active as an aggregate of helicase-I monomers (*24, 193*). Subsequent observations suggest that helicase I may be active as a monomer or a small multimer (*194;* E. G. Minkley, personal communication).

The NTPase activity of helicase I exhibits a preference for ATP (dATP), but also hydrolyzes the remaining six predominant NTPs (*193, 194*). Efforts to determine a K_m for NTP and a V_{max} for the DNA-dependent NTPase reaction using the various NTPs have been complicated by the unusual $MgCl_2$ requirements of the enzyme (*194*) and the apparent biphasic dependence on NTP concentration. Nevertheless, an apparent K_m for ATP of 0.27 mM has been reported (*193*). Additional data suggest the existence of a second, lower K_m for ATP of 2 μM (E. G. Minkley, personal communication). This would be consistent with the presence of two potential nucleotide binding sites within the helicase I polypeptide (*195*). The DNA-dependent ATPase reaction requires ssDNA; little or no activity is observed in the absence of DNA or in the presence of dsDNA. In addition, helicase I does not use RNA or ssDNA coated with SSB as an effector of the ATPase reaction.

Interestingly, the original studies of helicase I suggested that synthetic polydeoxyribonucleotides such as poly(dT) or poly(dA) are not effective in stimulating the ATPase reaction (*193*). This observation was explained when it was discovered that the extent of the helicase I ATPase reaction on linear DNA molecules is limited (*194*). Kinetic studies of the helicase I, DNA-dependent ATPase reaction using linear and circular M13 ssDNA indicate that helicase I processively translocates along ssDNA, presumably utilizing the energy released by the hydrolysis reaction to fuel movement (*194*). The ATPase reaction is linear with time in the presence of circular ssDNA, but is hardly detected when linear ssDNA is substituted for the circular molecule. That helicase I does, in fact, traverse the linear DNA has been demonstrated using unwinding assays.

The ATPase results appear to be due to the extreme processivity of helicase I, which has little tendency to dissociate from the DNA molecule, once bound. Thus, in the case of the linear DNA, the enzyme binds and moves to the end of the DNA molecule and remains associated with the DNA in a complex that does not hydrolyze ATP. In contrast, on the circular DNA molecule, the enzyme processively migrates around the circle, which functionally is infinitely long, and continues to hydrolyze ATP.

The unwinding reaction catalyzed by helicase I was originally demonstrated using partially duplex fd DNA and the S1 nuclease assay (24, 196). The unwinding of duplex DNA requires the concomitant hydrolysis of ATP and a region of ssDNA (>200 nt in length; 36) to which the enzyme binds initially. The unwinding reaction is processive in mechanism, as trapping of excess enzyme does not result in a reduced reaction rate. The polarity of the unwinding reaction is 5' to 3', as demonstrated with linear duplex fd DNA partially eroded with either exonuclease III or λ exonuclease (36) or the partial-duplex polarity assay described in Section I,A (194) (see Fig. 2).

More recently, the helicase-I unwinding reaction has been characterized using partial-duplex substrates (194). These studies also suggest a processive mechanism. This conclusion is supported by the fact that the extent of the unwinding reaction is directly proportional with helicase I concentration. Thus, the enzyme does not appear to turn over from one DNA substrate molecule to another, which is consistent with results obtained using the DNA-dependent ATPase assay as a measure of enzyme activity. Results from these experiments suggest that helicase I may be active as a monomer or a much smaller oligomer than previously thought.

The discovery that helicase I is encoded by the traI gene on the F plasmid implicates helicase I in the process of bacterial conjugation (197). It is inferred that helicase I is not involved in chromosomal metabolism. The product of traI is required for both physical and genetic transfer of the F plasmid from donor to recipient cells (198, 199). The DNA unwinding activity of helicase I seems ideally suited to drive the transfer of a single strand of DNA into the recipient bacterium.

Helicase I may also have a role in the site-specific nicking reaction that is believed to initiate the strand transfer of F DNA to the recipient cell (200, 201). The evidence for this derives from complementation studies using plasmids containing various regions of the F transfer (tra) operon (201) and from mapping studies (200). The site-specific nicking event is thought to be catalyzed by an endonuclease complex that is the product of the traY and traZ genes (198, 199). The traY gene lies near the proximal end of the tra operon, and the traZ gene, near the distal end. The traI gene also maps near the distal end of the tra operon. However, no site mutations in the traZ gene have ever been isolated. In fact, the traI gene and the traZ gene have never been separated by genetic complementation studies. Mapping studies have located the putative traZ gene at a site within or just upstream from the helicase I encoding sequence (200). These results, in conjunction with complementation results, have been interpreted to suggest that helicase I is bifunctional, having DNA unwinding and site-specific nicking activities. However, this has not been demonstrated biochemically. In fact, recent efforts to demonstrate site-specific nicking at the F *oriT* locus using helicase I alone, and in combination with the TraY protein, have been unsuccessful (E. E. Lahue and S. W. Matson, unpublished).

The complete sequencing of the helicase I gene has identified an in-frame restart polypeptide called TraI* (200, 201). Whether it has helicase activity is not known. However, the sequence data (195) place one of the ATP-binding-sequence motifs within TraI*, and it has been reported that the first 40 kDa of helicase I is not required for its helicase activity (197). The role, if any, of the TraI* restart polypeptide is not clear at present.

B. Helicase III

Helicase III was isolated in a search for additional DNA unwinding enzymes in a *rep*⁻ strain of *E. coli* (202–205). The protein was identified as an ssDNA-dependent ATPase eluting from a phosphocellulose column at a higher salt concentration (about 700 mM NaCl) than any of the previously identified helicases. The purified enzyme appears to be a single polypeptide (M_r = 20,000) and is the smallest helicase described to date. Glycerol gradient sedimentation suggests that the active enzyme has an M_r of nearly 40,000. Thus, helicase III may consist of two, presumably identical, polypeptides of 20,000 M_r each (202, 203).

The ssDNA-dependent ATPase activity of helicase III is dependent on the presence of Mg^{2+} and is maximally active with either φX174 or fd phage DNA. Little or no activity is observed in the absence of DNA or in the presence of dsDNA. Short homopolymeric DNAs also fail to activate the ATPase activity, and, interestingly, poly(dT) is only 15% as effective as φX174 DNA as an effector of the ATP hydrolysis reaction. Although poly(rU) and poly(rA) fail to activate the ATPase activity, poly(A)⁻ RNA does support the ATP hydrolysis reaction to a limited extent. The significance of this observation is unknown. The enzyme catalyzes the hydrolysis of both ATP and dATP with little or no activity observed using UTP, GTP, and dTTP. The K_m for ATP in the hydrolysis reaction is 100 μM, and the K_m for dATP is 240 μM (202).

The unwinding reaction catalyzed by helicase III was first demonstrated using a partial-duplex substrate and analyzed by resolving products on a sucrose gradient (202). In this case, the duplex region on the substrate was approximately 500 bp long. The unwinding reaction depends on the presence of ATP, and is partially dependent on the presence of *E. coli* SSB (204). Although SSB inhibits the ssDNA-dependent ATPase activity of helicase III, it stimulates the DNA unwinding reaction at low concentrations of helicase III, presumably by binding to the displaced strand. However, the helicase-III unwinding reaction is not absolutely dependent on the addition of SSB.

At higher concentrations of helicase III, the addition of SSB causes little or no stimulation of the unwinding reaction (*204*). Helicase III presumably requires a region of ssDNA on which to bind to initiate an unwinding reaction, although this has not been demonstrated directly. Helicase III will not unwind φX174-RF DNA that has been nicked by CisA protein, and thus will not substitute for Rep protein in this reaction. Analysis of the direction of the unwinding reaction indicates that the enzyme unwinds duplex DNA in the 5′-to-3′ direction (*204*), opposite those of Rep protein, helicase II, and helicase IV.

Interestingly, helicase III binds to both ssDNA and duplex DNA in the absence of ATP (*205*). In the presence of ATP, binding is confined to ssDNA. This is consistent with the fact that ssDNA activates the ATP hydrolysis reaction, while duplex DNA does not. Substitution of the poorly hydrolyzed analog, AMP-PNP, for ATP inhibits the ATP hydrolysis reaction catalyzed by helicase III and inhibits the binding of helicase III to ssDNA. This has been interpreted to suggest the presence of an enzyme–PO_4 or enzyme–ADP complex that is important for binding to ssDNA. In support of this notion, an ADP–ATP exchange reaction has been demonstrated. This reaction requires the presence of Mg^{2+}, but proceeds at a rate that is 1/2000 that of the rate of ATP hydrolysis. To date, this is the only helicase that has been reported to catalyze such an exchange reaction.

Although suggested by the above experimental evidence, an enzyme–intermediate complex has never been directly demonstrated. Nevertheless, this evidence has been used to formulate a hypothesis regarding the mechanism by which helicase III unwinds duplex DNA. The enzyme presumably binds an ssDNA initiator region and moves in a 5′-to-3′ direction to the junction of ssDNA and duplex DNA. Here, in the absence of ATP, helicase III binds the ds DNA just "ahead" of the junction. Upon binding and hydrolyzing ATP, the enzyme changes conformation and the conformation of the DNA to which it is bound, such that the DNA unwinds and ADP is released. The enzyme–PO_4 form is converted to free enzyme and is, once again, able to bind duplex DNA just ahead of the unwound fork, and the cycle is repeated stepwise until the DNA is unwound. This model for unwinding, whether by helicase III or any other helicase, awaits further experimental testing.

Although described biochemically, the gene encoding helicase III remains unknown and no mutants in helicase III are available. Thus, the physiological role of helicase III remains unknown.

C. Helicase IV

Helicase IV was originally called the 75-kDA helicase, to reflect the relative molecular mass of the polypeptide (*206*). The enzyme was isolated from an *E. coli* strain deficient in Rep protein, as was helicase III, and identified as an ssDNA-dependent ATPase with helicase activity that eluted from a phosphocellulose column at relatively high (650 m*M* KCl) salt concentrations. Reconstitution of active enzyme, after resolution on a dodecyl sulfate–polyacrylamide gel, confirmed that the 75-kDA polypeptide has active sites for both ssDNA-dependent ATPase and helicase activities. The enzyme has an M_r similar to those of helicase II, Rep protein, and PriA protein, but is distinct from these other *E. coli* helicases on the basis of biochemical, immunological, and genetic criteria (*260, 207*). Thus, helicase IV is a distinct helicase in the cell that appears, based on purification recoveries, to be present in relatively low abundance, perhaps as little as 10 copies per cell (*208*).

The ATPase activity of helicase IV is dependent on the addition of ssDNA; there is little or no activity in the absence of DNA or in the presence of duplex DNA (*206*). There is no apparent sequence specificity. Poly(dT) is as effective as M13 DNA as a cofactor in the ATPase reaction. Poly(rA) and SSB-coated M13 ssDNA fail to serve as effectors of the ATPase (*208*). The enzyme catalyzes the hydrolysis of both ATP and dATP with approximately equal efficiency and has a K_m for each of about 250 μ*M*. In addition, there is slight hydrolysis of GTP but at a level that is 1/30 that of ATP. The ssDNA-dependent ATPase reaction requires the presence of $MgCl_2$, and the non-hydrolyzable ATP analog, ATP(γ)S, is an inhibitor of the ATPase reaction (*208*).

The unwinding reaction catalyzed by helicase IV has been demonstrated using two partial-duplex substrates containing either 71 or 343 bp of duplex DNA (*206*). Unwinding is unidirectional in the 3'-to-5' direction and thus shares the same polarity as helicase II, Rep protein, and PriA protein. Unwinding of the 71-bp, partial-duplex molecule is quite efficient. Unwinding of the 343–bp partial duplex, on the other hand, is substantially reduced compared to unwinding of the 71-bp molecule. Even at high protein concentrations, less than 10% of the available duplex-DNA molecules were completely unwound by the enzyme. This phenomenon is shared with Rep protein, which also unwinds long duplex regions poorly in the absence of additional proteins (see above). It has been suggested that this may be due to a strand-switching event that results in unidirectional migration of the helicase off the partial-duplex substrate prior to completion of the unwinding reaction (*3, 33*). A strand-switching event has not been directly demonstrated, but would be consistent with the distributive interaction with ssDNA exhibited by helicase IV (*208*). The addition of *E. coli* SSB to unwinding reactions utilizing the 343-bp substrate stimulates the unwinding reaction about four-fold (*208*). However, even under these conditions, a large fraction of the substrate is not unwound by helicase IV.

The gene encoding helicase IV has been cloned, sequenced, and mapped on the *E. coli* chromosome (*207*). The helicase IV gene, referred to as *helD*, maps at 22 min on the *E. coli* map, approximately 4.8 kb from the *ompA* gene. The amino-acid sequence of helicase IV, deduced from the DNA sequence, shares several regions of similarity with both helicase II and Rep protein.

The physiological role of helicase IV is not known at present. There are no known mutations in the *helD* gene, and thus no phenotype for helicase IV mutants. However, in this context, it is interesting to note that helicase IV is identical with a protein identified in Hoffmann-Berling's laboratory as being able to rescue the temperature-sensitive growth defect in *uvrD^{ts}–rep* double mutants (H. Hoffmann-Berling, personal communication). In these experiments a *uvrD^{ts}–rep* double mutant was constructed and, although viable at the permissive temperature, failed to grow at the restrictive temperature. Temperature-resistant (pseudo)revertants were easily isolated, and a previously unidentified helicase activity was discovered in these cells. The activity was purified, antibodies directed against the protein were raised, and the gene was cloned. The gene encoding the protein cotransduced with the *ompA* gene at a frequency of more than 90%. Recent hybridization experiments suggest that this gene and *helD* are the same gene (S. W. Matson, unpublished). Thus, helicase IV may compensate for some essential activity of helicase II or Rep protein in the cell. What this activity might be and what helicase IV does under normal conditions are questions that remain to be answered.

Another putative helicase, also called helicase IV, has been described (*209*). In the absence of direct evidence for unwinding activity, I propose that this enzyme not be called a helicase at this time.

D. Rho Protein

Rho protein was initially isolated in a search for a protein factor(s) that would cause RNA polymerase to terminate transcription and release the RNA transcript at unique sites *in vitro* (*210*). Subsequent studies have confirmed that Rho protein is a transcription termination factor, required for the accurate termination of transcription at specific sites on the DNA template (for reviews, see *22* and *211*). The helicase activity of Rho protein, which catalyzes the unwinding of RNA·DNA hybrids and duplex RNA, has been described (*18*). This discovery may shed light on the mechanism by which Rho protein terminates transcription. The gene encoding Rho protein has been cloned and sequenced (*212*). The M_r of Rho protein, based on the DNA sequence of the *rho* gene, is 46,094. The active form of Rho protein is thought to be a hexamer of identical Rho monomers (*210, 213*). The gene encoding Rho protein is located at 85 min on the *E. coli* chromosome, and mutational studies suggest that Rho protein is essential for cell viability (*214*).

Like the other helicases found in *E. coli*, Rho protein has an associated NTPase activity (*215–217*). However, in contrast to the helicases described above, the NTPase activity of Rho protein is dependent on single-stranded RNA. Results from *in vitro* studies suggest that the dependence of Rho NTPase activity on the base composition and structure of the ssRNA effector is complex. There does not appear to be a conserved nucleotide sequence required for the binding of Rho protein, although an ssRNA lacking secondary structure and having cytidine residues appears to be important. *In vitro*, poly(rC) provides the best effector of the Rho protein ATPase activity (*217*). When poly(rC) is used as the nucleic acid effector, Rho protein catalyzes the hydrolysis of all four rNTPs (*216*), although ATP is preferred as the NTP substrate in the helicase reaction (*18, 19*). The NTPase activity of Rho protein is essential for termination of transcription (*219, 220*) as well as for helicase activity (*18, 19*). This presumably provides the energy required for translocation of Rho protein along ssRNA toward a paused RNA polymerase (*221*) and/or to unwind the RNA·DNA hybrid present in the transcription complex (*18, 19*).

An amino-terminal fragment of Rho protein, called N1, can bind RNA while a carboxy-terminal fragment, N2, contains the ATP binding site (*222*). The domain structure has been further refined using limited trypsin digestion as a probe of structure, and confirms an amino-terminal RNA-binding domain, an ATP-binding domain in the middle third of the protein, and a carboxy-terminal domain whose function remains unknown (*223*). Originally, the ATP binding site in N2 was proposed based on sequence homologies (*222*). More recently, site-directed mutagenesis (*224*) and photoaffinity labeling (*225*) have confirmed the roles of Lys-181 and Asp-265 in the binding of ATP to Rho protein. In addition, a direct requirement for ATP binding and hydrolysis in transcription termination has been shown through the use of mutant Rho polypeptides (*224*).

The RNA·DNA unwinding activity of Rho protein was demonstrated using a substrate consisting of a radioactively labeled RNA containing the *trp t'* Rho-dependent terminator annealed to a circular ssDNA through 28 nt of DNA complementary to the RNA at the 3' end of the transcript (*18*). Rho protein, in the absence of RNA polymerase, catalyzes the unwinding of this duplex region in a reaction that requires ATP (dATP) hydrolysis. The unwinding reaction is unidirectional in the 5'-to-3' direction with respect to the RNA molecule, as determined by changing the polarity of the annealed region. Moreover, substrates constructed with the *trp t'* terminator in the opposite orientation are not unwound by Rho protein, a result consistent with the fact that *trp t'* does not function as a terminator when in the opposite orientation (R. Wu and T. Platt, unpublished, cited in *18*).

Although Rho protein can unwind duplex RNA, provided that a specific sequence of ssRNA is provided for Rho protein binding, the enzyme does not unwind duplex DNA. The efficiency of the RNA·DNA unwinding reaction catalyzed by Rho protein has been improved by lowering the KCl and Mg^{2+} concentrations in the reaction mixture (*19*). Under these conditions, each Rho hexamer catalyzes the unwinding of approximately one RNA molecule, and the concentration of ATP required for maximal unwinding is reduced. Interestingly, these changes adversely affect the unwinding of an RNA duplex by Rho protein. RNA·DNA hybrid regions as long as 120 bp can be unwound by Rho protein; longer regions are not unwound by the helicase (*226*). In addition, the length of the ssRNA between the presumed Rho entry site and the RNA·DNA duplex (up to 450 nt) has little effect on the Rho helicase reaction. However, under conditions that favor unwinding of the RNA·DNA hybrid and inhibit duplex-RNA unwinding, the existence of a colinear region of duplex RNA prevents unwinding of the downstream RNA·DNA hybrid (*226*).

The observations cited above have suggested a model for Rho-dependent termination (*18*, *226*) in which Rho protein binds the RNA transcript at its entry site and then either tracks 5' to 3', or anchors at its entry site and tracks via secondary interactions with the RNA to the site of the transcription bubble. Presumably, ATP hydrolysis fuels this movement along ssRNA. Subsequently, the helicase activity of Rho protein unwinds the RNA·DNA duplex, causing the transcript and polymerase to dissociate from the DNA template.

VI. Summary

A great deal has been learned in the last 15 years with regard to how helicase enzymes participate in DNA metabolism and how they interact with their DNA substrates. However, many questions remain unanswered. Of critical importance is an understanding of how NTP hydrolysis and hydrogen-bond disruption are coupled. Several models exist and are being tested; none has been proven. In addition, an understanding of how a helicase disrupts the hydrogen bonds holding duplex DNA together is lacking. Recently, helicase enzymes that unwind duplex RNA and DNA·RNA hybrids have been described. In some cases, these are old enzymes with new activities. In other cases, these are new enzymes only recently discovered. The significance of these reactions in the cell remains to be clarified. However, with the availability of significant amounts of these enzymes in a highly purified state, and mutant alleles in most of the genes encoding them, the answers to these questions should be forthcoming.

The variety of helicases found in *E. coli*, and the myriad processes these enzymes are involved in, were perhaps unexpected. It seems likely that an equally large number of helicases will be discovered in eukaryotic cells. In fact, several helicases have been identified and purified from eukaryotic sources ranging from viruses to mouse cells (*4–13, 227–234*). Many of these helicases have been suggested to have roles in DNA replication, although this remains to be shown conclusively. Helicases with roles in DNA repair, recombination, and other aspects of DNA metabolism are likely to be forthcoming as we learn more about these processes in eukaryotic cells.

ACKNOWLEDGMENTS

I would like to thank T. M. Lohman, T. Platt, S. C. Kowalczykowski, K. J. Marians, N. Minkley, and H. Hoffmann-Berling for communication of results prior to publication. In addition, I thank Janet Yancey and Dan Bean for critical reading of this manuscript, other members of the laboratory for stimulating discussions, and Susan Whitfield for preparation of the artwork. Work from the author's laboratory was supported by National Institutes of Health Grant GM 33476 and American Cancer Society Grants MV-332, MV-435, NP-615, and FRA-315. S.W.M. is the recipient of an American Cancer Society Faculty Research Award.

REFERENCES

1. K. Geider and H. Hoffmann-Berling, *ARB* **50**, 233 (1981).
2. S. W. Matson and K. A. Kaiser-Rogers, *ARB* **59**, 289 (1990).
3. S. W. Matson, J. W. George, K. A. Kaiser-Rogers, E. E. Lahue, E. R. Wood and J. E. Yancey, *ICN–UCLA Symp. Mol. Cell. Biol.* **127**, 127 (1990).
4. U. Hubscher and H. P. Stalder, *NARes* **13**, 5471 (1985).
5. K. M. Downey, D. M. Andrews, X. Li, C. Castillo, C. K. Tan and A. G. So, *ICN–UCLA Symp. Mol. Cell. Biol.* **127**, 141 (1990).
6. Y. Hotta and H. Stern, *Bchem* **17**, 1872 (1978).
7. M. Seki, T. Enmoto, F. Hanaoka and M. Yamada, *Bchem* **26**, 2924 (1987).
8. E. H. A. Poll and R. M. Benbow, *Bchem* **27**, 8701 (1988).
9. A. Sugino, B. H. Ryu, T. Sugino, L. Naumovski and E. C. Friedberg, *JBC* **261**, 11744 (1986).
10. P. Sung, L. Prakash, S. W. Matson and S. Prakash, *PNAS* **84**, 8951 (1987).
11. A. Aboussekhra, R. Chanet, Z. Zgaga, C. Cassier-Chauvat, M. Heude and F. Fabre, *NARes* **17**, 7211 (1989).
12. H. Itzik, L. Naumovski and E. C. Friedberg, *JBC* **264**, 20532 (1989).
13. C. Tien-Hsien, J. Arenas and J. Abelson, *PNAS* **87**, 1571 (1990).
14. B. L. Bass and H. Weintraub, *Cell* **48**, 607 (1987).
15. M. R. Rebagliati and D. A. Melton, *Cell* **48**, 599 (1987).
16. M. Scheffner, R. Knippers and H. Stahl, *Cell* **57**, 955 (1989).
17. S. W. Matson, *PNAS* **86**, 4430 (1989).
18. C. A. Brennan, A. J. Dombroski and T. Platt, *Cell* **48**, 945 (1987).
19. C. A. Brennan, E. J. Steinmetz, P. Spear and T. Platt, *JBC* **265**, 5440 (1990).
20. B. K. Ray, T. G. Lawson, J. C. Kramer, M. H. Cladaras, J. A. Grifo, R. D. Abramson, W. C. Merrick and R. E. Thach, *JBC* **260**, 7651 (1985).

21. K. Nishi, F. Morel-Deville, J. W. B. Hershey, T. Leighton and J. Schnier, *Nature* **336**, 496 (1988).
22. T. Platt, *ARB* **55**, 339 (1986).
23. B. Kuhn, M. Abdel-Monem and H. Hoffmann-Berling, *CSHSQB* **43**, 63 (1978).
24. M. Abdel-Monem, H. Durwald and H. Hoffmann-Berling, *EJB* **65**, 441 (1976).
25. M. Duguet, G. Yarranton and M. Gefter, *CSHSQB* **43**, 335 (1978).
26. M. Venkatesan, L. L. Silver and N. G. Nossal, *JBC* **257**, 12426 (1982).
27. S. W. Matson, S. Tabor and C. C. Richardson, *JBC* **258**, 14017 (1983).
28. S. W. Matson, *JBC* **261**, 10169 (1986).
29. L. J. Roman and S. C. Kowalczykowski, *Bchem* **28**, 2863 (1989).
30. S. W. Matson and C. C. Richardson, *JBC* **258**, 14009 (1983).
31. C. C. Liu and B. M. Alberts, *JBC* **256**, 2813 (1981).
32. S. W. Matson and J. W. George, *JBC* **262**, 2066 (1987).
33. K. R. Smith, J. W. George, E. R. Wood and S. W. Matson, *JMB* submitted (1990).
34. C. V. Jongeneel, T. Formosa and B. M. Alberts, *JBC* **259**, 12925 (1984).
35. H. Krell, H. Durwald and H. Hoffmann-Berling, *EJB* **93**, 387 (1979).
36. B. Kuhn, M. Abdel-Monem, H. Krell and H. Hoffmann-Berling, *JBC* **254**, 11343 (1979).
37. D. T. Denhardt, D. H. Dressler and A. Hathaway, *PNAS* **57**, 813 (1967).
38. J. Colasanti and D. T. Denhardt, *MGG* **209**, 382 (1987).
39. S. Eisenberg, J. F. Scott and A. Kornberg, *PNAS* **73**, 1594 (1976).
40. J. F. Scott, S. Eisenberg, L. L. Bertsch and A. Kornberg, *PNAS* **74**, 193 (1977).
41. J. F. Scott and A. Kornberg, *JBC* **253**, 3292 (1978).
42. S. Eisenberg, J. Griffith and A. Kornberg, *PNAS* **74**, 3198 (1977).
43. G. T. Yarranton and M. L. Gefter, *PNAS* **76**, 1658 (1979).
44. C. A. Gilchrist and D. T. Denhardt, *NARes* **15**, 465 (1987).
45. H. Bialkowska-Hobrzanska and D. T. Denhardt, *Gene* **28**, 93 (1984).
46. H. Bialkowska-Hobrzanska and D. T. Denhardt, *J. Bact.* **164**, 1004 (1985).
47. T. M. Lohman, K. Chao, J. M. Green, S. Sage and G. T. Runyon, *JBC* **264**, 10139 (1989).
48. A. Kornberg, J. F. Scott and L. L. Bertsch, *JBC* **253**, 3298 (1978).
49. N. Arai, K.-I. Arai and A. Kornberg, *JBC* **256**, 5287 (1981).
50. N. Arai and A. Kornberg, *JBC* **256**, 5294 (1981).
51. K. R. Smith, J. E. Yancey and S. W. Matson, *JBC* **264**, 6119 (1989).
52. H. E. D. Lane and D. T. Denhardt, *JMB* **97**, 99 (1975).
53. G. Taucher-Scholz, M. Abdel-Monem and H. Hoffmann-Berling, *ICN–UCLA Symp. Mol. Cell. Biol.* **10**, 65 (1983).
54. J. S. Fassler, I. Tessman and E. S. Tessman, *J. Bact.* **161**, 609 (1985).
55. M. S. Lee and K. J. Marians, *PNAS* **84**, 8345 (1987).
56. R. S. Lasken and A. Kornberg, *JBC* **263**, 5512 (1988).
57. A. Kornberg and T. Baker, "DNA Replication," 2nd ed., in press. 1990.
58. S. Wickner and J. Hurwitz, *PNAS* **71**, 4120 (1974).
59. R. McMacken and A. Kornberg, *JBC* **253**, 3313 (1978).
60. K. J. Marians, *CRC Crit. Rev. Biochem.* **17**, 153 (1984).
61. J. Shlomai and A. Kornberg, *JBC* **255**, 6789 (1980).
62. K. Arai, R. Low, J. Kobori, J. Shlomai and A. Kornberg, *JBC* **256**, 5273 (1981).
63. K. Arai, R. Low and A. Kornberg, *PNAS* **78**, 707 (1981).
64. S. Wickner and J. Hurwitz, *ICN–UCLA Symp. Mol. Cell. Biol.* **3**, 227 (1975).
65. J. Weiner, R. McMacken and A. Kornberg, *PNAS* **73**, 752 (1976).
66. K. Arai and A. Kornberg, *PNAS* **78**, 69 (1981).
67. J. Shlomai and A. Kornberg, *JBC* **255**, 6794 (1980).
68. J. Shlomai and A. Kornberg, *PNAS* **77**, 799 (1980).

69. S. L. Zipursky and K. J. Marians, *PNAS* **77**, 6521 (1980).
70. S. L. Zipursky and K. J. Marians, *PNAS* **78**, 6111 (1981).
71. P. Abarzua, W. Soeller and K. J. Marians, *JBC* **259**, 14286 (1984).
72. W. Soeller, P. Abarzua and K. J. Marians, *JBC* **259**, 14293 (1984).
73. P. Nurse, R. J. DiGate, K. H. Zavitz, and K. J. Marians, *PNAS* **87**, 4615 (1990).
74. K. Ueda, R. McMacken and A. Kornberg, *JBC* **253**, 261 (1978).
75. L. J. Reha-Krantz and J. Hurwitz, *JBC* **253**, 4043 (1978).
76. K. Mensa-Wilmot, R. Seaby, C. Alfano, M. S. Wold, B. Gomes and R. McMacken, *JBC* **264**, 2853 (1989).
77. T. A. Baker, B. E. Funnell and A. Kornberg, *JBC* **262**, 6877 (1987).
78. K. I. Arai, S. I. Yasuda and A. Kornberg, *JBC* **256**, 5247 (1981).
79. J. H. LeBowitz and R. McMacken, *JBC* **261**, 4738 (1986).
81. K. I. Arai and A. Kornberg, *JBC* **256**, 5253 (1981).
82. L. J. Reha-Krantz and J. Hurwitz, *JBC* **253**, 4051 (1978).
83. R. W. Richardson and N. G. Nossal, *JBC* **264**, 4725 (1989).
84. N. Nakayama, N. Arai, M. W. Bond, Y. Kaziro and K. I. Arai, *JBC* **259**, 97 (1984).
85. T. A. Baker, K. Sekimizu, B. E. Funnell and A. Kornberg, *Cell* **45**, 53 (1986).
86. J. A. Kobori and A. Kornberg, *JBC* **257**, 13770 (1982).
87. A. Klein, E. Lanka and H. Schuster, *EJB* **105**, 1 (1980).
88. S. Wickner and J. Hurwitz, *PNAS* **72**, 921 (1975).
89. K. I. Arai and A. Kornberg, *JBC* **256**, 5253 (1981).
90. E. Wahle, R. S. Lasken and A. Kornberg, *JBC* **264**, 2469 (1989).
90a. C. Alfano and R. McMacken, *JBC* **264**, 10699 (1989).
91. F. Bonhoeffer, Z. *Vererbungsl.* **98**, 141 (1966).
92. Y. Horita, A. Ryter and F. Jacob, *CSHSQB* **33**, 677 (1968).
93. W. L. Fangman and A. Novick, *Genetics* **60**, 1 (1968).
94. P. L. Carl, *MGG* **109**, 107 (1970).
95. J. A. Wechsler and J. D. Gross, *MGG* **113**, 273 (1971).
96. J. W. Zyskind and D. W. Smith, *J. Bact.* **129**, 1476 (1977).
97. M. S. Lee and K. J. Marians, *JBC* **264**, 14531 (1989).
98. M. Mok and K. J. Marians, *JBC* **262**, 16644 (1987).
99. G. S. Khatri, T. MacAllister, P. R. Sista and D. Bastia, *Cell* **59**, 667 (1989).
100. E. H. Lee, A. Kornberg, M. Hidaka, T. Kobayashi and T. Horiuchi, *PNAS* **86**, 9104 (1989).
100a. P. L. Kuempel, A. J. Pelletier and T. M. Hill, *Cell* **59**, 581 (1989).
101. E. Richet and M. Kohiyama, *JBC* **251**, 808 (1976).
102. M. Abdel-Monem, M. Chanal and H. Hoffmann-Berling, *EJB* **79**, 33 (1977).
103. M. Abdel-Monem, H. Durwald and H. Hoffmann-Berling, *EJB* **79**, 39 (1977).
104. E. Richet, R. Kern, M. Kohiyama and Y. Hirota, *ICN–UCLA Symp. Mol. Cell. Biol.* **10**, 605 (1983).
105. K. Oeda, T. Horiuchi and M. Sekiguchi, *MGG* **184**, 191 (1981).
106. H. M. Arthur, D. Bramhill, P. B. Eastlake and P. T. Emmerson, *Gene* **19**, 285 (1982).
107. K. Oeda, T. Horiuchi and M. Sekiguchi, *Nature* **298**, 98 (1982).
108. V. F. Maples and S. R. Kushner, *PNAS* **79**, 5616 (1982).
109. I. D. Hickson, H. M. Arthur, D. Bramhill and P. T. Emmerson, *MGG* **190**, 265 (1983).
110. G. Taucher-Scholz and H. Hoffmann-Berling, *EJB* **137**, 573 (1983).
111. K. Kumura, K. Oeda, M. Akiyama, T. Horiuchi and M. Sekiguchi, *in* "Cellular Responses to DNA Damage" (E. C. Friedberg and B. A. Bridges, eds.), p. 51. Liss, New York, 1983.
112. K. Kumura and M. Sekiguchi, *JBC* **259**, 1560 (1984).

113. H. Ogawa, K. Shimada and J. Tomizawa, *MGG* **101,** 227 (1968).

114. G. B. Smirnov, E. V. Filkova and A. G. Skavronskaya, *MGG* **118,** 51 (1972).

115. P. W. Finch and P. T. Emmerson, *NARes* **12,** 5789 (1984).

116. G. T. Runyon and T. M. Lohman, *JBC* **264,** 17502 (1989).

117. G. T. Runyon, D. G. Bear and T. M. Lohman, *PNAS* **87,** 6383 (1990).

118. B. Kuhn and M. Abdel-Monem, *EJB* **125,** 63 (1982).

119. M. Klinkert, A. Klein and M. Abdel-Monem, *JBC* **255,** 9746 (1980).

120. E. C. Siegel and H. M. Race, *Mutat. Res.* **83,** 49 (1981).

121. C. Van Sluis, I. E. Mattern and M. C. Paterson, *Mutat. Res.* **25,** 273 (1974).

122. S. R. Kushner, J. Shepherd, G. Edwards and V. F. Maples, *ICN–UCLA Symp. Mol. Cell. Biól.* **9,** 251 (1978).

123. H. M. Arthur and R. G. Lloyd, *MGG* **180,** 185 (1980).

124. N. B. Kuemmerle and W. E. Masker, *NARes* **11,** 2193 (1983).

125. P. R. Caron, S. R. Kushner and L. Grossman, *PNAS* **82,** 4925 (1985).

126. I. Husain, B. Van Houten, D. C. Thomas, M. Abdel-Monem and A. Sancar, *PNAS* **82,** 6774 (1985).

127. C. P. Selby and A. Sancar, *Bchem* **27,** 7184 (1988).

128. A. Sancar and G. B. Sancar, *ARB* **57,** 29 (1988).

129. M.-S. Tang and K. C. Smith, *Mutat. Res.* **80,** 15 (1981).

130. E. C. Siegel, *J. Bact.* **113,** 161 (1973).

131. P. Modrich, *ARB* **56,** 435 (1987).

132. A. L. Lu, S. Clark and P. Modrich, *PNAS* **80,** 4639 (1983).

133. A. L. Lu, K. Welsh, S. Clark, S. S. Su and P. Modrich, *CSHSQB* **49,** 589 (1984).

134. R. S. Lahue, K. G. Au and P. Modrich, *Science* **245,** 160 (1989).

135. P. Modrich, *JBC* **264,** 6597 (1989).

136. J. Bauer, G. Krammer and R. Knippers, *MGG* **181,** 541 (1981).

137. P. Howard-Flanders and E. Bardwell, *J. Bact.* **148,** 739 (1981).

138. V. Lundblad and N. Kleckner, *in* "Molecular and Cellular Mechanisms of Mutagenesis" (J. R. Lemontt and W. M. Generoso, eds.), p. 245. Plenum, New York, 1982.

139. R. G. Lloyd, *MGG* **189,** 157 (1983).

140. H. M. Arthur and P. B. Eastlake, *Gene* **25,** 309 (1983).

141. D. Brunier, B. Peeters, L. Janniere, B. Michel, S. Sozhamannan and S. D. Ehrlich, *Proc. Int. Symp., 8th* in press (1989).

142. Z. I. Horii and A. J. Clark, *JMB* **80,** 327 (1973).

143. V. Lundblad and N. Kleckner, *Genetics* **109,** 3 (1985).

144. C. Rayssiguier, D. S. Thaler and M. Radman, *Nature* **342,** 396 (1989).

145. A. M. Easton and S. R. Kushner, *NARes* **11,** 8625 (1983).

146. Y. Yamamoto, T. Ogawa, H. Shinagawa, T. Nakayama, H. Matsuo, and H. Ogawa, *J. Biochem.* **99,** 1579 (1986).

147. K. Nakayama, N. Irino and H. Nakayama, *MGG* **192,** 391 (1983).

148. E. C. Siegel, *MGG* **191,** 397 (1983).

149. E. Y. Oh and L. Grossman, *PNAS* **84,** 3638 (1987).

150. E. Y. Oh and L. Grossman, *JBC* **264,** 1336 (1989).

151. D. C. Thomas, M. Levy and A. Sancar, *JBC* **260,** 9875 (1985).

152. T. W. Seeley and L. Grossman, *PNAS* **86,** 6577 (1989).

153. E. Y. Oh and L. Grossman, *NARes* **14,** 8557 (1987).

154. D. K. Orren and A. Sancar, *PNAS* **86,** 5237 (1989).

155. G. Buttin and M. Wright, *CSHSQB* **33,** 259 (1968).

156. M. Oishi, *PNAS* **64,** 1292 (1969).

157. S. D. Barbour and A. J. Clark, *PNAS* **65,** 955 (1970).

158. A. F. Taylor, *in* "Genetic Recombination" (R. Kucherlapati and G. R. Smith, eds., p. 231. American Society for Microbiology, Washington, D.C., 1988.
159. P. J. Goldmark and S. Linn, *PNAS* **67**, 434 (1970).
160. L. C. Eichler and I. R. Lehman, *JBC* **252**, 499 (1977).
161. E. A. Friedman and H. O. Smith, *JBC* **247**, 2846 (1972).
162. H. O. Smith and E. A. Friedman, *JBC* **247**, 2854 (1972).
163. P. J. Goldmark and S. Linn, *JBC* **247**, 1849 (1972).
164. A. Taylor and G. R. Smith, *in* "Mechanistic Studies of DNA Replication and Genetic Recombination" (B. Alberts, ed.), p. 909. Academic Press, New York, 1980.
165. A. Taylor and G. R. Smith, *Cell* **22**, 447 (1980).
166. K. M. Telander-Muskavitch and S. Linn, *JBC* **257**, 2641 (1982).
167. S. C. Kowalczykowski and L. J. Roman, *UCLA Symp. Mol. Cell. Biol.*, *New Ser.* **127**, 357 (1990).
168. P. W. Finch, R. E. Wilson, K. Brown, I. D. Hickson, A. E. Tomkinson and P. T. Emmerson, *NARes* **14**, 4437 (1986).
169. A. M. Chaudhury and G. R. Smith, *J. Bact.* **160**, 788 (1984).
170. R. P. Lieberman and M. Oishi, *PNAS* **71**, 4816 (1974).
171. S. K. Amundsen, A. F. Taylor, A. M. Chaudhury and G. R. Smith, *PNAS* **83**, 5558 (1986).
172. P. W. Finch, A. Storey, K. Brown, I. D. Hickson and P. T. Emmerson, *NARes* **14**, 8583 (1986).
173. I. D. Hickson and P. T. Emmerson, *Nature* **294**, 578 (1981).
174. P. W. Finch, A. Storey, K. E. Chapman, K. Brown, I. D. Hickson and P. T. E. Emmerson, *NARes* **14**, 8573 (1986).
175. N. S. Willets and D. W. Mount, *J. Bact.* **100**, 923 (1969).
176. K. M. Palas and S. R. Kushner, *JBC* **265**, 3447 (1990).
177. I. D. Hickson, C. N. Robson, K. E. Atkinson, L. Hutton and P. T. Emmerson, *JBC* **260**, 1224 (1985).
178. I. D. Hickson, K. E. Atkinson, L. Hutton, A. E. Tomkinson and P. T. Emmerson, *NARes* **12**, 3807 (1984).
179. D. A. Julin and I. R. Lehman, *JBC* **262**, 9044 (1987).
180. L. J. Roman and S. C. Kowalczykowski, *Bchem* **28**, 2873 (1989).
181. A. E. Karu and S. Linn, *PNAS* **69**, 2855 (1972).
182. A. E. Karu, V. MacKay, P. J. Goldmark and S. Linn, *JBC* **248**, 4874 (1973).
183. A. F. Taylor and G. R. Smith, *JMB* **185**, 431 (1985).
184. G. Braedt and G. R. Smith, *PNAS* **86**, 871 (1989).
185. V. M. Braughtigan, W. C. Childs and F. C. Neuhaus, *J. Bact.* **146**, 239 (1981).
186. N. S. Willets and A. J. Clark, *J. Bact.* **100**, 231 (1969).
187. E. A. Birge and K. B. Low, *JMB* **83**, 447 (1974).
188. J. D. Porter, T. McLaughlin and B. Low, *CSHSQB* **43**, 1043 (1978).
189. S. D. Yancey and R. D. Porter, *J. Bact.* **162**, 29 (1985).
190. L. J. Roman and S. C. Kowalczykowski, *JBC* **264**, 18340 (1989).
191. A. McPartland, L. Green and H. Echols, *Cell* **20**, 731 (1980).
192. S. Wickner, M. Wright and J. Hurwitz, *PNAS* **71**, 783 (1974).
192. V. F. Simon and S. Lederberg, *J. Bact.* **112**, 161 (1972).
193. M. Abdel-Monem and H. Hoffmann-Berling, *EJB* **65**, 431 (1976).
194. E. E. Lahue and S. W. Matson, *JBC* **263**, 3208 (1988).
195. H. D. Bradshaw, Jr., B. A. Traxler, E. G. Minkley, Jr., E. W. Nester and M. P. Gordon, *J. Bact.* in press (1990).
196. M. Abdel-Monem, H. Lauppe, J. Kartenbeck, H. Durwald and H. Hoffmann-Berling, *JMB* **110**, 667 (1977).

197. M. Abdel-Monem, G. Taucher-Scholz and M. Klinkert, *PNAS* **80,** 4659 (1983).
198. K. A. Ippen-Ihler and E. G. Minkley, Jr., *ARGen* **20,** 593 (1986).
199. N. Willets and R. Shurray, *in* "*Escherichia coli* and *Salmonella typhimurium*, Cellular and Molecular Biology," (J. L. Ingraham, K. B. Low, B. Magasanik, M. Schaechter, H. E. Umbarger and F. C. Neidhardt, eds.), p. 1110. American Society for Microbiology, Washington, D.C., 1987.
200. B. A. Traxler and E. G. Minkley, Jr., *J. Bact.* **169,** 3251 (1987).
201. B. A. Traxler and E. G. Minkley, Jr., *JMB* **204,** 205 (1988).
202. G. T. Yarranton, R. H. Das and M. L. Gefter, *JBC* **254,** 11997 (1979).
203. M. L. Gefter, *in* "The Enzymes" (P. D. Boyer, ed.), p. 367. Academic Press, New York, 1981.
204. G. T. Yarranton, R. H. Das and M. L. Gefter, *JBC* **254,** 12002 (1979).
205. R. H. Das, G. T. Yarranton and M. L. Gefter, *JBC* **255,** 8069 (1980).
206. E. R. Wood and S. W. Matson, *JBC* **262,** 15269 (1987).
207. E. R. Wood and S. W. Matson, *JBC* **264,** 8297 (1989).
208. E. R. Wood, "The Biochemical Analysis of *E. coli* Helicase IV and the Identification and Cloning of the Genetic Locus," Ph.D. thesis. University of North Carolina, Chapel Hill, North Carolina, 1989.
209. V. N. Trieu and D. McCarthy, *J. Bact.* **171,** 2128 (1989).
210. J. W. Roberts, *Nature* **224,** 1168 (1969).
211. P. H. von Hippel, D. G. Bear, W. W. Morgan and J. A. McSwiggen, *ARB* **53,** 389 (1984).
212. J. Pinkham and T. Platt, *NARes* **11,** 3531 (1983).
213. L. R. Finger and J. P. Richardson, *JMB* **156,** 203 (1982).
214. A. Das, D. Court and S. Adhya, *PNAS* **73,** 1959 (1976).
215. C. Lowery-Goldhammer and J. P. Richardson, *PNAS* **71,** 2003 (1974).
216. C. Lowery and J. P. Richardson, *JBC* **252,** 1375 (1977).
217. C. Lowery and J. P. Richardson, *JBC* **252,** 1381 (1977).
219. B. H. Howard and B. deCrombrugghe, *JBC* **251,** 2520 (1976).
220. J. P. Richardson and R. Conway, *Bchem* **19,** 4293 (1980).
221. G. Galluppi and J. P. Richardson, *JMB* **138,** 513 (1980).
222. A. J. Dombroski and T. Platt, *PNAS* **85,** 2538 (1988).
223. J. W. Dolan, N. F. Marshall and J. P. Richardson, *JBC* **265,** 5747 (1990).
224. A. J. Dombroski, C. A. Brennan, P. Spear and T. Platt, *JBC* **263,** 18802 (1988).
225. A. J. Dombroski, J. R. LaDine, R. L. Cross and T. Platt, *JBC* **263,** 18810 (1988).
226. E. J. Steinmetz, C. A. Brennan and T. Platt, *JBC* in press (1990).
227. H. Stahl, P. Droge and R. Knippers, *EMBO J.* **5,** 1939 (1986).
228. G. S. Goetz, F. B. Dean, J. Hurwitz and S. W. Matson, *JBC* **263,** 383 (1988).
229. M. Weikowski, M. W. Schwarz and H. Stahl, *JBC* **263,** 436 (1988).
230. J. J. Crute, E. S. Mocarski and I. R. Lehman, *NARes* **16,** 6585 (1988).
231. J. J. Crute, T. Tsurumi, L. Zhu, S. K. Weller, P. D. Olivo, M. D. Challberg, E. C. Mokarski and I. R. Lehmann, *PNAS* **86,** 2186 (1989).
232. Y. Tawaragi, T. Enomoto, Y. Watanabe, F. Hanaoka and M. Yamada, *Bchem* **23,** 529 (1984).
233. M. Seki, T. Enomoto, Y. Watanabe, Y. Tawaragi, K. Kawasaki, F. Hanaoka and M. Yamada, *Bchem* **25,** 3239 (1986).
234. M. Seki, T. Enomoto, J. Yanagisawa, F. Hanaoka and M. Ui, *Bchem* **27,** 1766 (1988).

Index

327